Topics in

Contemporary

Mathematics

Sixth Edition

Wiley Williams, Ph. D.
University of Louisville

Kendall Hunt
publishing company

Cover image © Shutterstock.com

www.kendallhunt.com
Send all inquiries to:
4050 Westmark Drive
Dubuque, IA 52004-1840

Contents

Preface

Topics in Contemporary Mathematics is an applications-driven text. Its topics are chosen to explore some of the ways in which mathematics is applied to solve concrete problems in the modern world. Hopefully you will not think of the question, "What is this stuff good for?"; it will be apparent what it is good for. The goal of this text is not to prepare you for a future mathematics course, but rather to prepare you to use and appreciate mathematics in your life as an informed citizen of today's world. The topics do not require sophisticated mathematical prerequisites (by *college* standards). *But that does not mean the material is easy!* We will develop and use whatever mathematical concepts are appropriate to deal with the topic at hand. (This is what is meant by an "applications-driven" text.) You *will* need to *think clearly and logically* about the topics, and *work at understanding* them. But the topics have been chosen to be some that people care about and that can be solved by careful application of mathematical thinking. The focus of the topics is somewhat outside the mainstream algebra topics that may have dominated your mathematical life until now. They are:

- Interest. How do banks calculate interest? What do all the interest rates quoted in bank ads mean? How can I make predictions about how my savings will grow, or how much I need to invest to have a certain amount of money in the future? How can I determine the rate my investment is earning, or how long it will take for the investment to grow to a certain size? What role do inflation and the Consumer Price Index play in this?

- Periodic Payments. If I borrow money, how does the bank calculate my payments? If I set up a retirement account, how can I estimate the amount of money I will have as the result of regular investments? How do taxes affect the value of my savings? If I make additional payments on my mortgage, how does that affect the length of time it takes to pay off the mortgage? How can I determine whether I should refinance my mortgage?

- Linear Programming. How should a manager allocate a finite amount of resources among the products his or her company produces so as to yield the largest profit?

- Voting Methods. How can the various, often conflicting, opinions of individuals be consolidated into a single choice for the whole group? Is there a way to do this that meets natural fairness criteria?

- Apportionment. How can indivisible objects be fairly divided among participants that are entitled to fractional shares? Any time a representative body divides its seats among constituent groups this problem arises. Is there a way to do this that meets natural fairness criteria and avoids certain historical paradoxes?

Step by step solutions to many problems are provided and may be especially helpful.

Interest

The financial crisis of 2007-13 that caused a recession was due, in part, to everyday people not understanding their debts. Home buyers signed up for mortgages with payments that escalated after a few years, assuming the house's value would increase as well. Other homebuyers were given mortgages they could not afford. Consumers ran up credit card debt beyond their means to pay.

In today's world it is extremely important that *everyone* understand situations involving loans and savings, and underlying each are the concepts and applications of interest, especially compound interest.

Here are some examples of questions you may face in your life that involve the effects of interest:

- You sign up for a credit card. The interest is stated as 15%. How does the credit card company calculate how much interest you owe?

- What is the difference between simple interest and compound interest?

- You want to save for a new computer.

    - How much do you need to set aside today so it will grow to the price of the computer?

    - Suppose you want to deposit a fixed amount each month to save for the computer. If you want to accumulate savings equal to the price of the computer in 2 years, how much should that monthly amount be?

    - Suppose you set aside $300 now in an account paying 4% interest compounded annually. How long will it take until I have enough money to buy the computer?

- What does an index number mean, and how are index numbers used?

- Why is $1000 today not "worth" the same as $1000 will be "worth" 5 years from now?

- Why does the price of a bond go up when interest rates goes down, and vice versa?

- When I take out a mortgage, how does the lender determine the amount of my monthly payment?

- Why is the cash value of a lottery less than the sum of the yearly payments offered as an alternative?

- Why is the total amount repaid over the life of a 15 year mortgage significantly less than the total amount repaid over the life of a 30 year mortgage at the same rate?

- Suppose you have saved $500,000 when you retire. You want to withdraw $4000 each month to live on. How long will it be until you have used up your savings?

- When is a Roth IRA a better choice than a regular IRA?

In the first two chapters of this text we will help you learn to analyse these situations intelligently.

Section 1.1   Percents

In order to understand situations involving interest you must first understand what percents mean and how they work. Percents also appear, for example, in unemployment rates, tuition increases, and inflation rates. **Percent** means "for every hundred", so it is a ratio of a number to 100. Thus

$$1\% = \frac{1}{100} = 0.01, \quad 50\% = \frac{50}{100} = 0.50 = 0.5 = \frac{1}{2}, \quad 6\% = \frac{6}{100} = 0.06, \quad 7.5\% = \frac{7.5}{100} = \frac{75}{1000} = 0.075$$

You probably learned a rule for converting a percent to a decimal, such as "remove the percent sign and move the decimal point two places to the left." While this is correct, students who do not understand percents may confuse this with the rule for converting a decimal to a percent, which involves moving the decimal point to the *right*. **Rather than memorizing a rule, you are strongly urged to first understand what percent means.**

Example 1 Write each percent as a decimal by using the idea that % means (1/100).
   (a) 18%   (b) 125%   (c) 0.4%   (d) 5.75%

<u>Solution</u> To convert a percent to a decimal, first use the "per hundred" meaning of percents.

   (a) 18% means "18 per hundred", so $18\% = 18\left(\frac{1}{100}\right) = \frac{18}{100} = 0.18$

   (b) 125% is more than 100%, so the answer will be more than 1 (1 = 100%)

   Reasoning: $125\% = 100\% + 25\% = 1 + \frac{25}{100} = 1 + 0.25 = 1.25$

   Or: $125\% = 125\left(\frac{1}{100}\right) = \frac{125}{100} = 1.25$

   (c) 0.4% is less than 1%, so the answer will be less than 0.01

   $$0.4\% = 0.4\left(\frac{1}{100}\right) = \frac{0.4}{100} = \frac{4}{1000} = 0.004$$

   (d) In 5.72% the 5 represents 5 hundredths, so the decimal will have a 5 in the hundredths place

   $$5.72\% = 5.72\left(\frac{1}{100}\right) = \frac{5.72}{100} = \frac{572}{10000} = 0.0572$$

Example 2 Write each decimal as a percent.
   (a) 0.45   (b) 2.5   (c) 0.008   (d) 0.0654

<u>Solution</u> To convert a decimal to a percent you must write the decimal as a fraction whose denominator is 100. Then the numerator is the percent.

   (a) 0.45 means "45 hundredths" or $\frac{45}{100}$, so $0.45 = 45\%$

   (b) 2.5 is 2.5 times 1, so the answer should be 2.5(100%) = 250%

   Also, $2.5 = 2 + \frac{5}{10} = \frac{25}{10} = \frac{250}{100} =$ "250 per hundred" = 250%

   (c) 0.008 is 8 thousandths, so $0.008 = \frac{8}{1000}$. To write this is a number over 100 we must divide the

   numerator and denominator by 10. Thus $0.008 = \frac{8}{1000} = \frac{0.8}{100} = 0.8\%$

   (d) $0.0654 = \frac{654}{10000} = \frac{6.54}{100} = 6.54\%$

The process of converting a fraction to a percent is similar to that of converting a decimal to a percent; you must find a fraction with denominator 100 that is equivalent to the given fraction. Equivalently, you can convert the fraction to a decimal (by dividing the numerator by the denominator), and then convert that decimal to a percent.

Example 3 Write each fraction as a percent.

(a) $\dfrac{1}{4}$ (b) $1\dfrac{3}{4}$ (c) $\dfrac{3}{8}$ (d) $\dfrac{2}{3}$

<u>Solution</u> (a) $\dfrac{1}{4} = \dfrac{1 \times 25}{4 \times 25} = \dfrac{25}{100} = 25\%$

(b) $1\dfrac{3}{4}$ is more than 1, so $1\dfrac{3}{4}$ should convert to more than 100%.

$$1\dfrac{3}{4} = \dfrac{7}{4} = \dfrac{7 \times 25}{4 \times 25} = \dfrac{175}{100} = 175\%$$

(c) $\dfrac{3}{8}$ We cannot convert this to a whole number over 100, since 8 is not a factor of 100, but we can

convert it to a whole number over 1000, because 1000 ÷ 8 = 125.

So $\dfrac{3}{8} = \dfrac{3 \times 125}{8 \times 125} = \dfrac{375}{1000} = \dfrac{37.5}{100} = 37.5\%$ (Alternately, divide 3 by 8: $\dfrac{3}{8} = 0.375 = 37.5\%$)

(d) $\dfrac{2}{3}$ This decimal does not have a terminating decimal. That is, when 2 is divided by 3 the result

is   0.666666.... where the 6's go on forever. This is written $0.\overline{6}$ or $0.6\overline{6}$ or $0.66\overline{6}$. So $\dfrac{2}{3}$ is $66.\overline{6}\%$.

(If you divide 2 by 3 on a calculator, you will not get 6's that go on forever, because your calculator cannot represent this in its display. Rather the calculator will round the right most digit it displays to 7. This is an example of a situation where the calculator's answer is not *exactly* correct; the answer has been rounded to fit in the calculator's display.)

Quiz Yourself: (Answers are at the end of this Section, before the Problems.)

1. Convert 18% to a decimal.   2. Convert 6.5% to a decimal.

3. Convert 0.352 to a percent.   4. Convert 0.004 to a percent.

5. Convert $\dfrac{1}{5}$ to a percent.   6. Convert $\dfrac{1}{16}$ to a percent.

Solving Percent Problems

Finding the solution of a problem involving percents usually requires the use of a version of the proportion that expresses the "per hundred" relationship, or an equivalent equation:

Proportion:	**Equation:**
$\dfrac{\text{Percent}}{100\%} = \dfrac{\text{Amount}}{\text{Base}}$, or	(Decimal Equivalent of Percent) × (Base) = Amount

In these **Base** refers to the quantity of which the percent is being taken. The **Amount** is the quantity that constitutes the percent of the **Base.** <u>In a problem it is important to identify the Base and Amount correctly.</u> Usually the equation form is used when the percent is known.

Example 4 In a certain year Blockbuster Video customers rented 880 million videos out of the 3.6 billion videos rented that year. What percent of the videos did Blockbuster customers rent? Round your answer to the nearest hundredth of a percent.

Solution According to the last sentence the percent is to be calculated of the videos, so 3.6 billion is the Base, and 880 million is the Amount. Set up the proportion:

$$\frac{\text{Percent}}{100\%} = \frac{880 \text{ million}}{3.6 \text{ billion}}, \text{ or } \frac{\text{Percent}}{100} = \frac{880 \text{ million}}{3600 \text{ million}}$$

Dividing 880 by 3600 gives 0.2444444.... Then Percent = 100(0.244444...) = 24.444444...%. Rounding this to the nearest hundredth of a percent, Blockbuster customers rented 24.44% of the videos that year.

Example 5 An investor received a payment of $480, which was 8% of the value of the investment. Find the value of the investment.

Solution The payment is 8% is of the value of the investment, so the value of the investment is the Base and the given $480 is the Amount. Using the equation form above:

(0.08)(Value) = $480
Value = ($480) / (0.08) = $6000.

The value of the investment was $6000.

Example 6 A broker will receive a 3% commission on the sale of a $280,000 house. Find the amount of the commission.

Solution The price of the house is the Base on which the commission is calculated, and the commission is the Amount equalling the percent of the Base. Convert 3% to 0.03 and use the equation form above:

(0.03)(280,000) = Amount
8400 = Amount

The amount of the commission is $8400.

Quiz Yourself: (Answers are at the end of this Section, before the Problems.)

7. In January 2007 Toyota sold 176,000 cars, which was about 16.5% of all the cars sold that month. About how many cars were sold in January 2007? Round your answer to the nearest thousand.

8. For 2010 the Federal Defense Budget was $554 billion out of a total budget of $3318 billion. What percent of the total budget was the Defense Budget? Round your answer to the nearest hundredth of a percent.

Credit Card Interest Calculations

A credit card interest rate is usually given as an annual rate, but it is applied monthly, and

Monthly interest rate = Annual interest rate / 12

Your **unpaid balance** is your previous balance minus any payments you made (but never less than 0). Your **interest amount** I is calculated using the unpaid balance as the Base and the Monthly interest rate as the percentage:

Interest Amount I = (Monthly interest rate)(Unpaid balance)

Example 7 Each month a credit card charges interest on the unpaid balance at 15% annual interest. Your previous balance was $380, and you make a $100 payment. How much interest will you be charged?

Solution Your unpaid balance is $380 - $100 = $280; this becomes the Amount of the interest calculation. Your monthly interest rate is 15% / 12 = 1.25% = 0.0125. Your interest Amount is I = (0.0125)$280 = $3.50.

Percent Change

When a Base amount is changed to a New Value, we can measure the change in two ways. The first way is to calculate the **change amount.**

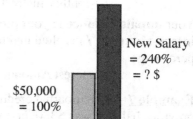

Change Amount = New Value – Base

Another way is to compare the Change Amount to the Base that was changed. This is done by computing the **percent change:**

$$\text{Percent Change} = \frac{\text{Change Amount}}{\text{Base}} \text{ (converted to a percent)}$$

For example, if an investment of $1000 generates a $60 interest payment, making the New Value of the account $1060, then $60 is the Change Amount, and the percent change is

$$\frac{60}{1000} = 0.06 = 6\%$$

The New Value of the investment is $1060. This new value is $\frac{1060}{1000} = 1.06 = 106\%$ of the original investment. This 106% represents 100% of the original investment plus the 6% interest payment.
In dealing with problems about changes and percents, it is important to decide whether the Amount in the percent proportion is the Change Amount or the New Value.

Example 8   In 2003 the Federal Gross Domestic Product (GDP) was $11.5 trillion dollars. In 2014 it was $17.4 trillion dollars.
      (a) What percent of the 2003 GDP was the 2014 GDP?
      (b) How much did the GDP change from 2003 to 2014? What percent change does this represent?

Solution (a) The Base is 11.5 trillion in 2003 and the New Value is 17.4 trillion

in 2014.

    By the percent proportion: $\frac{\text{Percent}}{100\%} = \frac{17.4}{11.5} = 1.51$; Percent = (100%)1.51 = 151%.

    (Note that 1.51 is the decimal equivalent of the percent, not the percent itself.)

    (b) The Change Amount is (17.4 trillion – 11.5 trillion) = 5.9 trillion dollars.

    So Percent Change $= \frac{5.9}{11.5} = 0.51$ which converts to 51%. (Note that 151% = 51% + 100%.)

Example 9 A certain web site states that to move from Louisville to San Francisco and maintain your current standard of living, your salary in San Francisco will need to be 240% of your current salary in Louisville. (!)
      (a) Explain why this 240% is not a percent change.
      (b) What is the percent change?
      (c) If your current salary is $50,000, what will your salary in San Francisco need to be to maintain the same standard of living?

Solution (a) Your new salary needs to be 240% of your current salary. The
    difference between your new salary and your current salary is not
    240% of your current salary. (See the diagram at right.)

    (b) The percent change is 240% - 100% = 140%; adding 140% to the
    current 100% you are earning gives a total new salary of 240% of
    your current salary.

    (c) Your new salary would need to be 240% of $50,000 = 2.4(50,000) =
    $120,000. This is an change of $70,000, which is 140% of $50,000.

Quiz Yourself: (Answers are at the end of this Section, before the Problems.)

9. Tuition at Big U increased from $7,850 per year to $8,320 per year. What percent change is this? Round your answer to the nearest hundredth of a percent.

10. In 2014 the value of a stock was $80. This was 160% of its value in 2008. What percent change is this? What was the value of the stock in 2008?

Brief Review of Fractions

A fraction $\frac{a}{b}$ means a parts of a whole that has been divided into b equal parts. If a out of b parts is equivalent to c out of d parts of the same whole then $\frac{a}{b} = \frac{c}{d}$. For example, $\frac{a}{b} = \frac{na}{nb}$ for any whole number n.

To **add two fractions** $\frac{a}{b}$ and $\frac{e}{f}$ we use a *common denominator*, which means a number than is a multiple of each of the denominators. One such common denominator is the product of the denominators bf. Then:

$$\frac{a}{b} + \frac{e}{f} = \frac{af}{bf} + \frac{be}{bf} = \frac{af + be}{bf}$$

Example: $\dfrac{2}{3} + \dfrac{1}{4} = \dfrac{2 \times 4}{3 \times 4} + \dfrac{3 \times 1}{3 \times 4} = \dfrac{8}{12} + \dfrac{3}{12} = \dfrac{11}{12}$

To **multiply two fractions** we multiply the numerators and denominators separately.

Example: $\dfrac{2}{3} \times \dfrac{1}{4} = \dfrac{2 \times 1}{3 \times 4} = \dfrac{2}{12} = \dfrac{1}{6}$

To **divide two fractions** first get them to a common denominator, then form the quotient of their numerators.

Example: $\dfrac{2}{3} \div \dfrac{1}{4} = \dfrac{2 \times 4}{3 \times 4} \div \dfrac{3 \times 1}{3 \times 4} = \dfrac{8}{12} \div \dfrac{3}{12} = 8 \div 3 = \dfrac{8}{3}$

Alternatively, to divide two fractions we can *invert the second fraction and then multiply it by the first*.

Example: $\dfrac{2}{3} \div \dfrac{1}{4} = \dfrac{2}{3} \times \dfrac{4}{1} = \dfrac{2 \times 4}{3 \times 1} = \dfrac{8}{3}$

Quiz Yourself: Calculate: 11. $\dfrac{2}{5} + \dfrac{3}{4}$ 12. $\dfrac{2}{5} \times \dfrac{3}{4}$ 13. $\dfrac{2}{5} \div \dfrac{3}{4}$

Answers to Quiz Yourself:

1. $18\% = \dfrac{18}{100} = 0.18$

2. $6.5\% = \dfrac{6.5}{100} = \dfrac{65}{1000} = 0.065$

3. $0.352 = \dfrac{352}{1000} = \dfrac{35.2}{100} = 35.2\%$

4. $0.004 = \dfrac{4}{1000} = \dfrac{0.4}{100} = 0.4\%$

5. $\dfrac{1}{5} = \dfrac{2}{10} = 0.2 = 20\%$

6. $\dfrac{1}{16} = \dfrac{1\times25}{16\times25} = \dfrac{1\times25}{400} = \dfrac{1\times25\times25}{400\times25} = \dfrac{625}{10000} = 0.0625 = 6.25\%$

7. $176{,}000 = 0.165(\text{Total Sales})$, so Total Sales $= 176{,}000 / 0.165 = 1{,}066{,}666.666\ldots \approx 1{,}067{,}000$ cars.

   (The symbol $\approx$ means "approximately" or "rounds to".)

8. $554 / 3{,}318 = 0.166968053\ldots.. = 16.6968053\ldots\% \approx 16.70\%$

9. Amount Increase $= \$8320 - \$7850 = \$470$. Percent change $= \$470/\$7850 = 0.05987\ldots = 5.987\ldots\% \approx 5.99\%$

10. Percent change $= 160\% - 100\% = 60\%$. (2014 value) $= 160\%(2008\text{ value})$, and $160\% = 1.6$.
    2008 value $=$ (2014 value) $/ 1.6 = 80 / 1.6 = \$50$.

11. $\dfrac{2}{5} + \dfrac{3}{4} = \dfrac{8}{20} + \dfrac{15}{20} = \dfrac{23}{20} = 1\dfrac{3}{20}$

12. $\dfrac{2}{5} \times \dfrac{3}{4} = \dfrac{2\times3}{5\times4} = \dfrac{3}{10}$

13. $\dfrac{2}{5} \div \dfrac{3}{4} = \dfrac{8}{20} \div \dfrac{15}{20} = \dfrac{8}{15}$

Problems for Section 1.1

Sharpen Your Skills: (Answers in back of text.)
Complete this table of equivalent percents, decimals, and fractions.

	Percent	Decimal	Fraction
1.	40%		
2.		0.6	
3.			$\frac{3}{20}$
4.	5.85%		
5.		0.0653	
6.			$\frac{3}{40}$

7. What is 28% of 350?

8. 20 is 16% of what number?

9. 6 is what percent of 40?

10. What is 12% of 125?

11. 84 is 15% of what number?

12. 8.4 is what percent of 48?

13. What is the percent change from 140 to 147?

14. What is the percent change from $1200 to $1278?

15. What is the percent change from $15,000 to $15,030?

16. What is the percent change from $1 billion to $1.1 billion?

Communicate the Concepts: (Answers in back of text.)

17. What is the meaning of percent?

18. What is the percent proportion?

19. What is the percent equation?

20. How do you determine the amount of monthly interest in a credit card calculation?

21. Given two amounts, how do we find the percent change from the smaller to the larger?

22. Given two amounts, how do we find the amount of change from the smaller to the larger?

Apply Your Knowledge: (Answers to odd-numbered problems in back of text.)

23. Of the 44 million people in the U. S. who do not have health insurance, 15.4 million are between the ages of 18 and 24. What percent of the people in the U. S. who do not have health insurance are between the ages of 18 and 24?

24. A person who had a salary of $60,000 was given a raise of $2400. What percentage of his old salary does this raise represent? Is this a percent change?

25. In a survey of middle school students 360 students, which was 45% of the students surveyed, said they had a television in their bedroom. How many students were surveyed?

26. A person receives an interest payment of $90, which represents 6% interest earned. What is the value of the investment?

27. In 2014, 54.3 million people e-filed their income taxes. This was a 20% increase over the number who e-filed in 2013. How many people e-filed in 2013? How many more people e-filed in 2014 than in 2013?

28. The population of the world in the year 2014 was 7.2 billion. This was a 25% increase over the population in 1990.
    (a) What was the population of the world in 1990?
    (b) How many more people were the in the world in 2014 than in 1990?

29. You buy a new pair of shoes, and the price plus sales tax (at a rate of 6%) equals $59.34. What was the price of the shoes?

30. A newspaper account says that consumer debt has risen 39% in the last five years, and now equals 1 trillion dollars. What was the amount of consumer debt five years ago?

31. Your current balance on a credit card charging 18% annual interest is $630. This month you made a payment of $200. How much interest will you be charged this month?

32. Your current balance on a credit card charging 16.5% annual interest is $800. This month you made a payment of $250. How much interest will you be charged this month?

33. Your current balance on a credit card charging 13.5% annual interest is $980. This month you made a payment of $500. How much interest will you be charged this month?

34. Your credit card charges 24% annual interest, and you currently have a balance of $1500. Assuming you make no further purchases, how much must you pay on the card to keep your balance from being larger than $1500 next month?

35. A man must pay his wife $1000 per month in child support. He is in the 20% income tax bracket. What amount of pre-tax income does he need to pay the $1000 after taxes?

Section 1.2 Simple Interest

When money is borrowed, lent, or invested, the original amount is the <u>Principal</u> or <u>Present Value</u>. (This is the Base of the percent calculation.) This principal earns <u>interest</u> for the lender or investor. Interest rates are usually stated as an annual rate, that is, as percent per year of the principal P. The amount I of <u>simple interest</u> on a principal P at an annual rate of interest $r\%$ will be $r\%$ of P for each year until the original principal changes. (So this amount of interest is the "Amount" in the previous section.) In general,

---

Amount of Simple Interest = I = Prt where $\begin{cases} P = \text{Principal} \\ r = \textit{annual} \text{ simple interest rate (as a decimal)} \\ t = \text{time in } \underline{\text{years or a fraction of a year}} \end{cases}$

In this formula it is crucial that the time t be written in years or fraction of a year!

If you borrow money for 3 months then $t = 3/12 = 1/4 = 0.25$ years. (We assume each month is $1/12$ of a year.) The interest owed is then only $1/4$ of, or 0.25 times, the amount of interest owed for a full year:

$I = Prt = \$1000 \times 0.11 \times 0.25 = \$27.50$, and the total amount you will repay is $\$1000 + \$27.50 = \$1027.50$

Here are some more examples of the use of the Simple Interest Formula above.

<u>Example 1</u> Find the amount of interest on a sixteen-month loan of $2000 if the annual interest rate is 6.3%.

<u>Solution</u> Here Principal = $2000, $r = 6.3\% = 0.063$, and time $= t = \dfrac{16 \text{ months}}{1 \text{ year}} = \dfrac{16 \text{ months}}{12 \text{ months}} = \dfrac{16}{12} = \dfrac{4}{3}$ year.

We calculate $I = Prt = (\$2000)(0.063)\left(\dfrac{4}{3}\right) = \dfrac{(\$2000)(0.063)(4)}{3} = \$168.00$

There will be $168.00 interest.

<u>Example 2</u> The simple interest charged on a four-month loan of $2000 is $81. Find the annual simple interest rate being charged.

<u>Solution</u>: Here $2000 is the Principal, $81 is the amount of interest I, and the time is $t = \dfrac{4}{12} = \dfrac{1}{3}$ year.

Substitute these in $I = Prt$ and solve for r.

$$81 = 2000(r)\left(\frac{1}{3}\right)$$

Multiply by 3: $243 = 2000(r)$

Divide both sides by 2000: $r = \dfrac{243}{2000} = 0.1215 = 12.15\%$

The simple interest rate is 12.15%.

Quiz Yourself: (Answers are at the end of this Section, before the Problems.)
1. If you borrow $200 for 9 months at 8% annual simple interest, how much interest will you pay?
2. If a bank charges $27 simple interest on a 15 month loan of $300, what interest rate did the bank use?

When money is invested, the value at any time in the future is the Principal plus the Interest Amount that has been earned. This value is called the **Future Value** of the investment and is denoted by F.

Simple Interest Future Value Formula: **Future Value at simple interest = Principal + Interest**

In symbols: $F = P + I = P + Prt$ which can also be written $I = F - P$

where P = Principal, r = <u>annual</u> simple interest rate (as a decimal), t = time <u>in years</u>

Example 3 Find the amount needed to pay off a simple interest loan of $1,000 for 6 months at a rate of 9% annual interest.

Solution: Here the principal is $P = \$1000$, the annual rate is $r = 0.09$, and the time is $t = 6/12 = 0.5$ years. Substitute these in the Simple Interest Formula:
$$F = P + Prt = \$1000 + \$1000(0.09)(0.5) = \$1000 + \$45 = \$1045.00.$$
The student must repay the original $1000 plus $45 interest, a total of $1045.

Example 4 What amount needs to be invested today at 4% annual simple interest in order to have it grow to $3000 in 9 months?

Solution: Since the $3000 is to be the value at the end of the 9 months, $\$3000 = F$. From what is given $r = 0.04$ and $t = 9/12 = 0.75$ years. Since the initial investment P is unknown we must solve:
$$\$3000 = P + P(0.04 \times 0.75)$$
Evaluate 0.04×0.75: $\$3000 = P + P(0.03)$

Factor out P: $\$3000 = P(1 + 0.03)$ *This is a crucial step!*

Divide both sides by 1.03: $P = \dfrac{\$3000}{1.03} = \$2912.62$ which we have rounded to the nearest penny.

Example 5 You are due a tax refund of $594. A tax service will give you the money one and one-half months early, but charge $40 up front to do so. What annual simple interest rate does this charge represent?

Solution: The tax service take the $40 charge out of your $594 refund, and will loan you
$P = F - I = \$594 - \$40 = \$554$. So $P = \$554$ and $I = \$40$.

Also the time of the loan is $t = 1.5/12 = 0.125$ years.

Substituting these into $I = Prt$ we have

(*) $40 = 554(r)(0.125)$

Method 1: Evaluate: $554(0.125) = 69.25$ So (*) simplifies to $40 = 69.25r$

Solve this by dividing both sides by 69.25: $r = 40 / 69.25 = 0.577617329 \ldots \approx 57.76\%$

Method 2: Divide both sides of (*) by $(554)(0.125)$: $r = \dfrac{40}{(554 \times 0.125)} = 0.577617329 \ldots \approx 57.76\%$

Both Methods of solution are acceptable. With Method 1, there are two simple expressions to evaluate, while with Method 2 there is only one expression, but that expression is more complicated. The keystrokes for Method 2 on your calculator are:

$$40 \div (\ 554 \ \times \ 0.125\ ) \ =$$

Be sure to include the parentheses on this calculation! This makes the calculator evaluate the denominator before dividing it into the numerator. Omitting the parentheses would yield $r = \dfrac{40}{554} \times 0.125$ ≈ 0.009025 which is incorrect.

Rounding Interest Rates

As in Example 5 above, interest rate calculations sometimes give decimals that do not terminate. In finance <u>it is conventional to round an interest rate to the nearest hundredth of a percent</u>. For example, if a calculation on the calculator gives the rate as a decimal $r = .0934256345....$ then the rate would be converted to the percentage $r = 9.34256345...\%$ Then rounded to the nearest hundredth of a percent this gives: $r = 9.34\%$.

Example 6 A student will have earned $1200 by August 15. How much can he borrow on April 15 at 8% annual simple interest if he will use his summer earnings to pay off the loan on August 15?

Solution: Again the principal P is unknown, but now $r = 0.08$ and $F = \$1200$. The time is $t = 4/12 = 1/3$ year since it is 4 months from April 15 to August 15. Substitute these in the Simple Interest Formula:

$$1200 = P + P \times 0.08 \times \frac{1}{3}$$

Factor out P: $\qquad\qquad 1200 = P(1 + 0.08 \times \frac{1}{3})$ *Again, this is a crucial step.*

Evaluate $0.08 \times \frac{1}{3}$: $\qquad 1200 = P(1 + 0.0266666666...)$

Divide both sides: $\qquad\qquad P = \dfrac{1200}{1.0266666666...} = \$1168.83$

Calculating the Answer

Many of our problems, such as the previous example, will require a calculator to obtain the final answer. **You should avoid rounding intermediate calculations any more than necessary.**

For example, rounding $0.08 \times \frac{1}{3}$ to, say, $0.08 \times 0.33 = 0.0264$, would cause the final answer of Example

6 to be $\dfrac{1200}{1.0264} = \$1169.13$. **In this problem that error is not large, but we will see examples later**

where such rounding does cause a large error, so begin now to *avoid such rounding*. On the other hand, had the interest rate been 9% then the calculation could have been done (mentally) exactly:

$0.09 \times \frac{1}{3} = 0.03$. Such *an exact calculation or simplification should be done*. Thus in Example 4 on the

previous page, since $0.75 = 3/4$ we have calculated $0.04 \times 0.75 = 0.03$ exactly, and used that to simplify

$1 + 0.04 \times 0.75$ to $1 + 0.03 = 1.03$ before dividing 3000 by it. In summary:

Preferred Calculator Method: Use algebra to solve for the unknown first, then evaluate the final expression. As you do the algebra, if you evaluate an intermediate expression, do not round the result more than what is displayed on your calculator.

Example 7 A student puts $600 into an account paying 4% annual simple interest. How long will it be until the value reaches $660?

Solution: $P = \$600$ and $F = \$660$, so the amount of interest to be earned is $I = \$60$, and $r = 4\% = 0.04$. Substituting these in $I = Prt$:

$\qquad\qquad \$60 = \$600(0.04)(t)$

$\qquad\qquad \$60 = \$24t$

$\qquad\qquad t = \$60 / \$24 = 2.5$ years.

Quiz Yourself: (Answer at the end of this Section, before the Problems.)

5. A student invests $200 in an account that pays 3% annual simple interest. How long will it be until the value of the account reaches $221?

Brief Review of Algebra

Think of an equation as being like a statement that the two sides of the equation "balance", in the same way a scale balances. From that point of view the rules of algebra maintain the initial balance. The **three basic rules of algebra** that apply to any situation involving an equation are:

1. You are allowed add, subtract, multiply, or divide by anything you want (except you can't divide by zero), *as long as you do the same thing to both sides of the equation.* (This also applies to raising both sides to a power, or taking a root of both sides, but we won't need these yet.)

2. You can exchange the left and right sides of an equation. Also, you can factor or expand some or all of the terms on either side of the equation, since those operations do not change the value of either side.

3. If a equals b, and b equals c, then a equals c.

We have already used these rule in working with percents:

Example 1 Solve $44 = 0.25(\text{Base})$

Solution: Divide both sides by 0.25. This results in 44 / (0.25) = Base. We usually interchange the sides and write: Base = 44 / 0.25   Then evaluate the right side: Base = 176.

The Simple Interest Future Value equation $F = P + Prt$ is a **linear equation**. We now give a review of how to solve such an equation for one of its variables.

Type I To solve a linear equation in which the unknown appears *only once*, we perform two steps:

1. Look at the side containing the variable. Subtract (from both sides) any terms on that appear on that side but don't contain the variable. Then simplify each side (add any like terms that can be added).

2. Using the equation that results from step 1, divide both sides of the equation by the coefficient of the unknown in this equation. The result will give the value of the unknown.

Example 2 Solve $\$1050 = \$1000 + \$1000(0.12)(t)$ for t.

Solution: Since there is only one instance of the unknown t, and since the other term on the side containing t is $1000, in Step 1 we subtract $1000 from both sides, then simplify:

$$\$1050 - \$1000 = \$1000(0.12)t$$

$$\$50 = \$120t$$

Then in Step 2 we divide both sides by $120, the coefficient of t. We also switch the sides, because usually the unknown appears to the left of the = sign.   Notice the value of t is always in years.

$$t = 50 / 120 = 5/12 \text{ of a year, or 5 months.}$$

Type II To solve a linear equation in which the unknown appears *more than once*, perform three steps:

1. Pick one side of the equation and subtract (from both sides) each term containing the unknown that appears on that side. Then subtract (from both sides) each term *not containing the unknown* that appears on the *other* side of the equation. After this step all the terms on one side will contain the unknown, and none of the terms on the other side will contain the unknown.

2. Factor the unknown out of each term on the side whose terms contain the unknown. This makes that side be a (perhaps complicated) constant times the unknown. Simplify both sides by adding terms that can be added.

3. Divide both sides by the coefficient of the unknown. The result gives the value of the unknown.

Example 3 Solve $\$2100 = P + P(0.06)(2)$ for P

Solution: Since the unknown P appears twice this is an equation of Type II. The right side has only terms containing the unknown, and the left side has only a term that does not contain the unknown, so we don't need to perform Step 1.   Since $P = P(1)$ we perform Step 2 by factoring the right side as follows:

$\$2100 = P(1) + P(0.12)$

$\$2100 = P(1 + 0.12)$

Then Step 3 is to divide by the coefficient of the unknown P (and switch sides):

$P = \$2100 / (1.012) = \$1875$

Example 4 Solve $1.4x + 350 = 2.53x - 520$

Solution Step 1: Subtract $1.4x$ from both sides: $350 = 2.53x - 520 - 1.4x$

Add 520 to both sides: $350 + 520 = 2.53x - 1.4x$

(We now have all the terms involving the variable on one side, and all the terms not involving the variable on the other side.)

Step 2: Simplify and factor: $870 = (2.53 - 1.4)x$

$870 = (1.13)x$

Step 3: Divide by the coefficient of the unknown: $870 / 1.13 = x$

Interchange sides: $x = 769.9115...$

Quiz Yourself:
6. Solve $2x - 1 = 7x + 9$ for x 7. Solve $150 = P + 1.5P$ for P
8. Solve $2500 = 2400 + 2400(r)(5/12)$ for r.

Answers to Quiz Yourself Problems
1. $P = \$200$, $t = 9/12$ years $= 0.75$ years, and $r = 0.08$. $I = Prt = (\$200)(0.08)(0.75) = \$12$.

2. $I = \$27$, $P = \$300$, $t = 15/12 = 1.25$ years. So $\$27 = \$300(r)(1.25)$. $r = \dfrac{27}{300 \times 1.25} = 0.072 = 7.2\%$

3. $I = \$30$ and $F = \$900$ so $P = F - I = \$870$ is what you actually receive. Since $t = 1/12$ year,
$\$30 = \$870(r)(1/12)$. $30 = 72.5r$ (Since $870 / 12 = 72.5$)
$r = 30/72.5 = 0.4137931...... = 41.37931...\%$ which rounds to 41.38%.

4. $F = \$900$, $r = 0.05$, $t = 15/12 = 1.25$ years. Substitute: $\$900 = P + P(0.05)(1.25)$
Evaluate: $\$900 = P + P(0.0625)$ Factor out P: $\$900 = P(1.0625)$
Divide: $P = \$900 / 1.0625 = \$847.06$ to the nearest penny.

5. To reach a value of $\$221$ the account must earn $\$221 - \$200 = \$21$ in interest. So $P = \$200$ and $I = \$21$.

Solve: $\$21 = \$200(0.03)(t)$ $t = \dfrac{21}{200 \times 0.03} = 3.5$ So it takes 3 and one-half years.

6. Subtract $2x$ from both sides: $-1 = 5x + 9$
Subtract 9 from both sides; $-10 = 5x$.
Divide by 5: $x = -10/5 = -2$.

7. Factor out P: $150 = P(1 + 1.5)$ Simplify: $150 = P(2.5)$ Divide: $P = 150/2.5 = 60$.

8. Subtract 2400 from both sides: $100 = 2400(r)(5/12)$
Evaluate right hand side: $100 = 1000r$
Divide by 1000: $r = 0.1 = 10\%$.

Problems for Section 1.2

Sharpen Your Skills: (Answers in back of text.)

1. Solve for r: $40 = 800(r)(2.5)$. Express your answer as a percent.

2. Solve for r: $33 = 1000(r)(1.5)$. Round the answer to the nearest hundredth percent.

3. Solve for P: $3300 = P + P(0.05)(2)$

4. Solve for P: $2075 = P + P(0.03)(1.25)$

5. Solve for r: $1300 = 1200 + 1200(r)(1.5)$ Round the answer to the nearest hundredth percent.

6. Solve for r: $831 = 800 + 800(r)(0.5)$ Round the answer to the nearest hundredth percent.

Communicate the Concepts: (Answers in back of text.)

7. Explain how to calculate the amount of simple interest if the Principal, annual simple interest rate, and length of time are known.

8. Explain how to find the amount of simple interest if the Principal and Future Value are known.

9. Explain why an investment earns the same amount of interest each year if simple interest is used.

10. Explain how the expression $P + Pr$ can be factored.

Apply Your Knowledge: (Answers to odd-numbered problems in back of text.)

In these problems all rates are annual simple interest rates. Assume each month is 1/12 of a year. Express any rate as a percent rounded to the nearest hundredth of a percent.

11. A man borrows $1,500 for 8 months at 15% annual simple interest. Find the amount of interest that the bank will charge, and the single amount he must repay at the end of the 8 months.

12. A college student borrows $1200 at 12% annual simple interest for 1 1/2 months. Find the amount of interest that the bank charges, and the single amount she must repay at the end of 1 1/2 months.

13. A student will get a $800 income tax refund on June 1. How much can she borrow from a loan agency on February 1 at 18% annual simple interest if she will use the refund to pay off the loan?

14. A student will inherit $20,000 on her 21st birthday. How much can she borrow fifteen months prior to that time against her inheritance if she is charged 9% annual simple interest?

15. Sam is due a $500 refund. A tax service will give him the money 2 months early, less a $40 fee. To what annual simple interest rate is this fee equivalent?

16. Frank's parents loan him $2500 for 3 months, but he must repay $2600 at the end of that time. What annual simple interest rate is he being charged?

17. A man used his stereo system valued at $160 as collateral on a loan from a pawnshop for 2 months. Their finance charge was $18, and they give him $142. What annual simple interest rate does this represent?

18. A student borrows $500 from her parents for 6 months, and they charge her 5% annual simple interest. How much will she need to repay her parents after the 6 months?

19. You are due a $650 tax refund. Your brother agrees to give you $600 now if you will give him the $650 three months from now. What annual simple interest rate is your brother earning on this deal?

Section 1.3   Annual Compound Interest

Most banks use <u>compound interest</u> on savings accounts. This means that interest is paid periodically, and each time interest is paid to the account that interest is calculated based on the amount of money currently in the account, not just on the original principal.

Example 1 Suppose $1000 is deposited in an account paying 4% interest, compounded annually. Find the value of the account after four years.

<u>Solution</u> The value at the end of one year is calculated by using the simple interest formula for one year, that is, with $t = 1$.

Value after 1 year = $1000 + 0.04 × $1000 = $1000 + $40 = $1,040.

For the second year, we begin with a value of $1,040.00, and *interest is earned on this entire amount.* Starting with this amount as our principal for the second year, and using the simple interest formula again for one year, we calculate the value F_2 at the end of the second year.

Value after 2 years = $1040 + 0.04 × $1040 = $1040 + $41.60 = $1,081.60.

Similarly, the values at the end of the third and fourth years are, respectively,

Value after 3 years = $1,081.60 + 0.04 × $1,081.60 = $1,081.60 + $43.26 = $1,124.86,

Value after 4 years = $1,124.86 + 0.04 × $1,124.86 = $1,124.86 + $44.99 = $1,169.85

Notice that the interest at the end of each year is added to the current value to get the new value, and the new value is used as the principal to calculate the interest for the next year. Moreover, the *amount* of interest added per year grows; $40 the first year, then $41.60, then $43.26, then $44.29. This is because the principal on which the interest is calculated is growing.

Now let us examine the compounding effect using a general principal P and general annual rate of interest r. If the interest is added at the end of each year, then the value at the end of one year is

$$P + rP(1) = P + rP = P(1 + r)$$

as in the simple interest calculation. This means that the annual interest rate is really the percent change (as discussed in Section 1.1) of the value of the investment. The second year's value is calculated using the value at the end of year 1 as the principal:

Value after 2 years = $P(1 + r) + P(1 + r)r = P(1 + r)(1 + r)$,   which simplifies to

Value after 2 years = $P(1+r)^2$

Similarly, the third year's value is calculated using the value after 2 years as the principal:

Value after 3 years = $P(1+r)^2 + P(1+r)^2 r = P(1+r)^2 (1+r)$,   which simplifies to

Value after 3 years = $P(1+r)^3$

Crucial Idea: This pattern of multiplying the previous year's value by $(1 + r)$ is repeated each successive year, so the exponent on $(1 + r)$ matches the number of years of the investment:

Year	Value
1	$P(1+r)$
2	$P(1+r)^2$
3	$P(1+r)^3$
4	$P(1+r)^4$

And so on.

From the pattern of these computations we can infer the formula for the Future Value of an account that uses annual compound interest:

> **A principal P invested at an <u>annual</u> <u>compound</u> interest rate r grows to**
> $$F = P(1+r)^t \text{ after } t \text{ years.}$$
>
> **The value F is called the <u>Future Value</u>, and the value P is called the <u>Present Value</u>. The <u>amount of interest earned</u> is $I = F - P$.**

Example 2 Suppose $1000 is deposited in an account paying 6% annual interest. Compare the value after 10 years using simple interest and compound interest, and also the amount of interest.

<u>Solution</u> (i) Using Simple Interest:

$$F = P + Prt = \$1000 + \$1000 \times 0.06 \times 10 = \$1600, \text{ so } \$600 \text{ in interest was earned.}$$

(ii) Using Compound Interest:

$$F = P(1+r)^t = \$1000(1+0.06)^{10} = \$1000 \times 1.06^{10} = \$1790.85,$$

so $1790.85 - $1000 = $790.85 in interest was earned.

Calculating the Answer

To evaluate 1000×1.06^{10} requires two operations, a multiplication and an exponentiation.

The standard order of operations is: when faced with a choice of operations, do exponentiation first, then multiplication or division, and finally addition or subtraction.

Here this means that exponentiation is done before multiplication. *This text assumes your calculator has algebraic logic and will respect this order of operations.*

To perform an exponentiation on your calculator you must use the $\wedge$ or y^x or x^y key. **In this text we will use $\wedge$ to denote this calculator key.** Assuming your calculator has algebraic logic, you may enter the expression in the same manner that it is read:

Calculator keystrokes for Example 2 (ii):   1000 $\times$ 1.06 y^x or x^y or $\wedge$ 10   =

Comparing Simple and Compound Interest over Time.

In Example 2 compound interest yields a significantly higher value than simple interest after 10 years, $1790.85 versus $1600. Figure 1.1 below shows how the value in an account grows over 10 years if the account starts with an initial principal $1000.

Year	F at 6% Simple Interest	F at 6% Compound Interest
1	$1060	$1060.00
2	$1120	$1123.60
3	$1180	$1191.02
4	$1240	$1262.48
5	$1300	$1338.23
6	$1360	$1418.52
7	$1420	$1503.63
8	$1480	$1593.85
9	$1540	$1689.48
10	$1600	$1790.85

Figure 1.1

In Figure 1.1 the values found using compound interest soon significantly exceed those found using simple interest. One explanation comes from the forms of the formulas for the values:

$$F = P(1 + rt) \qquad\qquad F = P(1+r)^t$$

Simple Interest   Compound Interest

The simple interest formula is a *linear* function of time t, because it can also be written as $F = Prt + P$. (Recall that $y = mx + b$ gives a straight line in the xy plane; here the variables t and F are related in the same manner as x and y in a usual linear function, so the graph will be a straight line.) On the other hand, with compound interest the formula uses an *exponential* function, because the variable t is an exponent. This causes the graph of compound interest to turn upward at an ever-increasing slope. In each case, the slope is the amount of interest earned each year. With simple interest, that amount of interest per year stays constant at rP. But with compound interest the amount of interest earned per year grows, because that amount is calculated as a percentage of the *current* value, not the *original* principal P.

Simple and Compound Interest as Iterative Processes

The values in Figure 1.1 also emphasize the iterative nature of interest calculations.

Simple interest pays the *same dollar amount* of interest each year; in Figure 1.1 it is 6% of $1000 = $60. So in the middle column $60 is *added* to each year's value to obtain the next year's value. The number t in the Simple Interest formula $F = P + Prt$ counts the number of times $I = Pr$ is added.

Compound interest pays the *same percentage of the previous year's value* each year; in Figure 1.1 it is 6% of the current value. In the last column each year's value is *multiplied* by $(1 + .06)$ to obtain the next year's value. The exponent t in the compound interest formula $F = P(1+r)^t$ counts the number of multiplications.

Figure 1.2 below shows a plot of the ordered pairs (year, value) computed in the table in Figure 1.1, but extended over 30 years. The simple interest ordered pairs lie along a straight line, visually illustrating the linear growth described above. The compound interest ordered pairs lie along a curve that is continually turning upward. **Notice that after 30 years the compound interest value is over twice the simple interest value.**

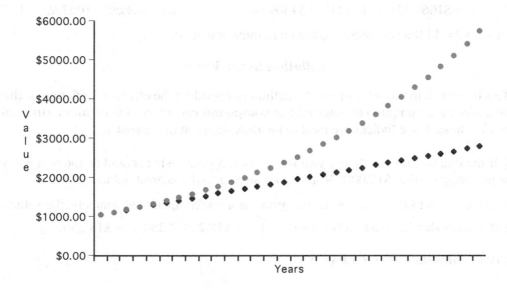

Figure 1.2

Example 3 At age 25 George has $10,000 and Marsha has $5000. Each has their money invested in an account paying 6% annual interest, but Marsha's pays compound interest and George's pays simple interest. Compare the values of their accounts at the end of 30 years.

Solution: Since George's account pays simple interest, he earns

$$I = Pr = (\$10,000)(.06) = \$600$$

each year for the next 30 years. At the end of 30 years he will have earned

$$I = (Pr)(t) = (\$600)(30) = \$18,000$$

and so his account will be worth

$$F = P + I = \$10,000 + \$18,000 = \$28,000.$$

On the other hand, Marsha's account pays compound interest, so each year its value increases by 6% of its current value, so the current value is multiplied by 1.06. After 30 years her account will be worth

$$F = P(1+r)^t = \$5000(1.06)^{30} = \$28,717.46.   \text{Keystrokes: } 5000 \times 1.06 \wedge 5 =$$

Quiz Yourself: (Answers at the end of this section, before the Problems.)

1. If $5000 is invested at 4% annual compound interest, what will be its value after 15 years? How much interest will you have earned?
2. Which investment will be worth more after 20 years, $4000 invested at 3% annual simple interest or $3000 invested at 4% compound interest?

Example 4 Suppose $950 is invested into an account earning 6% annual compound interest. After two years, all of the money that has accumulated is withdrawn and reinvested for four years in an account paying 7.2% annual compound interest. How much will the account be worth at the end of the entire six years? How much interest will have been earned?

Solution: After the first two years, the account will have accumulated to

$$F = \$950(1+0.06)^2 = \$1067.42   \text{Keystrokes: } 9500 \times 1.06 \wedge 2 =$$

This becomes the principal for the investment during the next four years. At the end of that four-year period (and the end of the entire six years) the account will have accumulated to

$$F = \$1067.42(1+0.072)^4 = \$1409.66.   \text{Keystrokes: } 1067.42 \times 1.072 \wedge 4 =$$

This represents $I = \$1409.66 - \$950 = \$459.66$ in interest earned.

Inflation in the Future

Inflation refers to growth in the price of goods. Estimates regarding the effects of inflation **in the future** are always made under the assumption of some annual **compound rate** of growth in prices. (In Section 1.8 we will see how Consumer Price Indices are used to measure inflation in the past.)

Example 5 If the inflation rate is 4% per year for the next 5 years, what should be the cost five years from now of a car presently costing $15,000? Round your answer to the nearest dollar.

Solution. Since the $15,000 price of the car grows at 4.0% compounded annually, the value of the car at the end of 5 years should be $15,000(1+0.04)^5 = \$18,249.79354... \approx \$18,250.$

Calculator keystrokes: $15000 \times 1.04 \wedge 5 =$

Quiz Yourself: (Answers below.)

3. Suppose $800 is invested at 4.2% annual interest for 5 years. After that time the money is moved to an account paying 5% annual interest. What will be the value of the money after 10 years in the second account? How much interest will you have earned after the 15 total years?

4. Suppose house prices increase at a rate of 3.5% per year for the next 4 years. What will be the price 4 years from now of a house currently costing $120,000? Round your answer to the nearest thousand dollars.

Answers to Quiz Yourself:

1. $F = \$5000(1.04)^{15} = \$9004.72$. $I = F - P = \$9004.72 - \$5000 = \$4004.72$

2. $4000 at 3% simple interest for 20 years: $\$4000 + \$4000(.03)(20) = \$6400$

   $3000 at 4% compound interest for 20 years: $\$3000(1.04)^{20} = \$6573.37$

   The second is larger.

3. After 5 years $F = \$800(1 + 0.042)^5 = \$800(1.042)^5 = \$982.72$

   After the next 10 years $F = \$982.72(1.05)^{10} = \$1600.75$. $I = \$1600.75 - \$800 = \$800.75$

4. Price $= \$120000(1 + 0.035)^4 = \$120000(1.035)^4 = 137,702.76 \approx \$138,000$.

Problems for Section 1.3

Sharpen Your Skills: (Answers in back of text.)

1. Calculate $\$1200(1.08)^{12}$

2. Calculate $\$900(1.07)^9$

Communicate the concepts: (Answers in back of text.)

3. Explain the difference between simple interest and compound interest.

4. Explain the meaning of each variable in the compound interest formula on page 18.

Apply Your Knowledge: Round all dollar amounts to the nearest penny unless instructed otherwise.
(Answers to odd-numbered problems in back of text.)

5. Most people can invest up to $2000 in an Individual Retirement Account (IRA) each year. Suppose you deposit $2,000 at age 21 in an account paying 6.2% compounded annually. How much will this single investment be worth when you reach (a) Age 50? (b) Age 65?

6. Suppose you deposit $2,000 at age 21 in an account paying 5.6% compounded annually. How much will this single investment be worth when you reach (a) Age 55?   (b) Age 70?

7. On his twenty-first birthday Bob put $1000 in an account paying 5.5% interest compounded annually. On his fortieth birthday Sam put $3000 into an account paying the same rate. How much will each of them have on his 55th birthday?

8. On her twenty-first birthday Jan put $2500 in an account paying 6.2% interest compounded annually. On her fiftieth birthday Mona put $6000 into an account paying the same rate. How much will each of them have on her 60th birthday?

9. John invests $2000 in account that pays 7% annual *simple* interest. Jane invests $1000 in an account that pays 7% annual *compound* interest. Compare their values after 35 years.

10. Suppose Jane's investment in Problem 9 only pays 6% annual compound interest. Compare the values of the two accounts after 35 years.

11. Mike deposits $2400 in an account paying 5% annual compound interest and leaves it for three years. Because interest rates have risen he moves all the money from that account to one paying 6.1% annual compound interest. What will be the value of his investment two years after he moves the money? How much interest will he have earned at the end of the five years?

12. Bank of Louisville offers a five-year "Rising Rate CD". It pays 5.8% annual compound interest for the first year, 6.1% annual compound interest for the next two years, and 6.5% annual compound interest for the last two years. If $1500 is invested in this CD, what will be its value at the end of the five-year period? How much interest will he have earned?

13. The cost of rental space for offices is projected to grow at an annual rate of 9.5% per year for the next four years. What should space costing $28 per square foot today rent for in four years? *Round your answer to the nearest dollar.*

14. If a loaf of bread costs $2.25 now, and the rate of inflation for the next 20 years is 3.5%, what should a loaf of bread cost 20 years from now?

15. If a gallon of milk costs $3.55 now, and the rate of inflation for the next 25 years is 3.2%, what should a gallon of milk cost 25 years from now?

16. Suppose new car prices rise at an annual rate of 3.8% per year for the next five years. What will be the price in five years of a BMW that costs $40,000 (to the nearest thousand dollars) today? *Round your answer to the nearest thousand dollars.*

17. For 2014-15 the full-time tuition per year for a resident undergraduate student at the University of Louisville was $10,236. College expenses have been growing at 8.5% per year recently. If this growth rate continues, what will be the tuition per year for a similar student for 2018-2019? *Round your answer to the nearest dollar.*

18. If housing costs continue to rise at 5.4% per year, what will a house currently costing $90,000 cost 8 years from now? *Round your answer to the nearest thousand dollars.*

Review Problems (Answers in back of text.)

19. A tax refund service offers to give you your $400 tax refund 2 months early, less a $19 fee. This is equivalent to a loan with a $19 fee. What would be the annual simple rate of such a loan?

20. If $2500 grows to $2800, what is the percent change in value?

Section 1.4   Compounding More Often; APY

Most banks pay compound interest, but the compounding is usually done more than once per year. We now investigate how such compounding affects the calculation of a future value or a present value. This will lead to a standard way of reporting an interest rate, called the Annual Percentage Yield.

Example 1 If $1000 is invested at 6% annual compound interest for 10 years, what will the Future Value of the account be if the interest is compounded
     (a) annually,
     (b) four times a year (quarterly), or
     (c) monthly (12 times per year)

<u>Solution</u>; (a) With annual compounding interest is calculated and paid into the account once at the end of each year of investment, so $F = \$1000(1+0.06)^{10} = \$1790.85$

(b) With quarterly compounding interest is paid into the account four times a year (every 3 months), but each is at a rate that is 1/4 the annual rate. In this example, that rate would be $0.06 / 4 = 0.015$. (This is called the **periodic interest rate** you earn for each three-month period.) However, the interest is paid 4 times per year for 10 years, or a total of 40 times (This is referred to as the **total number of compounding periods**.) So the value after 40 compoundings at 1.5% each will be

$$F = \$1000(1+0.015)^{4\times10} = \$1000(1.015)^{40} = \$1814.02$$

(c) With monthly compounding interest is paid 12 times a year at a rate that is 1/12 of the annual rate. Here that periodic rate is $6\% / 12 = 0.5\% = 0.005$. The total number of compoundings is 12 times a year for 10 years, or 120 compoundings. The value after 10 years (120 compoundings) will be

$$F = \$1000(1+0.005)^{12\times10} = \$1000(1.005)^{120} = \$1819.40$$

Generalizing the features in Example 1 leads to:

General Compound Interest Formula: $F = P(1+i)^m$

where

    F = Future Value = Value accumulated at end of compounding
    P = Present Value = starting Principal
    i = periodic interest rate = $\dfrac{\text{annual interest rate}}{\text{number of compoundings per year}}$

    m = total number of compoundings
       = (number of years) $\times$ (number of compoundings per year)

Example 1 Continued If you deposit $1000 at 6% annual compound interest for 10 years, what will the value be if the compounding is:
     (d) semi-annual (twice a year)
     (e) daily (365 times per year)

<u>Solution</u> (d) If the compounding is twice a year for 10 years there will be $m = 2(10) = 20$ compoundings at the periodic rate of $6\%/2 = 3\%$. So the value will be $F = 1000(1+0.03)^{20} = \$1806.11$.

(e) If the compounding is 365 times per year, then the periodic rate is $\dfrac{.06}{365} \approx 0.0001643$ and there will be $(10)(365) = 3650$ compoundings. The value may be calculated using either of the following:

$$F = \$1000\left(1+\frac{0.06}{365}\right)^{3650} \quad \text{or } F = \$1000(1.0001643)^{3650} \qquad \text{Both give } F = \$1822.03$$

<u>NOTE: DO NOT ROUND OFF YOUR VALUE OF i.</u> In Example 1 (e), the periodic interest rate is 0.06/365 is approximately 0.0001643. If that were rounded to, say, 0.00016, the value of F would be calculated as $F = \$1000(1.00016)^{3650} = \$1793.11$, a difference of almost \$30!

This reinforces the Preferred Calculator Method stated in Section 1.2: **<u>Make calculations without intermediate roundings</u>**.

Most students find it easier to calculate $\$1000\left(1+\dfrac{0.06}{365}\right)^{3650}$ than to evaluate $\dfrac{0.06}{365} = 0.0001643$ and

then re-enter that long number in the calculation of $\$1000(1.0001643)^{3650}$

If you do make intermediate evaluations, be sure to enter the **entire** result in the next calculation! Compound interest calculations are very sensitive to changes in the interest rate.

Picturing the Situation with a Time Line

The use of F for the "future value" of the account at an ending time, and P for the "present value", or original principal, of the account at a starting time will help you keep their relationship straight. A *time line* may also help. It is a visual device for presenting the key features of the compound interest problem. The line shows time progressing from left to right, *with time being measured in compounding periods*. This scale is indicated with numbers below the line. Above the line we place the dollar amounts involved in the problem. Here is a generic time line:

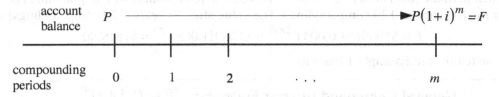

The arrow indicates that we are calculating the unknown future value F from the known present value P.

Example 2 Find the future value of an investment of \$10,000.00 after a period of six years and six months at 8% compounded quarterly.

Solution: Identify the values of the key variables: (i) $P = \$10,000.00$, (ii) write the time in years: $t = 6.5$ years, (iii) the annual rate as a decimal is $r = 8\% = 0.08$, and (iv) there are 4 compoundings per year. Then the periodic interest rate is $i = 0.08 / 4 = 0.02$, which is the rate per quarter, and the total number of compounding periods is $m = 4(6.5) = 26$ quarterly compoundings. The time line is

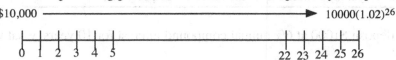

Using our variables in the Compound Interest Formula gives:

$$F = \$10000(1.02)^{26} = \$16{,}734.18.$$

Example 3 If you invest \$9,875.00 at 8.1% compounded monthly, how much will this investment be worth in 17 years?

Solution: Identify the values of the key variables: $P = \$9{,}875.00$, $n = 12$ compoundings per year, and annual rate $r = 0.081$. So $i = 0.081 / 12 = 0.00675$ is the interest rate per month and $m = nt = 12(17) = 204$ is the total number of compoundings. Using the Compound Interest Formula:

$$F = \$9{,}875\left(1+\frac{0.081}{12}\right)^{204} = \$9875(1.00675)^{204} = \$38{,}953.93.$$

Quiz Yourself: (Answers at the end of this section, before the problems.)
1. If $3000 is invested at 5% compounded semi-annually, what will it be worth after 10 years?
2. If you invest $5500 at 5.4% compounded monthly, what will it be worth after 8 years and 4 months? How much interest will you have earned?

Example 4 Bank of Louisville offers a 4 year "Rising Rate" Certificate of Deposit (CD) which pays 5.8% compounded daily for the first year, then 5.9% compounded daily for the second year, and finally 6.2% compounded daily for the last two years. If $1000 is invested in this account, how much will it be worth at the end of the 4 years?

Solution: Since there are 3 different rates used, we must break up the 4 years into the three time periods in which those rates apply. The future value F_1 at the end of the first year becomes the Present Value P_2 at the start of the second year, and the future value F_2 to which that grows at the end of the second year becomes the present value P_3 for the growth during the third time period (last two years). Here is the situation depicted in a time line:

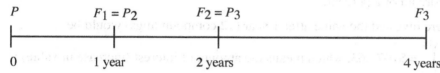

We proceed iteratively. For all the periods the compounding is daily. For the first and second years $t = 1$ year; for the third period $t = 2$ years. In each of the first two periods there are 365 compoundings, in the third period there are $2(365) = 730$ compoundings. So:

$$F_1 = \$1000\left(1 + \frac{0.058}{365}\right)^{365} = \$1059.71 = P_2$$

$$F_2 = \$1059.71\left(1 + \frac{0.059}{365}\right)^{365} = \$1124.11 = P_3$$

$$F_3 = \$1124.11\left(1 + \frac{0.062}{365}\right)^{730} = \$1272.50, \text{ the value at the end of the four years.}$$

Annual Percentage Yield (APY)

We saw in Example 1 that different numbers of compoundings per year can produce different future values at the same annual rate r. For example, if $1000 is invested at 8% compounded quarterly, the value at the end of one year is $\$1000\left(1 + 0.08/4\right)^4 = \$1082.43$. Thus the original $1000 investment earned interest of $82.43 during the year which represents a percentage increase for the year of $\frac{\$82.43}{\$1000} = 0.08243 = 8.243\%$ for one year. This percentage increase is called the APY of the investment.

> **The percentage increase in the value of an investment in one year is called the Annual Percentage Yield (APY) of the investment, and denoted by Y.**

According to the Truth in Lending Law, banks are now required to use the APY of an investment when they advertise the investment. This greatly simplifies the process of comparing investments that are compounded different numbers of time per year. Prior to this law consumers were forced to compute the values of an investment for each different rate and each different compounding frequency in order to determine the best investment.

Example 5 A student puts $400 in a "money market account", in which the daily interest rate varies. At the end of one year the value of the account has risen to $416.38. What was the APY of this investment for this year? Round your answer to the nearest hundredth of a percent.

Solution: During the year the value of the account has risen by I = $416.38 - $400.00 = $16.38. The percent change is $\dfrac{\$16.38}{\$400} = 0.04095 = 4.095\% \approx 4.10\%$. So the APY would be stated as 4.10%.

Note When writing the rounded value 4.10%, the 0 in the hundredths place should not be omitted. That 0 emphasizes that we know the hundredths place is 0. Writing 4.1% does not make such a statement, because 4.1% seems to have been rounded to the nearest tenth of a percent. If the result of rounding were 4.1% then the actual value could be anywhere between 4.05% and 4.15%, for any such number would round to 4.1%.

Example 6 Find the annual percentage yield for a rate of 7.50% compounded monthly. Round your answer to the nearest hundredth of a percent.

Solution: If $1000 were invested the value after 1 year (12 compoundings) would be

$$F = \$1000\left(1+\frac{0.075}{12}\right)^{12} = \$1077.63, \text{ which means the amount of interest (increase in value) is}$$

$1077.63 - $1000 = $77.63. This is a percent change of $77.63/$1000 = 0.07763 = 7.763....% which rounds to 7.76%.

If we had invested $2000 then $F = \$2000\left(1+\dfrac{0.075}{12}\right)^{12} = 2155.26$, so the percent change is

($2155.26 − $2000)/$2000 = $155.27/$2000 = 0.07763... = 7.763....% which rounds to 7.76%. **The APY Y does not depend on the amount of the principal.**

In a situation like Example 6, where the interest rate and compounding frequency are known and constant throughout the investment, there is a formula for APY. **Fill in the justifications for the steps below.**

Suppose a principal P is invested for one year and the annual rate r and compounded n times per year. Then: Statement   Justification

Value at end of year = $F = P\left(1+\dfrac{r}{n}\right)^n$ _____

Interest in 1 year = $P\left(1+\dfrac{r}{n}\right)^n - P$ _____

Percent change in Value = $\dfrac{P\left(1+\dfrac{r}{n}\right)^n - P}{P}$ _____

Simplify: APY $Y = \dfrac{P\left(\left(1+\dfrac{r}{n}\right)^n - 1\right)}{P} = \left(1+\dfrac{r}{n}\right)^n - 1$ _____

In summary:

> **The Annual Percentage Yield (APY), denoted Y, of an investment at an annual rate of r that is compounded n times per year may be calculated by** $Y = \left(1+\dfrac{r}{n}\right)^n - 1$.

Example 7 By comparing their APYs, decide whether an investment at the rate of 7.6% compounded quarterly is better or worse than an investment at the rate of 7.52% compounded daily. Round each APY to the nearest hundredth of a percent.

Solution: For the first investment $r = 0.076$ and $n = 4$ compoundings per year so using the APY formula above

$$Y = \left(1 + \frac{0.076}{4}\right)^4 - 1$$

When this is evaluated we obtain $Y = 0.07819\ldots = 7.819\ldots\%$. So $Y = 7.82\%$ when converted to a percentage and rounded to the nearest hundredth of a percent.

For the second investment $r = 0.0752$ and $n = 365$ compoundings per year so

$$Y = \left(1 + \frac{0.0752}{365}\right)^{365} - 1$$

When this is evaluated we obtain $Y = 0.07809\ldots = 7.809\ldots\%$ So $Y = 7.81\%$ when converted to a percentage and rounded to the nearest hundredth of a percent. Since the first investment has a higher APY it is a better investment. (In practice, banks are required to perform this calculation and advertise the APY of an investment.)

Quiz Yourself: (Answers on next page.) Round your APYs to the nearest hundredth of a percent.

3. If an investment of $350 grows to $361.23 in one year, what APY did the investment pay for that year?

4. What is the APY of an investment at 6.1% compounded quarterly?

5. Is 6% compounded daily a better or worse investment than 6.1% compounded quarterly? Find the APY of each, and compare them.

Answers to Quiz Yourself:

1. Earns $5\%/2 = 2.5\% = 0.025$ at each of the 20 compoundings; $F = \$3000(1+0.025)^{20} = \$4915.85$

2. Earns $5.4\%/12 = 0.45\%$ each month for $8(12) + 4 = 100$ months. $F = \$5500(1.0045)^{100} = \$8617.01$

   Amount of interest earned is $I = F - P = \$8617.01 - \$5500 = \$3117.01$

3. The amount of increase is $I = \$361.23 - \$350 = \$11.23$. The percent change is

   $$\frac{\$11.23}{\$350} = 0.0320857.... = 3.20857...\% \approx 3.21\% = Y.$$

4. $\$1000$ grows to $\$1000\left(1+\dfrac{0.061}{4}\right)^4 = \$1062.41$ in 1 year, a percent change of $Y = \$62.41\,/\,\$1000 =$

   $0.06241 \approx 6.24\%$. Or, here we can use the above formula: $Y = \left(1+\dfrac{0.061}{4}\right)^4 - 1 = 0.06241 \approx 6.24\%$.

5. For 6% compounded daily $Y = \left(1+\dfrac{0.06}{365}\right)^{365} - 1 = 0.0618313... = 0.0618313.. \approx 6.18\%$. Since this is a

   lower APY that we found in the previous problem, 6.1% compounded quarterly is a better investment.

Problems for Section 1.4

Sharpen Your Skills: (Answers in back of text.)

1. Evaluate $\$1200(1.012)^{36}$

2. Evaluate $\$360\left(1+\dfrac{0.05}{365}\right)^{730}$

3. Find the percent change from \$250 to \$260.

4. Find the percent change from \$550 to \$583.

5. Evaluate $\left(1+\dfrac{0.04}{365}\right)^{365}-1$ (Give answer as a percent rounded to nearest hundredth)

6. Evaluate $\left(1+\dfrac{0.05}{12}\right)^{12}-1$ (Give answer as a percent rounded to nearest hundredth)

Communicate the Concepts: (Answers in back of text.)

In problems 7 and 8, give the **meaning** (<u>use words</u>) of each of the variables listed below that appear in the formulas of this section, and give the correct **units** (dollars, months, years, etc.) or **form** (decimal, whole number, etc.) when they are used in the formulas.

7. (a) *P* Meaning: _____   Unit: _____

    (b) *t* Meaning: _____   Unit: _____

    (c) *i* Meaning: _____   Form _____

    (d) *m* Meaning: _____   Form _____

8. (a) *F* Meaning: _____   Unit: _____

    (b) *Y* Meaning: _____   Form: _____

    (c) *r* Meaning: _____   Form: _____

9. Explain the difference between the meanings of the variables *r* and *i*.

10. Explain the difference between the meanings of the variables *t* and *m*.

11. Explain the difference between the meanings of the variables *Y* and *r*.

12. Explain how the variables *P*, *I*, and *F* are related.

Apply Your Knowledge: In these problems all stated rates are annual compound interest rates unless otherwise stated. (Answers to odd-numbered problems in back of text.)

13. Suppose that, on the tenth birthday of your son, you invest \$7000 in a Certificate of Deposit (CD) paying interest at the annual rate of 5.4% compounded monthly. What will the value of the CD be on your son's eighteenth birthday? How much interest will you have earned?

14. To what amount will an investment of \$15,000.00 grow over a period of 8 years and 7 months if the investment earns 7.2% annual interest compounded monthly? How much interest will it have earned?

15. If you invest $4000 in an 18-month Certificate of Deposit (CD) that pays 6.9% annual interest compounded quarterly, what will be the value of your investment at the end of the 18 months? How much interest will you have earned?

16. If you invest $500 in a 9 month Certificate of Deposit (CD) that pays 6.8% annual interest compounded quarterly, what will be the value of your investment at the end of the 9 months? How much interest will you have earned?

17. If a money market account grows in value from $1325 to $1370 in one year, what APY did it earn for that year? Round your answer to the nearest hundredth of a percent.

18. The value of a certain stock rose from $23.50 to $24.75 in one year. If you had invested in the stock what APY would your investment have earned? Round your answer to the nearest hundredth of a percent.

19. An investment has a annual compound interest rate of 5.4%. Find the APY of the investment if it is subject to the following compounding frequencies:
    (a) Semi-annually   (b) Quarterly   (c) Monthly   (d) Daily (365 times/year)
    (e) Look at the APYs calculated in (a) – (d). What seems to happen to APY as the number of compoundings per year increases?

20. By comparing their APYs, decide which is better, an investment at 7.28% compounded monthly, an investment at 7.35% compounded quarterly, or an investment at 7.4% compounded semi-annually.

21. Bank A offers to turn your $500 into $529.16 in one year. Bank B offers 5.68% compounded daily. Find the APY of each investment and decide which offers a better deal for you.

22. Bank C offers 6.64% interest compounded quarterly. Bank D offers 6.52% compounded monthly. Find the APY of each investment and decide which offers a better deal for the investor.

23. A 1-year Certificate of Deposit pays 5.4% compounded monthly for the first 3 months and then 5.7% compounded monthly for the next 9 months. If $1500 is invested in the CD:
    (a) What will the CD be worth at the end of the year?
    (b) How much interest will it have earned?
    (c) Determine the APY of the investment by finding the percent change in value of the CD. Why can the formula on page 26 **not** be used here?

24. On January 1 George invests $1000 for 90 days in an account paying 5.5% compounded daily. At the end of that time he moves the money to a different account that pays 6% compounded monthly, where it stays for the rest of the year.
    (a) What will the investment be worth at the end of the year?
    (b) How much interest will it have earned?
    (c) Determine the APY of the investment by finding the percent change in value of the investment. Why can the formula on page 26 **not** be used here?

Review Problems: (Answers in back of text.)
25. Sue's parents loan her $1500 for 4 months, but she must repay $1600 at the end of that time. What annual simple interest rate are her parents charging her?

26. Hospital costs are currently rising at 9.5% per year. If a room now costs exactly $400 per night, what will it cost in ten years? Round your answer to the nearest dollar.

Section 1.5 Finding Present Value with Compound Interest

In some situations we know the future value F at the end of the investment but want to know the present value P required at the start of the investment. To find that P we substitute into the compound interest equation $F = P(1+i)^m$ and then solve for P by dividing both sides by $(1+i)^m$.

Example 1 How much must the parents of a child invest now in a CD paying 4.5% compounded annually in order to accumulate $30,000 for college at the end of the next 12 years? How much interest will the CD have earned?

Solution Since $30,000 is the desired value 12 years from now it is the future value F of the CD. The interest rate is $r = 0.045$, and the time is $t = 12$ years. The compounding is annual this so $i = r = 0.045$ and $m = 12$ annual compoundings. The unknown is the original principal (present value) P of the investment. Substituting these in the basic compound interest equation $F = P(1+i)^m$, we see that we must solve $P(1+0.045)^{12} = \$30,000$. Dividing both sides by $(1.045)^{12}$, we obtain $P = \dfrac{\$30,000}{(1.045)^{12}}$.

This evaluates as $P = \$17,689.92$. Therefore, to reach the $30,000 goal you must invest $$17,689.92 today. You will have earned I = F - P = $30,000 - $17,689.92 = $12,310.08.

Calculator Keystrokes: 30000 ÷ (1.045) ^ 12 =

The time line for a problem like Example 1 is shown below. The arrow indicates that now we are calculating an unknown P from a known F. This is sometimes called *depreciating* the Future Value.

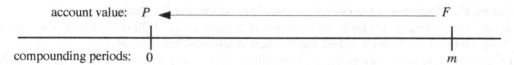

Example 2 Find the principal that must be invested for a period of 8 years at 5%, compounded monthly, to accumulate $15,000.00 at the end of that time. How much interest will have been earned?

Solution Since the compounding is done monthly, we have $i = 0.05 / 12$ as the rate per month, and $m = 12(8) = 96$ is the number of monthly compoundings.   The time line is:

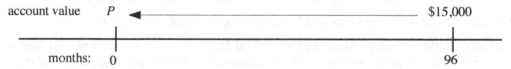

Thus we must solve: $$\$15,000 = P\left(1+\frac{0.05}{12}\right)^{96}$$

Divide both sides by $\left(1+\dfrac{0.05}{12}\right)^{96}$: $P = \dfrac{15,000}{\left(1+\dfrac{0.05}{12}\right)^{96}}$ Evaluate: $P = \$10,063.16$.

So you must invest $10,063.16 to reach your goal 8 years later. $I = \$15,000 - \$10,063.16 = \$4936.84$

Calculator Keystrokes: 15000 ÷ (1 + 0.05 ÷ 12) ^ 96 =

<u>Alternative Solution to Example 2:</u> We could have rounded $i = 0.05 \, / \, 12$ to 0.004166667. Then

$$\$15,000 = P(1.00416667)^{96} \quad \text{and} \quad P = \frac{15000}{(1.00416667)^{96}} = \$10,063.16 \text{ as in the solution above.}$$

CAREFUL: If you round $0.05 \, / \, 12$ to, say 0.004 you obtain $P = \dfrac{15000}{(1.004)^{96}} = \$10,224.80$, which has

an error of \$161.64. **Do not round intermediate calculations more than necessary!**

Example 3 To have \$17,000 on your daughter's seventeenth birthday, how much must you invest on her third birthday in a CD paying 2.6% compounded quarterly? How much interest will you have earned?

<u>Solution:</u> Between her third and her seventeenth birthdays is $t = 17 - 3 = 14$ years. So $m = 4(14) = 56$ quarterly compoundings. Putting the \$17,000 at her seventeenth birthday in the timeline we have:

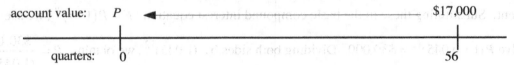

Also, the rate paid each quarter is $i = 0.026 \, / \, 4 = 0.0065$. So we must solve $17,000 = P(1 + 0.0065)^{56}$

Divide both sides by $(1 + 0.0065)^{56}$: $P = \dfrac{17,000}{(1.0065)^{56}} = \$11,827.07.$

So, if \$11,827.07 is invested on her third birthday she will have the \$17,000 on her seventeenth birthday. You will have earned $I = F - P = \$17,000 - \$11,827.07 = \$5172.93.$

Quiz Yourself: (Answers at the end of this Section, before the Problems.)
1. How much must you invest today in order for it to grow to \$15,000 in 8 years if your investment earns 7% compounded yearly? How much interest will you have earned?
2. To have \$5,000 on your 16th birthday, how much must your parents invest on your tenth birthday if the investment earns 4% compounded monthly? How much interest will they have earned?

How Does a Bond Differ From a CD?

A Certificate of Deposit (CD) pays a guaranteed interest rate r for a stated length of time t. The value F of the CD at the end of that time depends on the amount P of money invested: $F = P(1 + r)^t$. Usually the CD is issued by a bank or savings and loan, and is guaranteed by the FDIC.

On the other hand, a bond is issued by the Federal Treasury or by a company, and may not be guaranteed. The value F of the bond at the end of its stated time period t is fixed. The price P of the bond depends upon the rate r it pays, and is found by solving $F = P(1 + r)^t$ for P.

Example 4 The price today of a \$1000 5-year treasury bond depends on the interest rate of the bond. Find the price today if the annual interest rate is (a) 4%, (b) 3%, (c) 2%.

<u>Solution</u> Here F is fixed at \$1000 and $t = 5$ in all cases. If we solve $1,000 = P(1 + r)^5$ for P

we obtain $P = \dfrac{1,000}{(1 + r)^5}$. We can evaluate this for the values of r in (a), (b), and (c):

(a) $P = \dfrac{1,000}{(1.04)^5} = \$821.93$ (b) $P = \dfrac{1,000}{(1.03)^5} = \$862.61$ (c) $P = \dfrac{1,000}{(1.02)^5} = \$905.73$

Example 5 Suppose you bought the 5-year $1000 treasury bond at 3%. In Example 4 (b) its price was calculated to be $862.61. After 2 years, interest rates on treasury bonds have changed. How do you determine the value of your bond at that time?

Solution If your investment had been in a CD paying 3% you could calculate the Future Value of your $862.61 investment after 2 years: $F = \$862.61(1.03)^2 = \$915.14$. But with a bond, the value of the bond depends on the current rate being paid by bonds of a similar quality.

If the interest rates have fallen from 3% to 2.5%, the value of your bond is the price of a $1000 3-year bond (since there are 3 years remaining on your bond) at 2.5% interest. We solve:

$$1000 = P(1.025)^3 \quad \text{which yields} \quad P = 1000/(1.025)^3 = \$928.60$$

So when interest rates fell, your bond did better than a comparable CD would have done!

If the interest rates have risen from 3% to 3.5%, the value of your bond is the price of a $1000 3-year bond (since there are 3 years remaining on your bond) at 3.5% interest. We solve:

$$1000 = P(1.035)^3 \quad \text{which yields} \quad P = 1000/(1.035)^3 = \$901.94$$

So when interest rates rose, your bond did worse than a comparable CD would have done!

Note: If you hold your bond the full 5 years, you will still get the full $1000, but the value of the bond over the 5 years will vary as interest rates vary.

Conclusion: Bond prices and values fall as interest rates rise, and conversely.

Quiz Yourself: (Answers at the end of this Section, before the Problems.)
3. A 10-year treasury bond now pays 2.25%. What is the price of a $20,000 bond?
4. Six years after the purchase of the the bond in 3., interest rates are 3.5%. What is the value of the bond six years after its purchase?

More on Inflation

Example 6 If housing costs have risen at 8% per year for the last 10 years, what might a house valued at $160,000 now have cost 10 years ago? Round your answer to the nearest thousand dollars.

Solution. **Although $160,000 is the value of the house today, for the purposes of this calculation it is the "future value" because it occurs at the *end* of the time interval over which the value is growing.** That interval starts 10 years ago and ends today, as shown by the time line:

```
      P                              F = $160,000
      |                                   |
 10 years ago                           today
```

So $F = \$160,000$, $i = 0.08$, $m = 10$ yearly compoundings, and we solve $\$160,000 = P(1 + 0.08)^{10}$.

Divide both sides by $(1.08)^{10}$: $P = \dfrac{\$160,000}{(1.08)^{10}} = \$74,111$ which rounds to $74,000 to the nearest thousand dollars.

Note: Whether a value is a Present Value or Future Value of a calculation depends on whether the value occurs at the start or end of the time interval over which the growth occurs.

Example 7 A university currently estimates that 4 years of tuition, books, and living expenses average $40,000. You have a three-year-old child, and want to plan for her university education by making a deposit today into an account paying 7.5% compounded annually. You want your deposit to grow in the next 15 years to an amount equal to the cost of her education. But it is estimated that those costs will rise by 5% per year. How much should you deposit (to the nearest dollar)?

Solution: We are asked to find the present value of an unknown future amount of money, so we must first find that future amount of money.

Step I If education costs rise at 5% per year, then the current $P = \$40,000$ cost will grow to $F = 40,000(1+0.05)^{15} = \$83,157.13$ in fifteen years. (Only round at the end of the computations!)

Step II We now need to find the present value that must be invested today at 7.5% annually so that it will grow to the required cost of $83,157.13 at the end of 15 years.

Thus $F = \$83,157.13$. Using $r = 0.075$, and $m = 15$ compoundings we must solve

$$\$83,157.13 = P(1+0.075)^{15}$$

Divide by $(1+0.075)^{15}$: $P = \$83,157.13 / (1.075)^{15} = \$28,104.28.$

This rounds to $28,104 to the nearest dollar.

So if $28,104 is invested at 7.5% annual compound interest today, it will grow in 15 years to $83,157.13, and that is the projected cost of the 4 years of tuition, books, and living expenses.

Quiz Yourself: (Answer below.)

5. If the cost of a carton of soft drinks has risen by 8% per year, what would a carton costing $4.25 today have cost 6 years ago? Round your answer to the nearest penny.

Answers to Quiz Yourself:

1. $F = \$15,000, r = 0.07, m = t = 8$. Solve $\$15000 = P(1+0.07)^8$. $P = \$15000 / (1.07)^8 = \$8730.14$

   Calculator: 15000 ÷ (1.07) ^ 8 = Amount of Interest: $I = F - P = \$15,000 - \$8730.14 = \$6,269.86$

2. $F = \$5000, r = 0.04, i = 0.04/12$ There are 6 years of monthly compoundings, so m 6(12) = 72.

   Solve $\$5000 = P\left(1+\dfrac{0.04}{12}\right)^{72}$ Obtain $P = \$5000 / \left(1+\dfrac{0.04}{12}\right)^{72} = \$3934.71$

   Calculator: 5000 ÷ (1 + .04 ÷ 12) ^ 72 = Amount of Interest: $I = F - P = \$5000 - \$3934.71 = \$1065.29$

3. Solve $\$20,000 = P(1+0.0225)^{10}$ Obtain $P = \$20,000/(1.0225)^{10} = \$16,010.20$

4. 4 years remain on the bond. Solve $\$20,000 = P(1+0.035)^4$ Obtain $P = \$20,000/(1.035)^4 = \$17,428.84$

5. Because $4.25 is the price at the end of the growth, $F = \$4.25. r = 0.08, m = t = 6.$

   Solve $\$4.25 = P(1+0.08)^6$ Obtain $P = \$4.25 / (1.08)^6 = \$2.69$

Problems for Section 1.5

Sharpen Your Skills: Round each to the nearest penny. (Answers in the back of the text.)

1. Solve $2000 = P(1.02)^{20}$ for P.

2. Solve $4500 = P(1.045)^{35}$ for P.

3. Evaluate $\dfrac{\$2500}{\left(1+\dfrac{.05}{12}\right)^{48}}$

4. Evaluate $\dfrac{\$358}{\left(1+\dfrac{.04}{365}\right)^{4\times365}}$

Communicate the Concepts: (Answers in back of text.)

5. How do you decide whether a dollar amount is a Present Value or a Future Value?

6. Explain why bond prices fall as interest rates rise.

Apply Your Knowledge: (Answers to odd-numbered problems in back of text.) In these problems you are encouraged to draw a timeline like the one below, filling in the information given.

Account Value P F

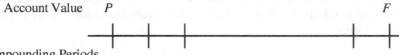

Compounding Periods

7. Suppose that you want to accumulate a total of $20,000 on your son's seventeenth birthday. To achieve this goal, how much should you invest on your son's third birthday in a certificate of deposit that pays 3.3% if that interest rate is as stated below. In each case, how much interest will you have earned?
    (a) Compounded annually?   (b) Compounded quarterly?

8. Suppose that you want to accumulate a total of $40,000 on your son's eighteenth birthday. How much should you invest on your son's sixth birthday in a certificate of deposit (CD) that pays interest at the rate of 6.6% compounded annually? How much interest will you have earned?

9. You want to accumulate $7,500.00 six years and nine months from now by purchasing a certificate of deposit at your bank. How much should you pay for the CD now if the bank's CDs pay interest at the rate of 4.35% compounded monthly? How much interest will you have earned?

10. How much should you invest at 7% compounded quarterly in order to accumulate $24,575.00 over a period of 8 years and six months? How much interest will you have earned?

11. How much should you invest today at 4.8% compounded monthly in order for it to grow to $20,000 when you retire in 35 years? How much interest will you have earned?

12. How much should you invest today in an account paying 6.1% annual compound interest in order for it to be worth $15,000 when you retire in 25 years? How much interest will you have earned?

13. What should be the price of a $10,000 10-year treasury bond paying 1.5% compounded annually?

14. A company wants to offer a $20,000 5-year bond paying 2.5% compounded annually? What should be its price?

15. At present 20-year Treasury bonds are paying 1.75% compounded annually.
    (a) What should be the price of a $5000 bond?
    (b) 7 years after the bond was purchased, interest rates are 2.5% compounded annually. What is the value of the bond then?

16. A school district issues 8-year construction bonds at 4.25%.
    (a) What should be the price of a $10,000 bond?
    (b) After 3 years interest rates have fallen to 3.5%, and the school district decides to buy back the bond. What is the value of the bond at that point? (This is a fair price for the bond.)

17. The cost of a hospital room has been rising at about 11% per year for the last 6 years. How much would a room costing $200 per day today have cost 6 years ago? Round your answer to the nearest dollar.

18. If clothing costs have risen at 7.0% per year for the past 10 years, what was the cost 10 years ago of a suit costing $300 today? Round your answer to the nearest dollar.

19. A new BMW presently costs $35,000, and the cost of such a car is currently rising at 5.0% per year. How much does a person need to invest today in an account paying 8.2% compounded annually in order to have value of the account reach the total cost of a BMW 6 years from now? Round your answer to the nearest thousand dollars.

20. A particular cruise currently costs $2,150, and the cost of such a cruise is rising at 3.5% per year. How much must you invest today in an account with an APY of 5% in order for the investment to grow to the total cost of such a cruise in 3 years? Round your answer to the nearest ten dollars.

Review problems (Answers in back of text.)
21. How much will a lump sum of $5,000 invested at 4.2% compounded monthly grow to in 4 years and 8 months?

22. Anita borrows $2500 from her parents and agrees to pay them 9% annual **simple** interest until she can repay them with a lump sum. How long will it be until the lump sum she will have to repay them will have grown to $2950?

Challenge Problem
23. In Example 7 the savings account is paying an interest rate greater than the rate at which higher education costs are rising. A more realistic situation is to have their sizes reversed. For example, the University of Louisville currently estimates that the cost of 4 years of tuition, books, and living expenses averages $36,000. It is estimated that those costs will rise by 8.5% per year for the foreseeable future. You have a five-year old child, and want to plan for his university education by making a deposit today into an account paying 3.6% compounded monthly. You want your deposit to grow by the time he is 18 to an amount equal to the cost of his education at UofL at that time. How much should you deposit today?

Section 1.6   Finding Interest Rates

In some problems involving compound interest we know the future value F at the end of the investment as well as the present value P required at the start of the investment. We are then asked to find the rate per compounding, i, that will cause the given Present Value to grow to the given Future Value in the stated number of compoundings, m.

Example 1 Suppose your parents invest $10,000 on your ninth birthday, and it accumulates to $19,000 on your seventeenth birthday. At what annual interest rate did this investment grow?

Solution by "Guess and Adjust" We know that P = $10,000, F = $19,000, and m = 17 - 9 = 8 compoundings. From the compound interest formula, these are related by

$$19,000 = 10,000(1+r)^8$$

We must determine r. There are two methods to do this. The first is to try a value of r, calculate the right hand side of the above equation using it, compare the result to the desired F, and use this to adjust our value for r. If we try $r = 8\%$ we calculate

$$F = 10,000(1+0.08)^8 = \$18,509.30$$

which is less than the desired $19,000. So we need a larger interest rate, and adjust r to 9%. We recalculate

$$F = 10,000(1+0.09)^8 = \$19,925.63$$

which is too large. Since the $18,509.30 obtained at 8% is closer to the desired $19,000 than is the $19,925.63 obtained at 9%, a reasonable next guess might be 8.4%. Using $r = 8.4\%$ we calculate

$$F = 10,000(1+0.084)^8 = \$19,064.89$$

This is a little too large, so let's try a rate slightly less than 8.4%, say 8.35%. We calculate

$$F = 10,000(1+0.0835)^8 = \$18,944.65$$

Using 8.36% yields $19,008.68. Using 8.355% yields $19,001.66. Using 8.354% leads to $19,000.26. Surely this is close enough to be acceptable.

Solution using algebra. While the above method eventually yields a good approximation to the exact rate, a more efficient method is to apply some algebra. We need to find r from the equation

$$19,000 = 10,000(1+r)^8$$

To solve this for r, first divide both sides by 10,000: $\dfrac{19,000}{10,000} = (1+r)^8$

Since it is easy to divide by 10,000, we should mentally simplify the quotient to 1.9.

$$1.9 = (1+r)^8$$

We now need to "remove" the exponent from $(1+r)^8$, that is, we need to "undo" raising (1+r) the 8th power. We do so by raising both sides of the equation to the 1/8 power. (This is equivalent to taking the eighth root of both sides, since 1/8 th power *means* eighth root, but, as we will see below, fractional exponents are easier to use on a calculator than roots.)

Raise both sides to 1/8 power: $(1.9)^{\frac{1}{8}} = 1 + r$ $\left(\text{since } \left((1+r)^8\right)^{\frac{1}{8}} = (1+r)^1 \right)$; See the Rules for

Exponents on page 41.

Finally, subtract 1 from both sides: $(1.9)^{\frac{1}{8}} - 1 = r = 0.0835381331...$

When written in percentage form and rounded to two decimal places this is 8.35%. Compare this to our result using the first method.

Calculating the Answer: A sequence of calculator keystrokes for the above calculation is

$$1.9 \quad y^x \text{ or } x^y \text{ or } \wedge \quad (\quad 1 \div 8 \quad) \quad - \quad 1 \quad =$$

The parentheses _must be included in this calculation_, because we want to evaluate $1 \div 8$ before using it as an exponent. If the parentheses are omitted, our evaluation would yield

$\dfrac{1.9^1}{8} - 1 = -0.7625$ which is impossible. If your calculator has a $\sqrt[x]{}$ key, you may calculate the

answer as $\sqrt[8]{1.9} - 1$ by using these keystrokes: $\quad 1.9 \quad \sqrt[x]{} \quad 8 \quad - \quad 1 \quad =$

Alternatively, since 1/8 has a terminating decimal, 0.125, we use this as the exponent and do not need the parentheses: $\qquad\qquad\qquad\qquad 1.9 \wedge .125 - 1 =$

Example 2 A bond selling for $2600 now can be redeemed in 12 years for $5500. What annual rate of compound interest does the bond pay? Round your answer to the nearest hundredth of a percent.

Solution In this problem $P = \$2600$, $F = \$5500$, and $m = 12$ annual compoundings. Substitute these in the Compound Interest Formula we have:

$$5500 = 2600(1+r)^{12}$$

Use a sequence of steps similar to the previous example:

Divide by 2600: $\qquad\qquad\qquad\qquad \dfrac{5500}{2600} = (1+r)^{12}$ (we choose not to simplify the fraction)

Raise to 1/12th power (take 12th root): $\quad \left(\dfrac{5500}{2600}\right)^{\!1/12} = 1 + r$

Exchange sides and subtract 1: $\qquad r = \left(\dfrac{5500}{2600}\right)^{\!1/12} - 1$

Evaluate: (5500 $\div$ 2600) $\wedge$ (1 $\div$ 12) $-$ 1 $=$

This gives $r = 0.644267.... = 6.4427...\%$. Rounding to two decimal places gives 6.44%.

Example 3 How would the answers to Example 1 (on the previous page) change if the interest were calculated (a) as simple interest, or (b) as a quarterly compound interest? Round your answer to the nearest hundredth of a percent.

Solution (a) The Simple Interest formula is $F = P + Prt$, as discussed in Section 1.2.

So we must solve $\qquad\qquad 19{,}000 = 10{,}000 + 10{,}000(r)(8)$

Subtract 10,000: $\qquad\qquad\qquad 9{,}000 = 80{,}000r$

Divide by 80,000 $\qquad\qquad r = \dfrac{9000}{80000} = 0.1125 = 11.25\%$ annual **_simple_** interest

(b) If the interest is compounded quarterly, then there are $8 \times 4 = 32$ compoundings at the rate of $r/4$.

So we must solve $\qquad\qquad 19{,}000 = 10{,}000\left(1+\dfrac{r}{4}\right)^{32}$

Divide by 10,000: $\quad 1.9 = \left(1+\dfrac{r}{4}\right)^{32}$ $\qquad$ Raise to (1/32) power: $\quad 1.9^{1/32} = 1 + \dfrac{r}{4}$

Subtract 1: $\quad 1.9^{1/32} - 1 = \dfrac{r}{4}$ $\qquad$ Multiply by 4: $\quad 4\left(1.9^{1/32} - 1\right) = r \approx 0.0810 = 8.10\%$

So at annual rate of 8.10% *compounded quarterly* $10,000 will grow to $19,000 in 8 years.

Quiz Yourself: (Answer at the end of this Section, before the Problems.)
1. If a savings bond costs $25 and is worth $50 after 15 years, what annual compound interest rate does the bond pay? Round your answer to the nearest hundredth of a percent.

Using APY in Future and Present Value Calculations

Once the APY Y of an investment has been found, we can use Y for the interest rate, and measure time t in years or fractions of a year rather than the number of compounding periods. So the compound interest formula may also be written:

> **If a principal P is invested at an APR of Y then the value F of the investment after t years may be calculated by $F = P(1+Y)^t$**

Example 4 A bank offers a 3-month certificate of deposit (CD) with an APY of 5.6%. If $1000 is invested in such a CD, how much money should be in the account at the end of 3 months? At the end of 9 months?

Solution: Using $Y = 0.056$ and $t = 3/12 = 0.25$ years in the formula above, we have

$F = \$1000(1+0.056)^{0.25} = \$1013.72$ after 3 months

For the value after 9 months = 0.75 years, $F = \$1000(1.056)^{0.75} = \$1041.71$.

Example 5 Suppose you want to make an investment today in an 18-month CD with APY of 6.4%. What investment today is necessary in order to have $5000 at the end of the 18 months?

Solution: Eighteen months = 1.5 years, and $F = \$5000$, so we solve

$\$5000 = P(1+0.064)^{1.5}$ and obtain $P = \dfrac{\$5000}{(1.064)^{1.5}} = \$4555.73$.

Another Method For Finding APY

In the previous examples of finding APY, there was a given annual rate r and number n of compoundings per year that were applicable throughout the term of the investment. In some situations, however, there is no single annual rate that applies throughout. We then must find the annual percentage rate of increase Y that causes the given present value to grow to a certain future value.

> **If an invested principal P grows to a resulting future value F in t years, then the APY Y of the investment can be found by solving $F = P(1+Y)^t$ for Y.**

Example 6 A money market account grows in value from $1500 to $1800 in two and one-half years. What single APY applies to the entire investment? Round your answer to the nearest hundredth of a percent.

Solution   Here $P = \$1500$, $F = \$1800$, and $t = 2.5$. We must solve $\$1800 = \$1500(1+Y)^{2.5}$

Divide by $1500: $\dfrac{18}{15} = (1+Y)^{2.5}$

Raise to 1/2.5 power: $\left(\dfrac{18}{15}\right)^{1/2.5} = 1+Y$

Subtract 1: $Y = \left(\dfrac{18}{15}\right)^{1/2.5} - 1$ Calculate: $Y = (18/15)^\wedge(1/2.5) - 1 =$

This gives $Y = 0.0756537569\ldots = 7.56537569\ldots\%$ which rounds to 7.57%.

Example 7 In 1975 the average price of a movie ticket was $2.05. By 2014, the average price had grown to $8.17. What annual rate of growth does this represent?

Solution: We must find the annual compound rate r that will cause $2.05 to grow to $8.17 in 2014 - 1975 = 39 years. Solve

$$8.17 = 2.05(1+r)^{39} \qquad \text{Divide by 2.05:} \quad \frac{8.17}{2.05} = (1+r)^{39}$$

Take 39th root: $\left(\dfrac{8.17}{2.05}\right)^{1/39} = 1+r$ Calculate: $r = \left(\dfrac{8.17}{2.05}\right)^{1/39} - 1 = 0.0360879$

As a percentage to two decimal places, the rate of growth is 3.61%.

Example 8 A bank offers a $1000 "rising rate" 2 year Certificate of Deposit (CD) which pays 5.7% annual interest compounded monthly for the first 6 months, 6% annual interest compounded monthly for the second 6 months, and 6.9% annual interest compounded monthly for the last year.
    (a) What will be the value of the CD at the end of the two years?
    (b) What is the APY of this CD?

Solution: (a) We must first find the future value of the $1000 investment in the CD, and then find the single annual interest rate that, if used for the entire year, would result in the same future value.
If $1000 is invested at 5.7% compounded monthly for 6 months, then $i = 0.057/12 = 0.00475$ each month and F_1 = value of the account after first 6 months = $1000(1.00475)^6$ = 1028.84

If this is reinvested for the second 6 months at 6% compounded monthly at $i = 0.06/12 = 0.005$ each month, then F_2 = value of the account after second 6 months = $1028.84(1.005)^6$ = 1060.09

If this is reinvested for the last year (12 months) at 6.9% compounded monthly, then $i = 0.069/12 = 0.00575$ at each monthly compounding, and the value of the account at the end of the second year is

$$F_3 = \text{value of the account after second year} = \$1060.09(1.00575)^{12} = \$1135.59$$

So the value of the CD at the end of the two years is $1135.59.

(b) Since the total time period of the CD is 2 years, and the CD grows in value from $1000 to $1135.59 in that time, the APY Y of this investment must satisfy:

$$\$1000(1+Y)^2 = \$1135.59.$$

Divide by $1000: $(1+Y)^2 = 1.13559$

Raise to 1/2 power: $(1 + Y) = (1.13559)^{0.5} = 1.06564...$

Subtract 1: The APY is $Y = .06564 \ldots$ or 6.56% rounded to the nearest hundredth percent.

Quiz Yourself: (Answers at the end of this Section, before the Problems.)
2. If you invest $2500 in an account paying an APY of 5.32%, what will it be worth after 15 months?
3. Suppose a "rising rate" 5-year CD pays 3.6% compounded monthly for the first 4 years, and 4.5% compounded monthly for the last year.
    (a) What will be the value of $2000 invested in such a CD after five years?
    (b) What is the APY of the CD?
4. In January 1981 the average price for a dozen eggs was $0.94. By January 2015 the price had risen to $2.11. What annual rate of inflation does this represent?

Review of Exponents

Recall that for a positive base b and a positive whole number exponent n, the expression b^n means b multiplied by itself until there are n factors of b in the product. So

$$3^4 = \underbrace{3 \times 3 \times 3 \times 3}_{4 \text{ factors}}$$

With this notation the basic rules of exponents are:

1. $\left(b^n\right)^m = b^{nm}$ 2. $b^n b^m = b^{n+m}$ 3. $\dfrac{b^n}{b^m} = b^{n-m}$ 4. $a^n b^n = (ab)^n$ 5. $\left(\dfrac{a}{b}\right)^n = \dfrac{a^n}{b^n}$

For example, $\left(3^4\right)^2 = (3 \times 3 \times 3 \times 3) \times (3 \times 3 \times 3 \times 3) = 3^8 = 3^{4 \times 2}$

$$3^4 \times 3^2 = (3 \times 3 \times 3 \times 3) \times (3 \times 3) = 3^{4+2} = 3^6 \qquad \left(\frac{3}{4}\right)^2 = \frac{3}{4} \times \frac{3}{4} = \frac{3 \times 3}{4 \times 4} = \frac{3^2}{4^2}$$

The meaning of a fractional exponent is set up so that these general rules work for fractional exponents too. For a positive whole number n we define

$$(b)^{1/n} = \sqrt[n]{b} \,, \qquad \text{(this is not a real number if } n \text{ is even and } b \text{ is negative)}$$

and then using the first rule above, $\left(b^n\right)^m = b^{nm}$, we define

$$(b)^{m/n} = \left((b)^{1/n}\right)^m = \left(\sqrt[n]{b}\right)^m = \sqrt[n]{b^m}$$

From this definition it follows that the basic rules of exponents also work when the exponents are positive fractions. In particular,

$$\left((b)^n\right)^{1/n} = \sqrt[n]{b^n} = b \quad \text{for any positive number } b.$$

Quiz Yourself on Exponents: (Answers on the next page.)
5. Simplify the following so that in each expression, each variable appears only once and all exponents are positive.

(i) $\dfrac{a^2 \left(bc^3\right)^4}{(ab)^2 \, c^6}$ (ii) $\dfrac{ab^2}{\sqrt{a^3 b^3}}$ (iii) $\left((1+r)^5\right)^{1/5}$

6. In chemistry, equations such as $V^2 = kP^3$ are used to show the relationship between variables. Solve this equation for V, then solve it for P. Express your solutions once using radicals and again using fractional exponents.

Answers to Quiz Yourself:

1. Solve $\$50 = \$25(1+Y)^{15}$ $2 = (1+Y)^{15}$ $2^{\frac{1}{15}} = 1+Y$ $Y = 2^{\frac{1}{15}} - 1 = 0.04729... = 4.73\%$

2. $t = 15/12 = 1.25$ years; $F = \$2500(1+0.0532)^{1.25} = \$2667.34$

3. (a) For first 4 years $i = 0.036/12 = 0.003$ and there are $4(12) = 48$ compoundings.

$\quad\quad F = \$2000(1.003)^{48} = \$2309.27$ is value after 4 years.

$\quad\quad$ The for last year $i = 0.045/12 = 0.00375$ and there are 12 compoundings.

$\quad\quad$ After fifth year the value is $F = \$2309.27(1.00375)^{12} = \$2415.36$

$\quad$ (b) Solve $\$2415.36 = \$2000(1+Y)^5$ Divide by $\$2000$: $1.20768 = (1+Y)^5$

$\quad\quad$ Take 5th root: $1.20768^{\frac{1}{5}} = 1+Y$

$\quad\quad$ Subtract 1: $Y = 1.20768^{\frac{1}{5}} - 1 = 0.03846143... = 3.85\%$

4. Solve $2.11 = 0.94(1+r)^{34}$ Divide by 0.94: $\dfrac{2.11}{0.94} = (1+r)^{34}$

$\quad\quad$ Take 34th root: $\left(\dfrac{2.11}{0.94}\right)^{\frac{1}{34}} = 1+r$

$\quad\quad$ Subtract 1: $r = \left(\dfrac{2.11}{0.94}\right)^{\frac{1}{34}} - 1 = 0.024066.... = 2.41\%$

5. (i) b^2c^6 (ii) $\sqrt{\dfrac{a}{b}}$ or $\dfrac{\sqrt{a}}{\sqrt{b}}$ or $\dfrac{a^{\frac{1}{2}}}{b^{\frac{1}{2}}}$ (iii) $\left((1+r)^5\right)^{\frac{1}{5}} = 1+r$

6.

$\quad\quad$ Solve for V: $V = \sqrt{kP^3} = k^{\frac{1}{2}}P^{\frac{3}{2}}$

$\quad\quad$ Solve for P: $\dfrac{V^2}{k} = P^3$; $P = \sqrt[3]{\dfrac{V^2}{k}} = \dfrac{V^{\frac{2}{3}}}{k^{\frac{1}{3}}}$

Problems for Section 1.6

Sharpen Your Skills: Round your answer to the nearest hundredth percent. (Answers in back of text.)

1. Calculate $Y = 1.73^{1/3} - 1$

2. Calculate $r = \left(\dfrac{13}{5}\right)^{1/9} - 1$

3. Solve $2.31 = (1+r)^5$

4. Solve $\$38 = \$30(1+r)^7$

Communicate the Concepts: (Answers in back of text.)

5. Explain how to find the APY of an investment if the principal, future value, and number of years of the investment are known.

6. Explain the steps necessary to solve $F = P(1+r)^t$ for r.

7. Explain why an expression like $2^{1/3}$ should not be calculated as $2^{0.33}$, but $2^{1/5}$ can be calculated as $2^{0.2}$.

8. Explain why the keystrokes $2 \wedge 1 / 9$ will not calculate $2^{1/9}$ accurately.

Apply Your Knowledge: **In these problems round all calculated rates to the nearest hundredth of a percent.** (Answers to odd-numbered problems in back of text.) In these problems you are encouraged to draw a timeline like the one below, filling in the information given.

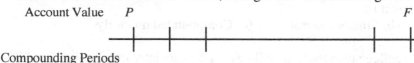

9. Suppose you invest $10,000 on your son's thirteenth birthday and it accumulates to $14,000 on his eighteenth birthday. What annual rate of compound interest did this investment earn?

10. Suppose you have $10,000 to invest on your daughter's sixth birthday. What annual rate of compound interest does your investment need to earn in order to grow to $35,000 on her eighteenth birthday?

11. A man buys a bond for $5,000 today. The sellers of the bond will pay the man $15,000 eighteen years from now. What annual rate of compound interest does this bond earn?

12. In 2015 a $100 Savings Bond actually cost $50, and took 16 years to reach its face value of $100. What annual rate of compound interest did this bond earn?

13. In 1968 a loaf of bread cost $0.27. In 2014 it cost $3.50. What annual rate of growth does this represent?

14. In 1959 postage for a first-class letter mailed within the United States was 4 cents. In 2014, the cost of that postage was 49 cents. What annual rate of growth (inflation rate) does this represent?

15. A bank offers a six-month CD with an APY of 3.1%. If $2000 is invested in such a CD, what will be the value of this investment at the end of the six months? At the end of two years and 3 months?

16. Savings Bank offers a two-and-one-half year CD with an APY of 4.3%. If $400 is invested in this CD, what will be its value at the end of the two and one-half years? How much interest will it have earned?

17. Jan has her eye on a $7000 car. How much does she need to invest today in a CD with an APY of 2.28% in order to have the $7000 she wants in three and one-half years? How much interest will she have earned?

18. A company wants to put aside money today in an account with 6.6% APY in order to accumulate $10,000 in 4 and one-half years. How much does the company need to invest today?

19. A bank offers a 2-year CD that pays 2% compounded quarterly the first 6 months, 2.5% compounded quarterly the second 6 months, and 3.6% compounded quarterly for the second year.
    (a) If $1000 is invested in this CD, what will it be worth after 2 years?
    (b) What is the APY of this CD?

20. A bank offers a 5 year CD which pays 2.4% compounded monthly the first year, 2.9% compounded monthly the second year, and 3.3% (annual interest) compounded monthly for each of the last 3 years.
    (a) If $1000 is invested in this CD, what will it be worth after 5 years?
    (b) What is the APY of this CD?

21. A man borrows $2000 and pays off the loan by paying the lender $2400 three years later. What rate of interest is he paying if the interest is:
    (a) Compounded annually   (b) Simple Interest   (c) Compounded quarterly

22. A student takes out a $10,000 college loan that she will pay off 5 years later by repaying $13,000. What rate of interest is she paying if the interest is:
    (a) Compounded annually   (b) Simple Interest   (c) Compounded quarterly

Review Problems: (Answers in back of text.)
23. Which of these has the highest APY?
    (a) 6.2% annual interest compounded quarterly
    (b) 6.1% annual interest compounded daily
    (c) An investment that grows in value from $300 to $319.08 in 1 year.

24. How much needs to be invested in an account paying 2.7% annual interest compounded monthly in order for it to grow to $3,000 in 5 years?

25. What should be the price of a $2500 6-year bond that pays 2.68% annual compound interest?

Section 1.7   Length of Time for Investment Growth

Example 1 Parents invest $9,500 on their son's ninth birthday at 3% compounded annually. What is the minimum number of years needed for this investment to grow to a value of at least $25,000.00?

Solution by Guess and Check After m yearly compoundings the $9,500 principal would accumulate to $F = \$9500(1+0.03)^m$. So we guess whole-number values of m until we find the smallest m so that $\$9500(1+0.03)^m \geq \$25,000$.

If we guess $m = 20$ we calculate $F = \$9500(1+0.03)^{20} = \$17,158.06$ Too low.

If we guess $m = 30$ we calculate $F = \$9500(1+0.03)^{30} = \$23,058.99$ Too low.

If we guess $m = 32$ we calculate $F = \$9500(1+0.03)^{32} = \$24,463.29$ A little low.

If we guess $m = 33$ we calculate $F = \$9500(1+0.03)^{33} = \$25,197.18$

The value does not *reach* $25,000 until 33 years after the son's ninth birthday. On his 33rd birthday $25,197.18 - $24,463.29 = $733.89 will be deposited into his account, making the value jump from less than $25,000 to more than $25,000 on that day.

Conclusion: It will take 33 years for the value to reach at least $25,000

The method of solution used above is rather tedious, and it would be even more so if the compounding were done monthly or daily. A more efficient method of solving such problems can be found by using logarithms. The method requires only one very important property of logarithms. (See also the Review of Logarithms at the end of this section.)

$$\boxed{\log(B^n) = n\log(B)}$$

In words this says that **the logarithm of a base raised to an exponent can be calculated by multiplying the exponent by the logarithm of the base.**

(A Review of Logarithms is given on page 48, but we will only need the above property in our work.)

Solution of Example 1 using Algebra: Solve $P(1+i)^m = F$ for m.

We have $P = \$9,500.00$, $r = 0.03$, $n = 1$ (annual compounding), and $F = 25,000$. The number of m yearly compoundings is unknown. We want to solve this expression for m:

$$\$9500(1+0.03)^m = \$25,000$$

Step 1: Divide by P = 9500: $(1.03)^m = \dfrac{25,000}{9,500}$

Step 2: Take logarithms of both sides of the equation $\log\left[(1.03)^m\right] = \log\left(\dfrac{25,000}{9,500}\right)$

Step 3: Apply property of logs $m\log(1.03) = \log\left(\dfrac{25,000}{9,500}\right)$

Step 4: Divide by coefficient of m, namely log(1.03): $m = \log\left(\dfrac{25,000}{9,500}\right) \div \log(1.03) = 32.7342.....$

Step 5: **Round m up to next whole number:** $m = 33$

Since the compounding is done annually, we would need to wait until the end of the 33rd year to get the interest that pushes us "over the top." Hence it will take a full 33 years before the value reaches at least $25,000, and the accumulation at the end of those 33 years would be

$$F = \$9500(1+0.03)^{33} = \$25,197.18$$

Notice that this agrees with our previous solution.

Calculating the Answer

You can calculate logarithms on your calculator using the **log** key.

On most calculators the log key must be pressed *before* the expression whose logarithm you want to calculate. (Such calculators include all graphing calculators, as well as the TI - 30X IIS.) In this case the keystrokes for Example 1 would be

log (25,000 ÷ 9,500) ÷ log 1.03 =

On many calculators the calculator will the supply the left parenthesis after log, and you must supply the right parenthesis. The calculation would look like log (25,000 ÷ 9,500) ÷ log (1.03) =

On other calculators, you must push the log key *after you have entered or evaluated the expression of which you want the logarithm.* For example, in the above expression you must calculate the quotient   25,000 ÷ 9,500   *before* pushing log to find its logarithm. With such a calculator the simplest keystroke sequence for the last computation is:

25,000 ÷ 9,500 = log ÷ 1.03 log =

Note: It is permissible to simplify a fraction like $\dfrac{25,000}{9,500}$ if we can do so exactly, such as dividing

numerator and denominator by 100: $\dfrac{25,000}{9,500} = \dfrac{250}{95}$

Then we would calculate   log (250 ÷ 95) ÷ log (1.03) =

Quiz Yourself: (Answer at the end of the Section, before the Problems.)
1. How many years will it take $1300 to grow to at least $5000 at 4% annual compound interest? How much will the investment be worth after that full number of years?

If the interest rate is compounded more than once per year, the length of time necessary for an investment to grow to a given value will be measured in <u>compounding periods</u>.

Example 2 You invest $5,000 on your son's fourth birthday at 7.2%, compounded semi-annually. What is the minimum number of six-month periods that this principal must be invested to accumulate at least $13,500.00? How long a period of time is this? At the end of this full number of six-month periods, what will the actual value of the investment be?

<u>Solution</u>: We have $P = \$5,000$, $r = 0.072$, $F = \$13,500$, and $i = 0.072 / 2 = 0.036$ is the rate applied at each 6-month compounding. We solve for m, **the number of six-month periods**.

$$5000(1+0.036)^m = 13,500$$

Step 1: Divide by 5000: $\qquad\qquad (1.036)^m = \dfrac{13,500}{5000}$

Step 2: Take logs of both sides $\qquad \log(1.036)^m = \log\left(\dfrac{13,500}{5000}\right)$

Step 3: Apply property of logs $\qquad m \log(1.036) = \log\left(\dfrac{135}{50}\right)$

Step 4: Divide by coefficient of m: $\qquad m = \log\left(\dfrac{135}{50}\right) \div \log(1.036) \ = \ 28.084...$

Step 5: **Round m up to next whole number:** $\qquad\qquad m = 29$

So the minimum number of six-month periods required to reach at least $13,500 is 29, and the number of *years* is 29 / 2 = 14.5 years, or 14 years and six months. At the end of 29 six-month periods, the actual value of the investment will be

$$F = \$5000(1+0.036)^{29} = \$13,994.50$$

Notice that after 28 periods $F = \$5000(1+0.036)^{28} = \$13,459.94$, which is less than $13,500.

Example 3 How will the answers to Example 2 change if the interest is compounded monthly?

Solution: Now time is measured as the number m of months and $i = 0.072 / 12 = 0.006$ is the periodic rate applied at each monthly compounding, so we must solve

$$5000(1.006)^m = 13{,}500$$

Using steps similar to those above we are led to $m = \log\left(\dfrac{135}{50}\right) \div \log(1.006) = 166.038...$

The minimum number of monthly compoundings is 167, which is $167/12 = 13.91666666...$ years. To convert this to years and months, multiply $13 \times 12 = 156$ to get the number of months in 13 years. Then 167 months is $167 - 156$ is 11 additional months. So the answer is 13 years 11 months. (Alternatively, $0.9166666.... \times 12 = 11$ calculates the number of months in $0.91666666...$ years.)

The actual value of the investment will be $F = 5000(1.006)^{167} = \$13{,}577.91$. Notice that it didn't

take as long to reach \$13,500 as it did in Example 2, because the APY of 7.2% compounded monthly is greater than the APY of 7.2% compounded annually.

Example 4 If money is invested at an APY of 7%, how long will it take for it to double in value?

Solution: The problem asks for the number of years m required for a present value P to grow to a future value that equals twice that present value, or $2P$. Because 7% is the APY, we substitute into the formula, given at the end of Section 1.5, that relates P, F, and t, $F = P(1+Y)^t$

We must solve $2P = P(1+0.07)^t$

    Step 1: Divide by P: $2 = (1.07)^t$

    Step 2: Take logs and apply property: $\log(2) = \log(1.07)^t$

    Step 3: Apply Property: $\log(2) = t\log(1.07)$

    Step 4: Divide by coefficient of t: $\log(2) \div \log(1.07) = t$

    Calculate: $t = 10.244768$ years or about $10\,\frac{1}{4}$ years

Notice that the length of time does not depend on the amount of money invested. That is, it takes just as long for \$1000 to grow to \$2000 as it does for \$10,000 to grow to \$20,000. Also, because we are using an APY here the length of time does not need to be a whole number of years.

Quiz Yourself: (Answer at the end of the Section, before the Problems.)
2. How many months will it take \$1300 to grow to \$5000 at 4.2% annual interest compounded monthly? How much will the investment be worth after that full number of months? How many years and months is this? How much interest will have been earned?
3. How long will it take money to triple in value at an APY of 5%?

Review of Logarithms

Think of b^x as defining a function, so that each input x yields an output that is the result of raising the fixed base b to the variable x power. If $b > 1$, then as the exponent x increases, the output b^x increases. This guarantees that two different inputs, say x and y, can not yield the same output:

$$b^x = b^y \text{ only when } x = y$$

Thus for a positive number a, there is one and only one x so that $b^x = a$. That number x is called the <u>logarithm of a using the base b</u>, written in symbols $\log_b(a)$.

In short, **$\log_b(a)$ means the power x to which the base b must be raised to yield a.**

Thus $\log_{10}(100) = \log_{10}(10^2) = 2$ because the base 10 raised to the power 2 yields 100.

The exact value of a logarithm is rarely a "nice" number, however. Nevertheless logarithms have many uses. Tables of approximate values of logarithms using base 10 were first developed as an aid in calculations before calculators were available. Such logarithms are called "common logarithms" and the notation "log" (without indicating a base) on your calculator means this kind of logarithm.

Logarithms are used to determine scales for quantities that grow exponentially, like earthquake magnitudes (Richter scale) and the loudness of sound (decibels). Logarithms are also useful in solving an equation in which the unknown is an exponent, such as the equations we solved in this section. This technique depends on the property mentioned in this section,

$$\log(b^m) = m\log(b)$$

(Read: **the log of a base to a power equals the power times the log of the base.**)

To see why this property is true, let $y = \log(b)$. Since the base of this logarithm is 10,

$$y = \log(b) \text{ means } 10^y = b.$$

Raising both sides to the m power gives $\qquad (10^y)^m = b^m$

Apply a rule of exponents to the left side: $\qquad 10^{my} = b^m$

By the definition of logarithm base 10, $\qquad my = \log(b^m)$

But $y = \log(b)$, so the previous equation is $\qquad m\log(b) = \log(b^m)$

<u>Example</u> Solve the equation $\quad 35 = 23(3)^x$

<u>Solution</u>   Divide both sides by 23: $\qquad \dfrac{35}{23} = 3^x$

Take logs of both sides: $\qquad \log\left(\dfrac{35}{23}\right) = \log(3^x)$

Apply our property of logs: $\qquad \log\left(\dfrac{35}{23}\right) = x\log(3)$

Divide both sides by log(3): $\qquad \dfrac{\log\left(\dfrac{35}{23}\right)}{\log(3)} = x$

This is the exact value. Use your calculator to get an approximate value of $x = 0.3821674....$

Quiz Yourself on Logarithms: (Answers below.)

4. A culture of bacteria double in size about very 5 hours; the relationship between the number N of

   bacteria and the time t in hours after noon is expressed by $N = 200(2)^{t/5}$.

   (a) How many bacteria are present at 3 pm?

   (b) At what time will there be 1000 bacteria present?

5. Solve $5000 = 100(0.5)^x$ for x. Check your answer by substituting it into the right hand side.

Answers to Quiz Yourself:

1. Solve $\$5000 = \$1300(1+0.04)^m$ $\dfrac{50}{13} = (1.04)^m$ $\log\left(\dfrac{50}{13}\right) = \log\left((1.04)^m\right) = m\log(1.04)$

   $m = \dfrac{\log\left(\dfrac{50}{13}\right)}{\log(1.04)} = 34.34....$ It takes 35 years.

   The actual value after 35 years is $F = \$1300(1.04)^{35} = \$5129.92$.

2. Question asks for the number of monthly compoundings at $i = 0.042/12 = 0.0035$.

   Solve $\$5000 = \$1300(1.0035)^m$ $\dfrac{50}{13} = (1.0035)^m$ $\log\left(\dfrac{50}{13}\right) = \log\left((1.0035)^m\right) = m\log(1.0035)$

   $M = \dfrac{\log\left(\dfrac{50}{13}\right)}{\log(1.0035)} = 385.55..$ It takes 386 months.

   The value after 386 months is $F = \$1300(1.0035)^{386} = \$5007.84$.   386 months = 386/12 =

   32.166666.. years. Since 32 years = 32(12) months = 384 months, which is 2 months short of 386

   months, 386 months = 32 years and 2 months. Amount of Interest = $I = \$5007.84 - \$1300 = \$3707.84$

3. Solve $3P = P(1+0.05)^t$ $3 = (1+0.05)^t$ $\log(3) = \log\left((1.05)^t\right) = t\log(1.05)$

   $\dfrac{\log(3)}{\log(1.05)} = t$ $t = 22.517...$ It takes about 22 and one-half years to double in value.

4. (a) Calculate: $200(2)^{3/5} =$ about 303 bacteria.

   (b) Solve $1000 = 200(2)^{t/5}$ $5 = (2)^{t/5}$ $\log(5) = \log\left((2)^{t/5}\right) = \dfrac{t}{5}\log(2)$

   $t = \dfrac{5\log(5)}{\log(2)} =$ about 11.6 hours after noon. Check: $200(2)^{11.6/5} = 998.7$

5. $x = \dfrac{\log(50)}{\log(0.5)} \approx -5.6438...$ Check: $100(0.5)^{-5.6438} = 4999.81 \approx 5000$

Problems for Section 1.7

Sharpen Your Skills: (Answers in back of text.)

1. Evaluate $\dfrac{\log(2.3)}{\log(1.04)}$

2. Evaluate $\dfrac{\log\left(\dfrac{5340}{1320}\right)}{\log\left(1+\dfrac{0.05}{12}\right)}$

In these three problems, find the smallest whole number m so that the right hand side is greater than or equal to the left hand side.

3. $4P = P(1+0.03)^m$

4. $\$2750 = \$500(1+0.0035)^m$

5. $\$783 = \$500(1.0025)^m$

Communicate the Concepts: (Answers in back of text.)

6. What is the property of logarithms that is used to find the required length of time for investment growth?

7. If compounding a given number of times a year is used, why does it take a whole number of compounding periods for an investment's value to reach a given goal?

8. Suppose M is a given number of months. Explain how to convert M to a number of years and a number of months less than 12.

9. Suppose Q is a given number of *quarters* of a year (three month periods). Explain how to convert Q to a number of years and a number of months.

10. Explain how to use the Guess and Check method to find the minimum number m of compoundings at the periodic interest rate i that are required in order for a principal of P to grow to a future value of F.

Apply Your Knowledge: (Answers to odd-numbered problems in back of text.)

11. Suppose you invest $12,000 at 3.3% compounded annually.
    (a) What is the minimum number of years that this principal must be invested if you want to have at least $20,000 in the account?
    (b) At the end of this number of years what will the actual amount in the account be? How much interest will have been earned?

12. At a certain school the tuition is $8,000 per year and growing at 5.8% compounded annually.
    (a) Assuming the current growth rate continues, how long will it be until the cost of tuition reaches at least $25,000?
    (b) At the end of this time what will the actual tuition be? Round your answer to the nearest dollar.

13. Suppose that you invest $3,750 at 4% compounded quarterly.
    (a) What is the minimum number of quarters that this principal must be invested to grow to at least $15,000? How many years and months is this?
    (b) At the end of this time what will the actual value of your investment be? How much interest will have been earned?

14. A man wants to accumulate $30,000. He has $5500 to invest at 5% compounded quarterly.
    (a) How many quarters will it take for him to accumulate at least $30,000? How many years and months is this?
    (b) What will the actual value of his investment be at the end of that time? How much interest will have been earned?

15. Marla wants to take a cruise that costs $4000. Right now she has $2800 invested in an account paying 6.3% interest compounded monthly. Assuming the cruise cost doesn't rise, how long (in years and months) will it be until her account has enough money to pay for the cruise?

16. How long (in years and months) will it take for $1400 to grow to $1700 if it is invested at 3.2% compounded quarterly?

17. How many days will it take for $45 to grow to $50 if it is invested at 2.7% compounded daily?

18. John has $532.50 in a savings account paying 6.5% compounded daily, and he's counting the days until he has at least the $600 he needs for a new computer. How many days will he have to wait?

19. Frank always wanted to be a millionaire, and he just inherited $400,000!
    (a) If he invests the $400,000 in an account paying 7.2% compounded monthly, how many months will it take for him to be a millionaire? How long is this in years and months?
    (b) If he invests the $400,000 in an account paying 7.2% simple interest, how long will it take for him to be a millionaire?

20. Frank's friend Sam won $600,000 in the lottery, and he wants to be a millionaire too. Answer the same questions for him as you did for Frank in Problem 19.
    (a) If Sam invests it in an account paying 7.2% compounded monthly, how many months will it take for him to be a millionaire? How long is this in years and months?
    (b) If Sam invests the $600,000 in an account paying 7.2% simple interest, how long will it take for him to be a millionaire?

21. How long will it take for money invested at a 6% APY to double in value?

22. How long will it take money invested at a 6% APY to triple in value?

23. How long will it take for money invested at 6% compounded quarterly to double in value? How long is this in years and months?

24. Banks often use a "Rule of 72", which says that it takes about $72 / r$ years for an investment to double in value at an APY of r%. Fill in the table below, calculating the values in the second column in the manner of Example 4 on page 47. How good is the rule?

Rate r%	Actual Time to Double in Value	$72/r$
4%		
6%	(See answer to Problem 21)	
8%		
9%		
12%		
18%		

Review Problems (Answers in back of text.)

25. If $800 is invested at 7.1% compounded daily for 5 years, what will the investment be worth at the end of that time? How much interest will have been earned?

26. A certain investment will double in value in 7 years and 3 months. What is the APY of this investment? Round your answer to the nearest hundredth of a percent.

27. How much must be invested today at 5.4% compounded quarterly in order for it to grow to $7500 in 5 years and 9 months?

28. A tax refund service will give you $250 today for your tax refund of $280, which you would receive in 3 weeks otherwise. Using one week = 1/52 of a year, what *annual simple* interest rate is the tax refund service charging?

Challenge Problem (Answer in back of text.)
29. In Problem 15 above Marla wants to take a cruise that costs $4000. Right now she has $1800 invested in an account paying 6.3% interest compounded monthly. Suppose that, as opposed to Problem 13, the cost of such a cruise actually rises at 3.6% per year compounded monthly. How many months will it take until the value of her investment is at least the cost of the cruise at that time in the future?

Section 1.8 Consumer Price Index and Purchasing Power

In previous sections we learned how to determine the effects of inflation when inflation is assumed to be occurring at a given rate per year. This is always the method used when dealing with inflation in the future since the future rate of inflation is not known and must be assumed. When dealing with inflation in the past, however, calculations are usually based on actual data collected by the government and expressed in terms of an **index**.

How Index Numbers Work

Index numbers are often used to compare measurements made at different times or in different places. One of the measurements is chosen as the Base, or *reference value*, of the particular index, and the other measurements are then given as percents of that Base. For example, column 2 of Table 1 below shows the Yearly Average Gasoline Price (per gallon) every five years from 1994 to 2014. To convert these measurements to indices (the plural of index) we first select a Base; here we have chosen the Average Gasoline Price for the year 1999 as the Base. In column 3 each of the other prices is expressed as a percentage of that Base and rounded to the nearest tenth of a percent. In column 4 we have removed the % sign to obtain the index for that year.

Year	Gas Price	Price as a percent of 1999 Price	Price Index Year 1999 = 100
1994	1.11	1.11 / 1.17 = 0.949 = 94.9%	94.9
1999	1.17	1.17 / 1.17 = 1.000 = 100.0%	100.0
2004	1.88	1.88 / 1.17 = 1.607 = 160.7%	160.7
2009	2.45	2.45 / 1.17 = 2.227 = 222.7%	222.7
2014	3.40	3.40 / 1.17 = 2.906 = 290.6%	290.6

Table 1 Gasoline Prices and Indices, Year 1999 = 100

Note: The statement "Year 1999 = 100" at the top of column 4 means that we have chosen the measurement for 1999 as the reference value. The reference value *always* has an index of 100.0.

To Calculate an Index Number for a Given Value:

Index Number of Given Value = (Given Value) / (Reference Value) × 100

rounded to the nearest tenth

Quiz Yourself: (Answer at the end of this Section, before the Problems.)
1. Complete the chart below for the indices (plural of index) if the measurement for the year 2004 is used as the reference value.

Year	Gas Price	Price as a percent of 2004 Price	Price Index Year 2004 = 100
1994	1.11		
1999	1.17		
2004	1.88		
2009	2.45		
2014	3.40		

Table 2 Gasoline Prices and Indices, Year 2004 = 100

Making Comparisons with Index Numbers

The primary use of index numbers is to make comparisons. Comparisons with the reference year are inherent in the indices. For example, In Table 1 the gas price index for the year 2014 is 290.6, so the average price of a gallon of gas in the year 2014 was 290.6% of the average price in 1999. Said another way, the price of gas in 2014 was 2.906 times as much as the price in 1999.

We can also make comparisons when neither value is the reference value. For example, suppose we want to use Table 1 to determine how much more expensive gas was in 2014 than in 1994. The answer may be found by dividing the index number for 2014 by the index number for 1994.

$$\frac{\text{Index number for 2014}}{\text{Index number for 1994}} = \frac{290.6}{94.9} \approx 3.06$$

So the 2014 price was 3.06 times the 1994 price. If it cost $20 to fill up a certain gas tank in 1994 it would have cost 3.06 times $20, or $61.20, to fill up the same tank in 2014.

Accuracy of Indices

We have assumed that all the interest rate and dollar amounts we were given were exactly the amount stated. For example, $2000 did not mean $1999.99. But indices are by definition accurate only to the nearest tenth. Thus the index number 290.6 is not exact. The actual value could be anywhere between 290.55 and 290.65, for numbers in that range round to 290.6 when rounded to the nearest tenth. Similarly, the index number 94.9 stands for some number between 94.85 and 94.95. When we take a quotient of indices, as we did at the top of this page, the result is not exactly accurate either. Actually:

$$\frac{290.6}{94.9} \text{ could be anywhere between } \frac{290.55}{94.95} = 3.0600315\ldots \text{ and } \frac{290.65}{94.85} = 3.064372\ldots$$

All of these calculations give 3.06 when rounded to the nearest hundredth. So we are certain that $\frac{290.6}{94.9}$ is 3.06 to the nearest hundredth, but we are not certain what the thousandths place is. Although $\frac{290.6}{94.9} = 3.064$ to the nearest thousandth, we can not say what the thousandths place will be. So in answering the question at the top of the page about the 2014 price to fill up the gas tank we should **not** calculate (3.064)($20) = $61.28. **We cannot know the answer to that accuracy!** In general:

Significant Digits

The number of **significant digits** in an index number equals the number of digits (including 0) starting from the left most digit and counting to the right to the tenths place.

Example: 290.6 has 4 significant digits, and 94.0 has 3 significant digits.

RULE FOR SIGNIFICANT DIGITS OF INDEX NUMBER CALCULATIONS: When making a calculation involving an index number, the result should be rounded to have no more significant digits than the smallest number of significant digits of the index numbers involved.

Example: $\frac{31.0}{107.6} \times 10,000$ calculates exactly as 2881.04089... Since 31.0 has 3 significant digits and 107.6 has four significant digits, if these are index numbers then the result of the calculation should be rounded to have 3 significant digits. So the calculation 2881.040089 should be rounded to 3 places from the leftmost place. That is the tens place. The result should be rounded to 2880.

Quiz Yourself: (Answer at the end of this Section, before the problems.)
2. Use your indices from Table 2 on the previous page to determine how much it would have cost in 2009 to fill up a gas tank that cost $15.00 to fill up in 1994. Round your answer using the above rule.

The Consumer Price Index

The Consumer Price Index, abbreviated CPI, for a given year represents the average cost that year of a standard "market basket" of items covered by the CPI, as a percentage of a reference value set at the average for the years 1982-4. For example, the CPI of 124.0 in 1989 means that in 1989 this market basket cost 124% of what it cost in 1982-4. (As noted above, each index is rounded to the nearest tenth.)

Table 2 Consumer Price Indices (CPI) for the years 1961 - 2104											
Year	CPI	Year	CPI	Year	CPI	Year	CPI	Year	CPI	Year	CPI
1961	29.9	1971	40.5	1981	90.9	1991	136.2	2001	177.1	2011	224.9
1962	30.2	1972	41.8	1982	96.5	1992	140.3	2002	179.9	2012	229.6
1963	30.6	1973	44.4	1983	99.6	1993	144.5	2003	184.0	2013	233.0
1964	31.0	1974	49.3	1984	103.9	1994	148.2	2004	188.9	2014	236.7
1965	31.5	1975	53.8	1985	107.6	1995	152.4	2005	195.3		
1966	32.4	1976	56.9	1986	109.6	1996	156.9	2006	201.6		
1967	33.4	1977	60.6	1987	113.6	1997	160.5	2007	207.3		
1968	34.8	1978	65.2	1988	118.3	1998	163.0	2008	215.3		
1969	36.7	1979	72.6	1989	124.0	1999	166.6	2009	214.5		
1970	38.8	1980	82.4	1990	130.7	2000	172.2	2010	217.2		

Table 3

The **inflation rate** from one year to the next is defined as percent change in the CPI.

Example 1 What was the inflation rate from 1998 to 1999?

Solution From 1998 to 1999 the CPI changed from 163.0 to 166.6, a change of $166.6 - 163.0 = 3.6$. As a percent of the 1998 CPI of 163.0 this is $\dfrac{3.6}{163.0} = 0.02208589.. = 2.208589...\% \approx 2.2\%$

(Since 3.6 only has 2 significant digits, so does the answer.)

> **Quiz Yourself:** (Answer at the end of this Section, before the Problems.)
> 3. What was the inflation rate from 1979 to 1980? Round your answer using the rule for significant digits on page 54.

Using the CPI to Compare Dollar Amounts and Purchasing Power in the Past

The Consumer Price Indices are used to determine what dollar amount in one year is equivalent to a given dollar amount in another year. This is done by setting up a proportion in which the ratio of CPIs equals the corresponding ratio of dollar amounts:

> To determine the dollar amount in Year A dollars that is equivalent to a given dollar amount in Year B dollars, solve the proportion $\dfrac{\textbf{Equivalent Dollar Amount in Year A dollars}}{\textbf{Given Dollar Amount in Year B dollars}} = \dfrac{\textbf{Year A CPI}}{\textbf{Year B CPI}}$
>
> This process is called "**adjusting for inflation**".

Example 2 If a family in 1970 had a yearly budget of $10,000, what would be the equivalent budget in 2014? This could also be asked as, "What budget in 2014 would equal the 1970 budget *adjusted for inflation?*

Solution Solve the proportion $\dfrac{\text{Equivalent Budget in 2014}}{\text{Budget in 1970}} = \dfrac{\text{2014 CPI}}{\text{1970 CPI}}$ Substituting the CPIs and

the $10,000 1970 budget, this becomes $\dfrac{\text{Equivalent Budget in 2014}}{\$10,000} = \dfrac{236.7}{38.8}$.

So Equivalent Budget in 2014 $= \left(\dfrac{236.7}{38.8}\right)\$10,000 \approx \$61,000$. (In economics this might be stated

as saying that a 1970 budget of $10,000 is equivalent to a $61,000 budget "in 2014 dollars".)
Since the 1970 CPI has only 3 significant digits we have rounded to 3 significant digits.

Example 3 A family spent $1000 per month in 1988 for groceries. What would be the equivalent price in 1977 dollars (i.e. adjusted for inflation)?

Solution In the table the find that the 1988 CPI was 118.3 and the 1977 CPI was 60.6. So
$\dfrac{\text{Equivalent Price in 1977 dollars}}{\text{Price in 1988 dollars}} = \left(\dfrac{\text{1977 CPI}}{\text{1988 CPI}}\right)$ becomes $\dfrac{\text{Equivalent Price in 1977 dollars}}{\$1000} = \left(\dfrac{60.6}{118.3}\right)$

Multiplying both sides by $1000: Equivalent Price in 1977 dollars $= \left(\dfrac{60.6}{118.3}\right) \times \$1000 = \$512.26 \approx \$512$

Because the 1977 CPI has only 3 significant digits, the result can only have 3 significant digits, so our answer should be rounded to $512.

In the previous example, the $512 is also called the *purchasing power of the $1000 from 1988 measured in 1977 dollars*. Purchasing Power is calculated the same way we adjust for inflation:

Purchasing Power is Proportional to CPI:

$$\dfrac{\textbf{Purchasing Power in Year A dollars}}{\textbf{Purchasing Power in Year B dollars}} = \dfrac{\textbf{Year A CPI}}{\textbf{Year B CPI}}$$

Purchasing Power calculations must be made when comparing salaries from different years.

Example 4 A professor's 1966 salary of $10,000 had grown to $70,000 by 2014.
  (a) What was the purchasing power of his 1966 salary in 2014 dollars?
  (b) Which salary had the largest purchasing power?

Solution: We read from Table 3 that the CPI for 1966 was 32.4 and the CPI for 2014 was 236.7.
(a) To determine the purchasing power of his 1966 salary in 1990 dollars we set up the proportion
$$\dfrac{\text{Purchasing Power in 2014 Dollars}}{\$10,000} = \left(\dfrac{236.7}{32.4}\right)$$

Multiplying by $10,000 gives: Purchasing Power in 2014 Dollars $= \left(\dfrac{236.7}{32.4}\right) \times \$10,000 = \$73,100$

(The rounding was done because 32.4 has only 3 significant digits.) This means that $10,000 in 1966 would purchase what $73,100 would purchase in 2014.
(b) Since both salaries are now measured in the "same year's dollars," we can compare $70,000 2014 salary to the Purchasing Power $73,100 in 2014 of the 1966 salary. The 1966 salary had a larger purchasing power. Even though his salary had risen significantly, it actually now has less purchasing power!

Quiz Yourself: (Answers at the end of this Section, before the Problems.)

4. How much larger were prices in 2014 than in 2004? If a family has a budget of $30,000 in 2014, what would that budget have been in 2004 when adjusted for inflation? Use the CPI table on page 55. Round your answers using the rule for significant digits on page 54.

5. What is the purchasing power of a 1994 salary of $25,000, if adjusted to 2014 dollars? Is that purchasing power more than a 2014 salary of $50,000? Use the CPI table on page 55. Round your answers using the rule for significant digits on page 54.

Purchasing Power Calculations in the Future

Example 5 Suppose an engineer has a 2014 salary of $80,000. If the annual rate of inflation for the next 15 years is 4.0%, what income in 2029 (when she retires) will be needed to have the same purchasing power? Round your answer to the nearest thousand dollars.

> Solution: **Here we cannot use the CPI table because it does not predict the future**. However, the assumption of a 4.0% annual inflation rate allows us to project the $80,000 salary into the future using standard compound interest calculations as in Section 1.3. To "keep up with inflation" the $80,000 salary would need to grow for 15 years at 4.0% annual compound rate of growth. So we calculate:

$$80,000(1+0.04)^{15} = \$144,075.48 \approx \$140,000$$

So her 2029 income needs to be about $140,000 in order to keep her present purchasing power, that is, to keep up with inflation.

Calculating Purchasing Power with a Given Inflation Rate i

(A) The future amount, m years from now, having the same purchasing power as a given current amount, can be determined by *multiplying* the current amount by $(1+i)^m$:

$$\begin{array}{l} \text{Future Amount } m \text{ years from now having} \\ \text{same Purchasing Power as Current Amount} \end{array} = \text{Current Amount} \times (1+i)^m$$

(B) The current amount, having the same purchasing power as a given future amount m years from now, can be determined by *dividing* the future amount by $(1+i)^m$:

$$\begin{array}{l} \text{Current Amount having same Purchasing Power} \\ \text{as Future Amount } m \text{ years from now} \end{array} = \frac{\text{Future Amount}}{(1+i)^m}$$

The reasoning behind these formulas may be seen by thinking about the timelines involved. For formula (A) the idea is that a given Current Amount must *grow* by a factor of $(1+i)^m$ to keep up with inflation. For formula (B) a given Future Amount must be *shrunk* by a factor of $(1+i)^m$ to undo that growth and arrive at the Current Amount with the same purchasing power.

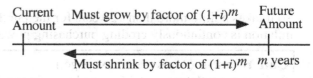

Formula (A) was used to solve Example 5. Example 6 below shows how formula (B) is used.

Example 6 A teacher retires in 2014 at a fixed retirement benefit of $30,000 per year. Assuming inflation is 4.0% per year, what will be the purchasing power of the benefit she receives 15 years from now, that is, what current amount would have the same purchasing power as the $30,000 benefit she receives 15 years from now? Round your answer to the nearest thousand dollars.

Solution: We must determine the current amount having the same purchasing power as the $30,000 benefit the teacher receives 15 years from now. Using formula (B) we calculate:

$$\text{Current Amount (in 2014 dollars)} = \frac{\$30,000}{(1.04)^{15}} = \$16,657.94 \approx \$17,000$$

It is discouraging to see what seems to be a comfortable retirement benefit eroded to about half its original purchasing power after only 15 years, and at a "moderate" inflation rate.

Quiz Yourself: (Answers at the end of this Section, before the Problems.)
6. If inflation is at 3.6% in the future, what salary 6 years from now would be equivalent to a salary of $56,000 today? Round your answer to the nearest hundred dollars.
7. You will inherit $80,000 in 10 years. If inflation is at 4.1% during those 10 years, what current amount has the same purchasing power as your inheritance? Round to the nearest hundred dollars.

The next example shows how we can use logarithms, as in Section 1.7, to determine how long it would take for purchasing power to shrink to a given size.

Example 7 Suppose you retire with a retirement benefit fixed at $45,000 per year. While this seems generous, you are concerned that its purchasing power will be eroded. If inflation is at 5.0% in the future, how long will it be until the purchasing power of your benefit is cut to $25,000 or less, that is, have no more purchasing power than $25,000 does currently?

Solution: You will receive $45,000 each year. You must find m so that the $45,000 you receive in the mth year has the same purchasing power as a $25,000 amount currently does.

Using formula (B) above we must solve $\$25,000 = \dfrac{\$45,000}{(1.05)^{m}}$ for m.

Multiply by $(1.05)^{m}$: $25,000(1.05)^{m} = 45,000$

Proceed as in Section 1.7; divide by 25,000: $(1.05)^{m} = \dfrac{45}{25}$

Take logs and use property of logs: $m\log(1.05) = \log\left(\dfrac{45}{25}\right)$

Divide by $\log(1.05)$: $m = \dfrac{\log\left(\dfrac{45}{25}\right)}{\log(1.05)} = 12.047$

So it takes a little more than 12 years for the purchasing power to decrease to $25,000. Note that since inflation is continuously eroding purchasing power, we do not need to make m be a whole number.

Quiz Yourself: (Answer on next page.)
8. Suppose inflation is at 3.2%, and you are receiving a pension of $30,000 per year that does not change with inflation. Approximately how many years will it take until the purchasing power of your pension that year is no more than $12,000 in today's dollars?

Answers to Quiz Yourself:

1.

Year	Gas Price	Price as a percent of 2004 Price	Price Index Year 2004 = 100
1994	1.11	1.11 / 1.88 = 0.590 = 59.0%	59.0
1999	1.17	1.17 / 1.88 = 0.622 = 62.2%	62.2
2004	1.88	1.88 / 1.88 = 1.000 = 100.0%	100.0
2009	2.45	2.45 / 1.88 = 1.634 = 163.4%	163.4
2014	3.40	3.40 / 1.88 = 1.809 = 180.9%	180.9

2. $\dfrac{2009 \text{ index}}{1994 \text{ index}} \times (1994 \text{ cost}) = \dfrac{163.4}{59.0} \times \$15 = \$41.54.. = \$41.5$ Answer should have three significant

digits since this is the smallest number of significant digits in 163.4 and 59.0.

3. (1980 CPI – 1979 CPI) / (1979 CPI) = (82.4 – 72.6) / 72.6 = 9.8 / 72.6 = .134986… $\approx 13\%$.   Answer should have the same number of significant digits as 9.8 does.

4. Prices in 2014 were 217.2 / 172.2 = 1.261 times as great as in 2000, rounding to 4 significant digits. Adjusting a \$30,000 budget in 2000 for inflation, the equivalent budget in 2010 would be 1.261 (\$30,000) = \$37,830.

5. To adjust a 1994 salary of \$25,000 to 2014 dollars we solve $\dfrac{2014 \text{ CPI}}{1994 \text{ CPI}} = \dfrac{2014 \text{ Purchasing Power}}{1994 \text{ Purchasing Power}}$ or

$\dfrac{236.7}{148.2} = \dfrac{2014 \text{ Purchasing Power}}{\$25,000}$ So 2014 Purchasing Power $= \$25,000 \left(\dfrac{236.7}{148.2} \right) = \$39,929.15$

Since the indices here have 4 significant digits, the answer is \$39,930.

6. $\$56,000(1.036)^6 = \$69,238 \approx \$69,200$

7. Using Formula (B), the \$80,000 must shrink by a factor of $(1+0.041)^{10}$, to

$\dfrac{\$80,000}{(1+0.041)^{10}} = \$53,528 \approx \$53,500.$

8. Solve $\$12,000 = \dfrac{\$30,000}{(1.032)^m}$ for m:

Multiply by $(1.032)^m$: $\qquad\qquad\qquad 12,000(1.032)^m = 30,000$

Divide by 12,000: $\qquad\qquad\qquad\qquad (1.032)^m = \dfrac{30}{12}$

Take logs and use property of logs: $\qquad m \log(1.032) = \log\left(\dfrac{30}{12} \right)$

Divide by log(1.032): $\qquad\qquad\qquad m = \dfrac{\log\left(\dfrac{30}{12} \right)}{\log(1.032)} = 29.089…$

This indicates the value reaches \$30,000 shortly after the end of the 29th year.

Problems for Section 1.8

Sharpen Your Skills: Round your answers using the rule for significant digits on page 54. (Answers in back of text.)

1. What is the percent change from 83.9 to 90.4?

2. What is the percent change from 217 to 215?

3. Using the table of CPIs on page 55, what was the rate of inflation from 1980 to 1981?

4. Using the table of CPIs on page 55, what was the rate of inflation from 2008 to 2009?

Communicate the Concepts: (Answers in back of text.)

5. Explain how to compute an index of a given value from a reference value and the given value.

6. Explain how to adjust a price for inflation from one year's dollars to another year's dollars.

7. Explain how to determine how a salary must grow in order to "keep up with inflation."

8. Explain why the purchasing power of a dollar amount shrinks over the years if there is inflation.

Apply Your Knowledge: In these problems use CPI and gas price data as needed from the tables in this section. Round your answers using the rule for significant digits on page 54. (Answers to odd-numbered problems in back of text.)

9. What would it cost in 2014 to fill up a gas tank that cost $25 to fill up in 2004?

10. What would it have cost in 1994 to fill up a gas tank that cost $45 to fill up in 2009?

11. What would $68,000 in 1990 convert to in 1970 dollars if it is adjusted for inflation?

12. What would $88,000 in 2010 convert to in 1990 dollars if it is adjusted for inflation?

13. What is the purchasing power of a 1975 salary of $28,000, in year 2014 dollars?

14. What is the purchasing power of a 1980 salary of $35,000, in year 2003 dollars?

15. Which had a larger purchasing power, a 1978 salary of $14,000 or a 2014 salary of $51,000? (Hint: you should compare the salaries after they have been converted to "same years dollars". You may convert both to 1978 dollars or both to 2014 dollars.)

16. Which had the larger purchasing power, a 1980 salary of $40,000 or a 1997 salary of $79,000? Justify your answer.

17. In 1965 an LP record cost $4.98. How much would that be, adjusted for inflation, in year 2014 dollars? How does that compare with the list price of a CD today?

18. In 1970, a certain college mathematics book cost $19.95. What would be the equivalent price in year 2010 dollars, adjusted for inflation? How does that compare with what you paid for your last mathematics textbook? (In 1970, there were no photographs, graphics, or color.)

19. In 1985 a pound of coffee cost $2.61. What would be the equivalent price in year 2014 dollars, adjusted for inflation? How does that compare with what a pound of coffee cost in 2014, namely $6.00? Has the price of coffee grown faster than the overall inflation?

20. In 1982 the average baseball salary was $412,000; in 2007 the average salary was $2.94 million. What would be the 1982 average salary in "2007 dollars", that is, adjusted for inflation? Have baseball salaries grown faster than overall inflation

21. Suppose your salary in 2015 was $35,000. If the annual rate of inflation for the next 10 years is 3.0%, what annual salary will you need to have in 2025 to have the same purchasing power as with your 2015 salary? Round your answer to the nearest thousand dollars.

22. Suppose your salary in 2015 was $50,000. If the annual rate of inflation for the next 20 years is 3.2%, what annual salary will you need to have in 2035 to have the same purchasing power as with your 2015 salary? Round your answer to the nearest thousand dollars.

23. Suppose you retire with a retirement benefit fixed at $50,000 per year. If inflation is at 4.5% in the future, how long will it be until the purchasing power of your benefit is cut to $30,000, that is, has the same purchasing power as a current amount of $30,000?

24. Suppose you retire with a retirement benefit fixed at $60,000 per year. If inflation is at 4.5% in the future, how long will it be until the purchasing power of your benefit is cut to $40,000, that is, has the same purchasing power as a current amount of $40,000?

Review Problems. (Answers in back of text.)
25. Determine annual compound rate of growth in the CPI during the time period 1960-86. Round your answer to the nearest hundredth of a percent.

26. Determine annual compound rate of growth in the cost of living during the time period 1976-86. Round your answer to the nearest hundredth of a percent.

27. Suppose $2350 is invested at 6% annual interest compounded monthly.
    (a) What will be the value of the investment after 3 years and 5 months?
    (b) How long (in years and months) will it be until the investment is worth at least $10,000?

28. Quick Loan will loan you $500 for 2 months but charge you $25 interest. What annual **simple** interest rate are they charging? Round your answer to the nearest hundredth of a percent.

29. If interest rates are currently 2.2%, what should be the price of a $4,000 6-year bond?

1.9   Overview and Review Problems for Chapter 1

In Section 1.1 we learned that $\text{Percent Change} = \dfrac{\text{New Value - Base}}{\text{Base}}$ converted to a percent.

The basic formulas of Chapter 1 regarding interest are:

$$I = Prt, \quad F = P + Prt = P(1 + rt) \qquad \textbf{(Simple Interest Formulas)}$$

P = Original Principal borrowed I = amount of Interest charged
r = annual interest rate F = value at end of growth
t = number of years.

    In these calculations we use ordinary simple interest, which assumes each month is 1/12 of a year.

$$F = P(1+i)^m, \quad I = F - P \qquad \textbf{(Compound Interest Formulas)}$$

F = Future Value of lump sum = value at end of compounding = value at end of growth
P = Present Value of lump sum = Principal = initial investment = value at beginning of growth
i = interest rate earned at each compounding m = total number of compoundings
r = (nominal) annual interest rate, t = number of years I = Amount of Interest
Notice that there are four fundamental variables $F, P, m,$ and i. In many problems, you know 3 of these 4 variables and want to find the other variable:

(i) In Section 1.2 we learned about simple interest and learned how to find the unknown variable if the values of the others is known.

(ii) In Sections 1.3 and 1.4, we knew P, i, and m, and found F using the above formula. The annual percentage yield (APY) Y of the investment is the percent increase in the value of the investment in 1 year. If the annual rate r and number n of compoundings per year are known and constant then

$$Y = \left(1 + \frac{r}{n}\right)^n - 1.$$

(iii) In Section 1.5, we knew F, i, and m, and wanted to find P. So we solved the basic formula for P.

(iv) In Section 1.6 we knew $F, P,$ and m, and wanted to find i. So we solved the basic equation for i by using Guess and Check or by using roots (fractional exponents).

We also saw that if Y is the APY then the basic compound interest formula becomes $F = P(1+Y)^t$

where t is in years and Y is the APY. This may be used to determine F or Y.

(v) In Section 1.7, we knew F, P, and i, and wanted to find m. So we solved the basic formula for m. We did this by Guess and Check or by using logarithms to solve the equation algebraically for m.

(vi) In Section 1.8 we learned the meaning of index numbers and how to calculate them for a given reference value. We learned about significant digits and the accuracy of index numbers. We learned how to use historical data about the CPI to adjust for inflation and compare the purchasing power of amounts from different years in the past.

$$\frac{\text{Equivalent Dollar Amount in Year A dollars}}{\text{Given Dollar Amount in Year B dollars}} = \frac{\text{Year A CPI}}{\text{Year B CPI}} = \frac{\text{Purchasing Power in Year A dollars}}{\text{Purchasing Power in Year B dollars}}$$

We also learned how to convert the purchasing power of a dollar amount from one year's dollars to a different year's dollars in the future:

$$\begin{array}{l}\text{Future Amount } m \text{ years from now having} \\ \text{same Purchasing Power as Current Amount}\end{array} = \text{Current Amount} \times (1+i)^m$$

$$\begin{array}{l}\text{Current Amount having same Purchasing Power} \\ \text{as Future Amount } m \text{ years from now}\end{array} = \frac{\text{Future Amount}}{(1+i)^m}$$

If you understand the two basic formulas at the top of the page and the algebra needed to solve for the various variables, you need not memorize any other formulas (except, perhaps, those for APY). Your job on most problems will be to determine which of the variables are known, which variable is sought, and correctly solve the basic formula for that variable, or apply the correct formula.

Review Problems for Chapter 1
(Answers in back of text.)

1. Give the meaning (<u>use words</u>) of each of the variables listed below that appear in the formulas of this chapter, and give the correct units (dollars, months, etc.) or form (decimal, whole number, etc.) when they are used in the formulas.

   a) F _____ Unit: _____

   b) P _____ Unit: _____

   c) m _____ Form _____

   d) t _____ Unit: _____

   e) i _____ Form _____

   f) Y _____ Form: _____

   g) r _____ Form: _____

   h) I _____ Unit _____

2. You deposit $1,600.00 in a savings account paying 6.25% annual interest compounded quarterly. What will be the value sixteen years later?

3. Suppose that you want to buy a CD on your son's fifth birthday that will be worth $35,000 on your son's eighteenth birthday. How much should you invest if the CD pays 9.3% compounded monthly?

4. Suppose that you invest $10,000.00 and it grows to $35,000.00 in 13 years. What annual compound interest rate did the investment earn? Round your answer to the nearest hundredth of a percent.

5. An executive had a salary of $12,000 in 1970. What would the purchasing power of that salary have been in 1995,? Round your answer in accordance with the rule on page 54. (The 1970 CPI was 38.8, the 1995 CPI was 152.4.)

6. If you want to accumulate $5,500.00 four years and nine months from now by purchasing a certificate of deposit at your bank, how much should you pay for the CD now if the bank's CDs pay interest at the rate of 8.4% compounded monthly?

7. Find the future value of an investment of $13,590 over a period of 10 years if the interest rate is 4.36% compounded daily.

8. In 1965, when the CPI was 31.5, the price of a loaf of bread was $0.15. What would be the equivalent price of a loaf of bread in 2014 dollars, adjusted for inflation? (The 2014 CPI was 236.7.)

9. What is the minimum number of months you must invest $3,500 at 5.4% compounded monthly in order to accumulate at least $6500? How long is this in years and months? What would your exact value be at the end of that full number of months?

10. By what effective annual percentage rate did the cost of living rise between 1975 and 1990? Round your answer to the nearest hundredth of a percent. (1975 CPI = 53.8, 1990 CPI = 130.7)

11. What is the APY of an investment at the nominal annual interest rate of 9.2% compounded monthly? Round your answer to the nearest hundredth of a percent.

12. How long will it take a $1000 investment to double in value if it earns 3% compounded semi-annually? How much will you actually have at the end of that time period?

13. A money market account grew in value from $400 to $413.73 in one year. What APY did this investment pay for that year? Round your answer to the nearest hundredth of a percent.

14. A new car costs $36,000 and the cost of such a car is currently rising at 4% annually. How much does a person need to invest today in an account paying 9.2% compounded annually in order to have the total cost of the RX-7 in 5 years? Round your answer to the nearest thousand dollars.

15. A student borrows $300 from Quick Loan on March 1 and pays it off by paying back $320 on June 1. What annual simple interest rate is the student being charged? Round your answer to the nearest hundredth of a percent.

16. Albert buys a Certificate of Deposit for $2,500 on September 1, 2015. The CD will be worth $7,500 on September 1, 2029. What annual rate of interest does this CD earn if it is compounded annually? Round your answer to the nearest hundredth of a percent.

17. A bank offers a nine-month CD with an APY of 5.1%. If $1000 is invested in such a CD, what will be the value of this investment at the end of nine months?

18. If your fixed retirement benefit is $70,000, and if inflation is at a rate of 3.6% annually in the future, how long will it be until your retirement benefit only has the purchasing power of a $40,000 benefit today?

19. In 1995 a pound of coffee cost $2.35, and in 2000 it cost $3.05. If the year 2000 cost is chosen as the reference value, what will the index value for the cost of a pound of coffee in 1995?

20. Determine the price today of a $2,000 5-year bond paying 3.2% compounded annually.

Chapter 2   Periodic Payments

In Chapter 1 we discussed financial situations involving a single lump sum. Many of our most important investments, however, involve a sequence of payments. These include a car loan, a home mortgage, and saving for retirement. In this Chapter we will expand our knowledge of compound interest situations begun in Chapter 1 to deal with situations involving a sequence of payments.

Section 2.1   Future Accumulation of a Sequence of Payments

Example 1 Suppose you invest $1000 per year, at the end of each year, for 4 years into an account that pays 5% annual interest. What will be the value of the account just after the last payment?

Solution: There are four payments of $1000, one at the end of each year. Each earns compound interest until the end of the 4-year time period. The first payment earns interest from the end of the first year to the end of the fourth year, which is three years. Similarly the second payment earns interest for 2 years (end of second year to end of fourth year) and the third payment earns interest for 1 year. The last payment earns no interest because there is no time between when the last payment is made and the time at which we are computing the value. Using our basic compound interest formula, we calculate that the future values of the four payments will be $\$1000(1.05)^3$, $\$1000(1.05)^2$, $\$1000(1.05)$, and $\$1000$ respectively. The total value of the payments is the sum of the values of the individual payments, so

(*)   Total Future Value $= \$1000(1.05)^3 + \$1000(1.05)^2 + \$1000(1.05) + \$1000$

As in Chapter 2, we visualize the situation with a time line. The payments are made at different points along the time line, but their value is calculated at a common future time. **The total future value of the sequence of payments is called its Future Accumulation** and denoted *FA*.

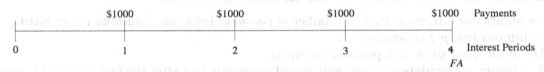

There are at least two possible ways to actually calculate the future accumulation.

Method 1: Calculate the future value of each of the four terms in (*) and then add them:

(*) $FA = \$1000(1.05)^3 + \$1000(1.05)^2 + \$1000(1.05) + \$1000$
$ = \$1157.63 \quad + \$1102.50 \quad + \$1050 \quad + \$1000$
$ = \$4310.13$

Method 2: This second method is not easier in this particular example, but it will allow us to develop a formula that is very efficient. Multiply both sides of equation (*) by 1.05. (This raises each exponent on the right by 1.) Then subtract equation (*) from the result:

(1.05)(*): $(1.05)FA = \$1000(1.05)^4 + \$1000(1.05)^3 + \$1000(1.05)^2 + \$1000(1.05)$

(*): $\underline{ FA = \$1000(1.05)^3 + \$1000(1.05)^2 + \$1000(1.05) + \$1000}$

Subtract: $(1.05)FA - FA = \$1000(1.05)^4 - \$1000$

Factor: $(1.05 - 1)FA = \$1000((1.05)^4 - 1)$

Divide: $FA = \$1000 \dfrac{\left((1.05)^4 - 1\right)}{(1.05 - 1)} = \$1000 \dfrac{\left((1.05)^4 - 1\right)}{0.05}$

When this last expression is evaluated on a calculator, the result is $FA = \$4310.13$, which agrees with what we obtained using Method 1.

Calculator Considerations: You may evaluate $1000\dfrac{\left((1.05)^4 - 1\right)}{0.05}$ by pressing the keys as we would in

reading the expression. Be sure to insert parentheses around the numerator to cause the entire numerator to be divided by 0.05. Also, parentheses are not necessary around the 1.05 as we already added 1 and 0.05.

Keystrokes: 1000 × (1.05 ∧ 4 - 1) ÷ .05 =

General Sequences of Payments

The essential feature of Example 1 is that it involved **a sequence of equal payments made at equal time intervals.** Other examples include automatic savings plans, automobile or home loans, regular payments from retirement accounts, and winnings from a lottery. In some of these you are making the payments, in others you are receiving the payments, but they all fit this description.

When dealing with a sequence of payments we will call the time between successive payments the **payment interval**. The **term** is the time from the beginning of the first payment interval to the end of the last payment interval.

We will only consider sequences of payments satisfying these conditions:

(i) The payments begin and end on fixed dates. Payments on most life insurance policies do not meet this condition, because premium payments stop only when you die.
(ii) The payment intervals and the intervals between interest compoundings coincide. For example, if payments are made monthly then interest is compounded monthly.
(iii) Unless otherwise stated, we require that the first payment is made at the end of the first payment interval, the second payment is made at the end of the second payment interval, and so on.

To standardize our calculations, we will use the following notation:

m = number of interest periods = number of payment intervals = number of payments,
i = interest rate *per compounding*.
PMT = the amount of each periodic payment,
FA = future accumulation of the sequence of payments just after the last payment is made (which is the end of the term) = total future value of the sequence of payments.

It will help to display each sequence of payments on a **time line** using the interest period as the unit of measure. The beginning of the term (0 on the time scale), the end of the term (m on the time scale), and a few of the periods should be shown. Payment amounts should be indicated above the time line at the points when they are made. Shown below is the general format. Compare this to Example 1.

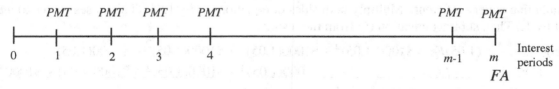

Using Method 2 from Example 1 as a model, we now develop a general formula for *FA*. Referring to the time line, the last payment earns no interest. The next to last payment draws interest for one (1) interest period and grows to $PMT(1 + i)$, the second to last payment draws interest for two (2) interest periods and grows to $PMT(1+i)^2$, etc. Finally, the first payment draws interest for m - 1 interest periods and grows to $PMT(1+i)^{m-1}$. Thus the total future value of the sequence of payments is given by formula (**):

$$(**)\qquad FA = PMT(1+i)^{m-1} + \ldots + PMT(1+i)^2 + PMT(1+i) + PMT$$

Multiply both sides of (**) by $(1 + i)$. (This raises each exponent on the right hand side by 1.) Then subtract equation (**) from the result:

$(1+i)(**)$: $(1 + i)FA = PMT(1+i)^{m} + \ldots\ldots\ldots + PMT(1+i)^{3} + PMT(1+i)^{2} + PMT(1 + i)$

$(**)$: $FA = \underline{\hspace{1.5cm} PMT(1+i)^{m-1} + \ldots\ldots + PMT(1+i)^{2} + PMT(1 + i) + PMT}$

Subtract: $(1 + i)FA \text{ - } FA = PMT(1+i)^{m} \text{ - } PMT$

(No other terms appear on the right because all other terms cancel when the subtraction is done.)

Factor: $[(1 + i) \text{ - } 1]FA = PMT[\,(1+i)^{m} \text{ - } 1]$

Divide: $FA = PMT\dfrac{\left((1+i)^{m}-1\right)}{\left((1+i)-1\right)}.$

Simplifying the denominator to i, we obtain our general formula:

---

(1) $FA = PMT\dfrac{\left((1+i)^{m}-1\right)}{i}$ **Future Accumulation FA of a Sequence of Payments**

(just after the last payment is made)

where PMT is the payment amount, i is the interest rate *per period,*
and m is the *total* number of payments (and interest periods).

Example 2 For the past ten years your uncle has been depositing $500 at the end of each year in a savings account that pays 3.5% compounded annually. What was the value of the account just after the tenth deposit? How much interest had been earned?

Solution: The periodic payment is $PMT = \$500$. Since the payments and interest compounding are done annually, $i = 0.035$ and $m = 10$ compoundings. The time line is:

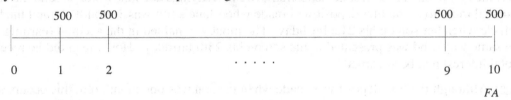

Inserting the values of the variables into (1), the future accumulation of the sequence of payments is

$$FA = \$500\dfrac{\left((1+0.035)^{10}-1\right)}{0.035} = \$5865.70$$

Calculator Keystrokes: 500 $\times$ (1.035   ^   10 $-$ 1   ) $\div$ .035   =

Calculating the Amount of Interest Earned If a sequence of payments earned <u>no</u> interest, its future value would be the product of the periodic payment times the number of payments, i. e. $PMT \times m$. So the difference between FA and this product is the amount of interest earned:

Total Interest Earned from savings is $I = FA \text{ - } m \times PMT$

In Example 2, there were 10 payments of $500 each, so a total of $10 \times \$500 = \$5{,}000$ was paid in. The amount of interest earned was $5,865.70 - $5,000 = $865.70.

Example 3 Find the value, just after the last payment, of a sequence of payments of $2,275 made at the end of every 6 months if the payments are made for 8 years and 6 months and money earns 5.4% compounded semi-annually. How much interest will have been earned by the payments?

Solution: The periodic payment amount is $PMT = \$2{,}275$ and the interest rate per payment period (every six months) is $i = 0.054/2 = 0.027$ since there are 2 payments per year. The total number of payments is $m = 8 \times 2 + 1 = 17$ since there are 2 per year for eight years, plus one more at the end of the additional six months. The time line is:

Again inserting these values into formula (1), the future accumulation of the sequence of payments is

$$FA = \$2275\,\frac{\left((1.027)^{17}-1\right)}{0.027} = \$48{,}271.04$$

Keystrokes: 2275 × (1.027 ^ 17 - 1) ÷ 0.027 =

The amount of interest earned was $48,271.04 - 17 × $2,275 = $9,596.04.

Quiz Yourself: (Answer at the end of this section, before the problems.)
1. A company deposits $200 at the end of each quarter for 7 years and 9 months into an account earning 5% compounded quarterly. To what value will the account accumulate just after the last payment is made? How much interest will the account have earned?

If the sequence of deposits stops for some reason, the amount in the account at that time should then be treated like a lump sum, as in Chapter 1. The next example shows how to deal with this.

Example 4 At the end of each month Jane deposited $100 in a savings account which credits interest at 5.7% compounded monthly. The first deposit was made when Jane's son was 1 month old and the last deposit was made when her son on his 21st birthday. The money remained in the account (earning interest in the same way) and was presented to the son on his 25th birthday. How much did he receive? How much total interest had been earned?

Solution: Although the first deposit was made when the son was one month old, this occurs at the end of the first payment interval, so the term of the sequence of payments actually began when the son was born. We seek the value on the son's 25th birthday. Since the sequence of payments stops on his 21st birthday, that is the end of the term of the sequence of payments and there are $21 \times 12 = 252$ payments. After his 21st birthday, the account can be considered as a single lump sum since no more payments are made. This lump sum stays invested for $4 \times 12 = 48$ more interest periods. The time line below describes the situation, with X denoting the final value we seek.

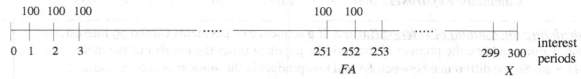

Step 1: We first calculate the future accumulation FA of the sequence of payments on the date of the last deposit, i.e. the son's 21st birthday. We have $PMT = \$100$, $i = 0.057 / 12 = 0.00475$ per month, and $m = 21(12) = 252$ payments. Inserting these into formula (1):

$$FA = \$100\,\frac{\left((1.00475)^{252}-1\right)}{0.00475} = \$48{,}437.98$$

This is the amount accumulated on the date of the last deposit (when the 252nd deposit is made).

Step 2: Then the money remained in the account for 4 more years, again at 5.7% compounded monthly. Since no more payments are made the *FA* becomes the principal that grows for 4 years. Using the compound interest formula from Chapter 1, with $m = 4 \times 12 = 48$ compoundings and $i = 0.00475$ per compounding, the value on his 25th birthday is

$$X = FA(1.00475)^{48} = \$48{,}437.98(1.00475)^{48} = \$60{,}809.40$$

To find the amount of interest, we subtract from this the total amount of the payments, $PMT \times m = \$100 \times 252 = \$25{,}200$. Thus the total amount of interest is $\$60{,}809.40 - \$25{,}200 = \$35{,}609.40$.

If the deposits are made into an account that already has money in it, this money should be treated as a lump sum separate from the sequence of deposits. Here is an example of how to deal with this.

Example 5 Sam has $4,235 in his savings account, which pays 6.2% compounded quarterly. He plans to make deposits of $250 at the end of each quarter into the account. If he does so, how much will his savings account be worth in 6 years? How much interest will his account have earned in that time?
  Solution: The total value of his savings will equal the future value F of his current lump sum plus the future accumulation FA of the sequence of payments he will make. In both, $i = .062 / 4 = 0.0155$ per compounding and $m = 6 \times 4 = 24$ compoundings. The time line below shows this.

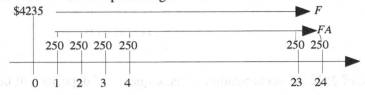

(i) For the lump sum:

$$F = \$4{,}235(1.0155)^{24} = \$6256.11$$

(ii) For the sequence of deposits:

$$FA = \$250 \frac{\left((1.0155)^{24} - 1\right)}{0.0155} = \$7201.60$$

So the total value of his savings will be the sum of these, $13,457.71.
To find the amount of interest, we subtract from this total value the $4235 he started with, as well as the total of the deposits he made, $24(\$250) = \$6000$.

$$\text{Total Interest} = \$13{,}457.71 - \$4{,}235 - \$6{,}000 = \$3{,}132.11.$$

Quiz Yourself: (Answers on next page.)
2. Starting in January 2015, Sue deposits $150 at the end of each month in an account paying 4.2% interest compounded monthly. She stops making deposits after December 31, 2026, and left the money in the account. What will the account be worth on December 31, 2033? How much interest will have been earned?
3. A company currently has $5000 in an account paying 4.8% compounded quarterly. If they begin depositing $400 at the end of each quarter, what will be the total value of the account after 9 years? How much interest will the account have earned during the 9 years?

Answers to Quiz Yourself:

1. $PMT = \$200$, $i = 0.05 / 4 = 0.0125$, $m = 7 \times 4 + 3 = 31$ quarterly compoundings.

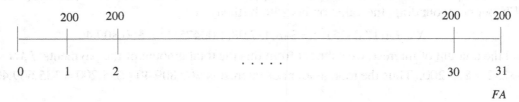

$$FA = \$200 \frac{\left((1.0125)^{31} - 1\right)}{0.0125} = \$7516.14 \quad \text{Interest earned} = \$7516.14 - 31 \times \$200 = \$1316.14$$

2. $PMT = \$150$, $i = 0.042 / 12 = 0.0035$ The years 2015 through 2026 encompass 12 years of payments. During the 12 years of deposits she makes $m = 12 \times 12 = 144$ deposits. During the next 7 years $7 \times 12 = 84$ more compoundings occur.

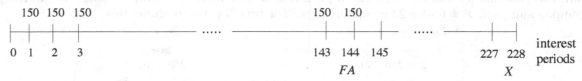

Step 1: At the end of 2026 the accumulation of the sequence of deposits will be:

$$FA = \$150 \frac{\left((1.0035)^{144} - 1\right)}{0.0035} = \$28{,}023.15$$

Step 2: At the end of 2026 this value becomes the principal invested from 2026 to 2033. During that 7 years the account will pay 84 compoundings at $i = 0.035$. At the end of that time the value will be

$$X = F = \$28{,}023.15 (1.0035)^{84} = \$37{,}581.72 .$$

The interest earned will be $\$37{,}581.72 - 144 \times \$150 = \$15{,}981.72$

3. $i = 0.048 / 4 = 0.012$ $m = 9 \times 4 = 36$ quarterly compoundings and deposits.
   Total Value = F of the original \$5000 plus the FA of the 36 deposits of \$400.

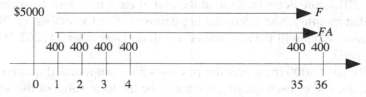

(i) For the lump sum: $\qquad\qquad\qquad F = \$5000(1.012)^{36} = \$7681.90$

(ii) For the sequence of deposits: $\qquad FA = \$400 \frac{\left((1.012)^{36} - 1\right)}{0.012} = \$17{,}879.31$

The total value of the account after 9 years is the sum of these, $\$25{,}561.21$

The interest earned in the 9 years is $\$25{,}561.21 - \$5000 - 36 \times \$400 = \$6161.21$

Problems for Section 2.1

Sharpen your skills: (Answers in back of text.)
Give the keystrokes to evaluate to evaluate each of these, and determine its value.

1. $\$300\dfrac{\left((1.005)^{54}-1\right)}{0.005}$

2. $\$50\dfrac{\left((1.004)^{176}-1\right)}{0.004}$

Communicate the Concepts: (Answers in back of text.)

3. Explain the meaning of *FA* and *PMT* in Formula (1).

4. What assumption(s) are made in Formula (1) about when payments are made?

5. Explain how to determine the total amount of interest earned in a given amount of time when a sequence of equal payments are made into a savings account.

6. Explain how to determine the total value in the future of an account that currently contains money and into which a sequence of deposits will be made.

Apply Your Knowledge: (Answers to odd-numbered problems in back of text.) You are encouraged to sketch a timeline and fill in the relevant information before working the problem.

7. Find the value, just after the last payment, of an account in which you invest $1500 at the end of each year for 5 years and which pays 6% annual interest. Find the value two ways:
   (a) Calculate the future values of each of the individual payments, and add these.
   (b) Use the general formula (1) for the total future accumulation.

8. Find the value, just after the last payment, of an account in which you invest $5000 at the end of each year for 6 years and which pays 8% annual interest, in the following two ways:
   (a) Calculate the future values of each of the individual payments, and add these.
   (b) Use the general formula (1) for the total future accumulation.

9. Find the future accumulation of the following sequences of payments using formula (1). Assume the payments are made at the ends of the compounding periods
   (a) $600 a year for 12 years at 4% annual compound interest.
   (b) $250 a month for 6 years, 3 months, at 6% compounded monthly.
   (c) $500 per quarter for 8 years, 9 months, at 6% compounded quarterly.

10. Don saves $200 at the end of each six months and invests it at 6.8% compounded semi-annually. How much will he have in the account at the end of 14 years? What amount of interest will his investments have earned?

11. Joan deposits $80 at the end of each month for 15 years into an account which pays 3% compounded monthly. How much will she have in the account at the end of that time? What amount of interest will her investments have earned?

12. Marty is investing $250 at the end of each month in an account that pays 6.6% compounded monthly. How much will she have in the account in 25 years? What amount of interest will her investments have earned?

13. At age 20 John starts making a contribution of $1000 at the end of each year into a retirement account that pays 7% annually. He continues to do so for 15 years, until he is 35, and then quits making contributions. If he leaves the money in the account until he is 65, how much money will be in the account? How much of that money is interest he has earned?

14. Suppose John (in problem 13) makes the $1000 contributions at the end of each year for 20 years from age 30 to age 50 (instead of what was stated in Problem 13) and then quits. If he leaves the money in the account until he reaches age 65, how much money will be in the account? How much of that money is interest he has earned?

15. Suppose John (in Problem 13 and 14) makes the $1000 contributions at the end of each year for 25 years from age 35 to age 60 (instead of what was stated in Problem 13) and then quits. If he leaves the money in the account until he reaches age 65, how much money will be in the account? How much of that money is interest he has earned?

16. What conclusions do you draw from the calculations in problems 13 - 15? Which seems to be more important, starting your retirement saving early or saving for a longer time?

17. Jim's parents have established a savings account to save for his college education. He just had his seventh birthday, and the account has $5,823.00 in it. They plan to make a deposit of $150 at the end of each month into the account until he reaches age 18. If they do so and the account pays 6.6% annual interest compounded monthly, how much money will be in the account on his 18th birthday? How much total interest will the account have earned between his seventh and 18th birthdays?

18. Jane's parents have established a savings account to save for their retirement. The account currently has $15,675.00 in it. They plan to make a deposit of $175 at the end of each month into the account for the next 20 years. Assuming they make the deposits and the account continues to pay 6% annual interest compounded monthly, how much money will be in the account 20 years from now? How much total interest will the account have earned during the 20 years?

19. (a) At age 22 George began depositing $100 per month into an account earning 9% interest compounded monthly.

    i) What will be the total value of the account when George reaches age 70?

    ii) How much of the value of the account will be interest when George reaches age 70?

    (b) George's brother Frank did not begin saving for retirement until he reached age 32, but thinks that if he begins depositing $200 per month at age 32 into an account also paying 9% interest compounded monthly he can accumulate as much savings as George by age 70.

    i) How much money will be in Frank's account when he reaches age 70?

    ii) How much of the money in Frank's account at age 70 will be interest?

    (c) Does Frank's plan work? That is, will he have accumulated as much money as George at age 70? Explain.

20. You have been saving for your retirement, and have accumulated $44,000 at age 50. If you put $300 per month into a savings account paying 3% interest compounded monthly, what will be the amount of your total savings when you reach age 65? How much total interest will you have earned between the ages of 50 and 65.

Section 2.2   Present Value of a Sequence of Payments, and Amortized Loans

When a customer signs a contract to purchase something, but does not have the money to pay cash for it, the customer may take out a loan from a financial institution. That institution pays the store or dealer the price of the item, and the customer agrees to make a sequence of payments in order to repay the financial institution. Included in those payments will be interest that the customer agrees to pay, as well as the original principal, which is the purchase price of the item less any down payment or trade-in.

Most loans of more than one year are **amortized** loans, which means that the payment amounts are the same, but the Principal of the loan is the sum of the present values of the payments at the time the loan was made. As we will see in Section 2.4, this means that although the payment amounts are the same, the part of the payment that goes toward the principal varies from month to month. In a later section of this chapter we will also discuss **installment** loans which use the **Add-on Interest** method for determining the amount of each payment.

Example 1 Suppose the four payments of $1000 in Example 1 of Section 2.1, one at the end of each year for four years, were being made to repay an amortized loan on which interest of 5% was charged. What was the principal (present value) of the loan when it was made?

Solution Now we are being asked to find the value of the sequence of payments at the *start* of the term of the payments, rather than at the end as in Section 2.1. We call this value the **Present Value** *PV* **of the sequence of payments, which is the amortized loan amount that could be paid off by the sequence of payments.** On a time line scale *PV* is shown at time 0.

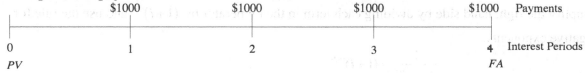

Using the Compound Interest formula as in Section 1.4, each payment's present value P is related to the payment amount $1000 by

$$\$1000 = P(1.05)^m, \text{ or } P = \frac{\$1000}{(1.05)^m}, \text{ where } m \text{ is the number of years since the loan began.}$$

Thus the *total* present value of the sequence of payments, *PV*, is the sum of these for $m = 1, 2, 3, 4$:

$$PV = \frac{\$1000}{(1.05)^1} + \frac{\$1000}{(1.05)^2} + \frac{\$1000}{(1.05)^3} + \frac{\$1000}{(1.05)^4}$$

$$= \$952.38 + \$907.03 + \$863.84 + \$822.70 = \$3545.95.$$

So the loan principal that can be paid off by the sequence of payments is $3,545.95. Because the present value of the loan equals the sum of the present values of the payments, we think of the loan principal as being equivalent to the sequence of payments. More precisely, **two financial obligations are financially equivalent if they have the same value when compared at the same point in time.**

In Section 2.1 we saw that this same sequence of payments was financially equivalent to a future value of $4310.12 just after the last payment (which is four years after the date of the loan). The time line below shows the time relationship between the sequence of payments, the value of the loan principal (which is the present value of the sequence of payments), and the value of an account if the payments were made into it (which is the future value *FA* of the sequence of payments). *All three are financially equivalent.*

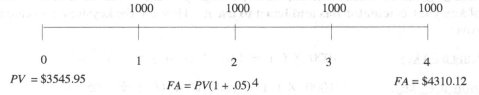

Notice in the previous example that *PV* and *FA* are different amounts, but are considered financially equivalent because the earlier one, *PV*, may be invested at 5% and will grow to the later one, *FA*.

In general, suppose you make a sequence of *m* payments of *PMT* each, with money earning a periodic interest rate of *i*. The present value *PV* and future accumulation *FA* of the sequence of payments are financially equivalent lump sums; they are related in the manner discussed in Chapter 1, namely

$$(*)\ PV(1+i)^m = FA$$

Recall that formula (1) from Section 2.1 provides a general way to calculate *FA* from the payment amounts:

$$(1)\ FA = PMT\frac{\left((1+i)^m - 1\right)}{i}.$$

Substitute the right hand side of (1) for *FA* in (*) to obtain: $PV(1+i)^m = PMT\dfrac{\left((1+i)^m - 1\right)}{i}$

To solve this for *PV* divide both sides by $(1+i)^m$: $PV = PMT\dfrac{\left((1+i)^m - 1\right)}{i}\dfrac{1}{(1+i)^m}$

Simplify the right hand side by dividing each term in the numerator by $(1+i)^m$ and use the rule for negative exponents:

$$\frac{1}{(1+i)^m} = (1+i)^{-m}$$

These steps yield a general formula for finding the loan principal paid off by the sequence of payments:

$(2)\ PV = PMT\dfrac{\left(1-(1+i)^{-m}\right)}{i}$ **Present Value of a Sequence of Payments**

(Amortized Loan Principal Paid Off by the Payments)

where *PMT* is the periodic payment amount, *i* is the interest rate *per payment period*, and *m* is the *total* number of payments.

To convince ourselves that this really works, let's use it to recalculate the value of the loan in Example 1. Substituting *PMT* = $1000, *i* = 0.05, and *m* = 4 into (3) we calculate

$$PV = \$1000\frac{\left(1-(1.05)^{-4}\right)}{0.05} = \$3{,}545.95$$

This agrees with our calculation above.

Calculating the Answer: Negative numbers are <u>not</u> entered into a calculator by using the subtraction key - , but rather by using either the negative key, which looks like (-), or the change of sign key, which on most calculators looks like +/- . The (-) is pushed <u>before</u> the number is entered, whereas the +/- key is pushed <u>after</u> the number is entered, thereby changing its sign. **You need to determine which kind of key your calculator has and learn to use it**. Here are the keystrokes to calculate the expression above:

<u>Using a (-) key:</u>   1000 X (1 - 1.05 ^ (-) 4) ÷ .05 =

<u>Using a +/- key:</u>   1000 X (1 - 1.05 y^x 4 +/-) ÷ .05 =

Example 2 Find the amortized loan principal (present value) that is paid off by making $85 per month payments for 2 years if interest is 8.1% compounded monthly. How much interest will the borrower have paid?

Solution Identify the values of the variables in Formula (2): $PMT = \$85$, $i = 0.081/12 = 0.00675$, and $m = 2(12) = 24$ monthly payments. Substituting these into formula (2):

$$PV = \$85\frac{\left(1-(1.00675)^{-24}\right)}{0.00675} = \$1877.50 \quad \text{Keystrokes: } 85 \times (\ 1 - 1.00675 \wedge (-)\ 24\ ) \div 0.00675$$

The present value (principal) of the loan paid off by the payments is $1877.50.

To find the amount of interest, first determine the total of all the payments: 24 x $85 = $2040. Those payments include both principal repaid and interest paid. Since the total principal repaid was just found to be $1877.50, the amount of interest repaid must be the difference between this and the total payments, $2040. So the amount of interest is $2040 - $1877.50 = $162.50.

Finding the Interest Paid on an Amortized Loan

If an amortized loan with principal PV is paid off by making a sequence of m payments of PMT each, then the amount of interest that will be paid on the loan is the difference between the total amount of payments and the loan principal PV:

Interest Paid on Amortized Loan = $m \times PMT - PV$

Quiz Yourself: (Answer at the end of this section, before the problems.)
1. What is the principal of an amortized loan that will be paid off with a sequence of quarterly payments of $175 for 6 years at 5.4% compounded quarterly? How much interest will the borrower have paid?

Example 3 Best Buy offers a TV for $200 down and $25 per month for the next 12 months. If interest is charged at 9% compounded monthly, find the cash value (actual price) of the TV. How much total interest will the customer pay with this offer?

Solution: **The down payment is not a part of the sequence of payments.** In general,

---

If part or all of the price of an item is paid off by a loan with periodic payments, then

$$\textit{Cash Value of Item} = \frac{\textit{Loan Principal of}}{\textit{Periodic Payments}} + \frac{\textit{Down Payment}}{\textit{(if any)}} + \frac{\textit{Trade - in}}{\textit{(if any)}}$$

In this problem there is no trade-in, so the cash value (actual price) of the TV is the $200 down payment plus the present value of the sequence of 12 monthly payments of $25 each. The following time line illustrates the situation, with C denoting the cash value.

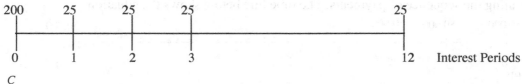

Since $i = 0.09 / 12 = 0.0075$, the present value of the sequence of 12 payments of $25 each is

$$PV = \$25\frac{\left(1-(1.0075)^{-12}\right)}{0.0075} = \$285.87$$

Thus the cash value is $C = \$200 + \$285.87 = \$485.87$. Since a total of $25 \times 12 = $300.00 was paid by the customer on his loan, the amount of interest is $300 - $285.87 = $14.13.

Example 4. A car dealer offers to sell you a new car if you trade in your old car worth $3500, make a down payment of $1200, and make monthly payments of $300 for four years. Assuming you can borrow money at 7.5% compounded monthly, what is the cash value of the deal he is offering on the new car? How much interest would you pay?

Solution: We first need to find the loan principal of the sequence of payments you will make in repaying the loan. From the information given, $PMT = \$300$ and $m = 12(4) = 48$ payments. On the timeline we have shown the down payment and trade-in at time 0, which is when they change hands.

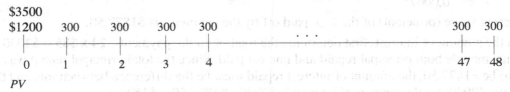

The interest rate per period is $i = 0.075/12 = 0.00625$ Using formula (2) we calculate

$$PV = \$300\frac{\left(1-(1.00625)^{-48}\right)}{(0.00625)} = \$12,407.51$$

To find the cash value we must add to this the $3500 trade-in and the $1200 down to obtain a total of $17,107.51 as the cash value of the deal. The amount of interest is 48($300) - $12,407.51 = $1992.49.

The cash value calculated in Example 4 is important! This is the amount you should compare to what other sources tell you the car is worth. If you have reason to believe the car (in Example 4) is worth only $12,000, then this is not a good deal. But if you believe it is worth $13,000 then this *is* a good deal.

> **Quiz Yourself:** (Answer at the end of this section, before the problems.)
> 2. A car dealer offers to sell you a new car if you agree to make a $2500 down payment and take out a 5 year amortized loan at 6% compounded monthly with monthly payments of $421.70. What is the cash value of this deal? How much interest will you pay? If you believe the car is worth $23,000, is this a good deal?

When the first payment in a sequence is made at the **start** of the first payment interval, we must treat it like a down payment. Here is an example of such a situation.

Example 5 You just won a one million dollar Lottery! You will receive $50,000 per year for the next 20 years, starting today, a total of $1,000,000. If the current interest rate 6.6% compounded annually, what is the actual cash equivalent of this sequence of payments? (Such a cash equivalent is the value of the <u>cash option</u> that you must select or reject when you purchase your lottery ticket.)

Solution: The cash equivalent of the payments today is the present value equivalent to the sequence of payments. <u>Because the first payment is being made today,</u> it is not made at the end of a year interval. So we will consider the first payment separately (like a down payment), with the other 19 payments constituting the sequence of payments. The time line below shows the situation.

With these assumptions, the sequence of $m = 19$ payments has $PMT = \$50,000$ and $i = 0.066$. So

$$PV = \$50,000\frac{\left(1-(1.066)^{-19}\right)}{0.066} = \$532,650.01$$

The total value of your winnings is PV + the initial $50,000 = $582,650.01. This is much less than the advertised 1 million dollars.

Example 6 Suppose the interest rate in Example 5 is only 3% compounded annually. Should this make the cash value larger or smaller? Determine the cash value of the sequence of payments with this interest rate and revisit your answer.

Solution: Replacing 0.066 by 0.03 in the calculation in Example 5,

$$\text{Cash Value} = \$50,000 + \$50,000\frac{\left(1-(1.03)^{-19}\right)}{0.03} = \$50,000 + \$716,189.96 = \$766,189.76$$

This is a significantly larger cash value! One line of reasoning to justify why we obtained a larger cash value is that with a smaller interest rate each $50,000 payment has a smaller amount of interest in it, and thus a larger amount of principal. If this is true for each payment then it is true for their sum, the original principal, and cash value.

Example 7 Your company says that when you retire you will receive $4000 per month for the next 20 years, the first paid the day you retire. If the bank charges 3.6% compounded monthly, what lump sum will the company have to give the bank today to pay for all the payments, including the first one given as soon as you retire? (This is the cash value of your retirement pension.)

Solution: There are $20 \times 12 = 240$ payments, but the first one is made at the start of the first payment interval. The company will have to pay the bank the first payment of $4000 plus the *PV* of the sequence of 239 other payments at the ends of the 239 months. $i = 0.036 / 12 = 0.003$.

$$\text{Lump Sum} = \$4000 + \$4000\frac{\left(1-(1.003)^{-239}\right)}{0.003} = \$681,681.32$$

Example 8 A couple is getting divorced and their assets are being split between them. The wife has a pension paying her $1500 per month, and her life expectancy is 28 years 3 months. To divide their assets the mediator must determine the cash value of her pension. What is it if money is worth 2.9% compounded monthly?

Solution: There will be $28 \times 12 + 3 = 339$ payments. $i = 0.029 / 12 = 0.002416667$

$$\text{Cash Value} = \$1500\frac{\left(1-(1.002416667)^{-339}\right)}{0.002416667} = \$346,842.64$$

Quiz Yourself: (Answer on next page.)
3. You just won a lottery of $60,000,000. One option is to receive 30 yearly payments of $2 million each, with the first being made today. Another is to receive the cash value today of that sequence of payments. Determine that cash value today if the current interest rate is 4% compounded annually.
4. You company offers you a retirement package consisting of $2500 per month for the next 10 years, paid at the start of each month. If money is currently worth 2.7% compounded monthly, what is the cash value of this package?

Answers to Quiz Yourself:

1. $i = 0.054 / 4 = 0.0135$ $m = 6 \times 4 = 24$ quarterly payments of $175.

$$PV = \$175 \frac{\left(1-(1.0135)^{-24}\right)}{0.0135} = \$3567.15$$

Amount of Interest Paid = $m(PMT) - PV = 24(\$175) - \$3567.15 = \$632.85$

2. $i = 0.06 / 12 = 0.005$ $m = 5 \times 12 = 60$ monthly payments of $421.70.

The principal of the sequence of payments is $PV = \$421.70 \dfrac{\left(1-(1.005)^{-60}\right)}{0.005} = \$21,812.67$

Amount of Interest Paid = $m(PMT) - PV = 60(\$421.70) - \$21,812.67 = \$3489.33$

Cash Value = $21,812.67 + $2500 = $24,312.67. This is more than the $23,000 you think the car is worth. Since the Cash Value is more than you think the car is worth, it is not a good deal.

3. You will receive a payment today and payments at the ends of the next 29 years. Cash Value =

$$\$2,000,000 + \$2,000,000 \frac{\left(1-(1.04)^{-29}\right)}{0.04} = \$2,000,000 + \$33,967,429.27 = \$35,967,429.27$$

4. You will receive a $2500 payment today and payments at the ends of the next 119 months.
   $i = 0.027 / 12 = 0.0025$.   So

$$\text{Cash Value} = \$2500 + \$2500 \frac{\left(1-(1.0025)^{-119}\right)}{0.0025} = \$2500 + \$257,051.64 = \$259,551.64$$

Problems for Section 2.2

Sharpen Your Skills: (Answers in back of text.)

1. Explain how to obtain the negative of a number on your calculator.

2. Give the keystrokes to evaluate $\$175\dfrac{\left(1-(1.0135)^{-24}\right)}{0.0135}$ on your calculator, and find its value.

3. Give the keystrokes to evaluate $\$65\dfrac{\left(1-\left(1+\dfrac{0.07}{12}\right)^{-36}\right)}{\left(\dfrac{0.07}{12}\right)}$ on your calculator, and find its value.

Communicate the Concepts: (Answers in back of text.)

4. Explain the meaning of *PV* in formula (2) in relation to the sequence of payments.

5. Explain how to find the total amount of interest paid over the life of an amortized loan.

6. What assumption(s) are made in Formula (2) about when payments are made?

7. Explain how to find the cash value of an amortized loan together with a down payment.

8. Explain why the first of 20 lottery winnings payments is not considered part of the sequence when using the Present Value formula (2).

Apply Your Knowledge: (Answers to odd-numbered problems in back of text.)

9. Find the present value of the following sequences of payments, that is, the principal that could be paid off by making this sequence of payments. Assume the payments are made at the ends of the payment intervals.
   (a) $600 a year for 12 years at 5% annual interest.
   (b) $250 a month for 6 years, 3 months, at 6% compounded monthly.
   (c) $500 per quarter for 8 years, 9 months, at 6% compounded quarterly.

10. What is the loan principal of an automobile loan paid off with monthly payments of $330 for four years, assuming you borrow money at 8.7% compounded monthly and the first payment is due one month after the start of the loan? How much total interest would you pay with this loan?

11. If a loan is made at 5.2% compounded quarterly, what loan value today could be paid off by making 15 quarterly payments of $500 each, the first due 3 months from today? How much total interest will be paid with this loan?

12. A business expects to generate enough profit to make quarterly payments of $800 at the end of each quarter for the next 7 years. If they can borrow money at 8.4% compounded quarterly, what loan value can they pay off with this sequence of payments? How much total interest will they pay?

13. You want to buy a new car. The seller, figuring interest at 5.7% compounded monthly, says you can have the car if you pay $2,000 down and promise to pay $250 every month for the next 5 years. What is the cash value of the car today? How much total interest would you pay with this deal?

14. A car dealer, figuring interest at 7.8% compound monthly, offers to sell you a new car if you trade in your car which is worth $5000, pay an additional $1500 down, and agree to pay $370 every month for the next three years.
   (a) What is the cash value of the car today?
   (b) How much total interest would you pay with this deal?

15. A car dealer offers to sell you a new car that he says is priced at $15,500 by taking your down payment of $3,000 and making you a loan at 6.3% annual interest compounded monthly for 4 years, resulting in a monthly payment of $300. What is the actual cash value of his deal (down payment plus loan value)? Is this cash value more or less than what the dealer says you are paying?

16. A car dealer offers to sell you a new car that he says is priced at $12,000 by taking your down payment of $1,250 and making you a loan at 9.3% annual interest compounded monthly for 3 years, resulting in a monthly payment of $350. What is the actual cash value of his deal (down payment plus loan value)?

17. In the Mega Millions lottery of January 5, 2015 each of the two winners could receive $190,000,000 paid in 25 equal annual installments, the first in January 2015. What was the cash value in January 2015 of this sequence of payments, if money was worth 3.5% compounded yearly?

18. Kentucky is considering introducing a new $4,800,000 lottery that will be paid out by making equal monthly payments at the start of each month for the next ten years, with the first payment upon winning. If money is worth 6.3% compounded monthly, what is the cash value of winning such a lottery?

19. Your company says that when you retire you will receive $3000 per month for the next 25 years, paid at the *start* of each month. If the bank charges 4.2% compounded monthly, what lump sum will the company have to give the bank today to pay for all the payments, including the first one given as soon as you retire? (This is the cash value of your retirement pension.)

20. Your company says that when you retire you will receive $5000 per month for the next 35 years, paid at the *start* of each month. If the bank charges 4.8% compounded monthly, what lump sum will the company have to give the bank today to pay for all the payments, including the first one given as soon as you retire? (This is the cash value of your retirement pension.)

21. A couple is getting divorced and their assets are being split between them. The wife has a pension paying her $2350 per month, and her life expectancy is 22 years 7 months. To divide their assets the mediator must determine the cash value of her pension. What is it if money is worth 3.0% compounded monthly?

22. A couple is getting divorced and their assets are being split between them. The husband has a pension paying him $2570 per month, and his life expectancy is 18 years 5 months. To divide their assets the mediator must determine the cash value of his pension. What is it if money is worth 3.2% compounded monthly?

Section 2.3 Finding the Required Periodic Payment

Formula (1) in Section 2.1 provides a way to calculate the Future Accumulation *FA*, when the periodic payment *PMT*, the interest rate *i* per period, and the number *m* of payments are known. Formula (2) in Section 2.2 provides a way to calculate the Present Value *PV* of an amortized loan when the periodic payment *PMT*, the interest rate *i* per period, and the number *m* of payments of an amortized loan are known. In many such situations, however, we know *FA* and must determine the periodic payment amount *PMT* necessary to accumulate *FA*, or know *PV* and must determine the periodic payment amount *PMT* necessary to pay off a loan amount of *PV*. To do this we must solve equations (1) and (2) for *PMT*.

Example 1 A family wants to start a savings account for college expenses ten years from now, and will make their first deposit at the end of this month. What equal monthly deposits in an account paying 3.6% compounded monthly are needed in order to accumulate $25,000 just after the last deposit ten years from now? How much interest will the account have earned?

Solution: From the information given $i = 0.036 / 12 = 0.003$, $m = 12 \times 10 = 120$ payments. The $25,000 is the future accumulation, because it is the value to be accumulated at the *end* of the sequence of payments. The time line shows the situation.

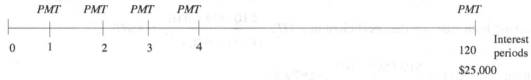

Since this problem is about a future accumulation, we substitute the given values in Formula (1):

$$FA = PMT\left(\frac{(1+i)^m - 1}{i}\right) \quad \text{becomes} \quad \$25,000 = PMT\left(\frac{(1+0.003)^{120} - 1}{0.003}\right)$$

To solve for *PMT* multiply both sides by 0.003: $\$25,000 \times 0.003 = PMT\left((1+0.003)^{120} - 1\right)$

and then divide both sides by the coefficient of *PMT*: $\dfrac{\$25,000 \times 0.003}{\left((1+0.003)^{120} - 1\right)} = PMT$

So $PMT = \dfrac{\$25,000 \times 0.003}{\left((1.003)^{120} - 1\right)} = \$173.39$ Since the *FA* gives the total of deposits and interest, the total

interest amount is given by $I = FA - m \times PMT = \$25,000 - 120(\$173.39) = \$4193.20$.

> *Calculating the Answer:*
> The denominator **must** be in parentheses. The keystrokes to evaluate the *PMT* above are:
>
> 25000 X 0.003 ÷ (1.003 ^ 120 - 1) =

In general, to solve formula (1): $FA = PMT\left(\dfrac{(1+i)^m - 1}{i}\right)$ for *PMT* we multiply both sides of each

equation by the reciprocal of the fraction on the right side. This yields:

> (3) $PMT = \dfrac{FA \times i}{\left((1+i)^m - 1\right)} =$ **Periodic Payment needed to accumulate future accumulation of *FA***

Example 2. A college student is given $10,000 for his college expenses for 4 years. He invests the money in an account paying 4% annual interest compounded quarterly. What equal quarterly withdrawals can he make for the following 4 years so as to completely exhaust the account at the end of the four years? How much interest will he have during the 4 years?

Solution: This problem is about a loan of $10,000 from the student to his account that is paid back in

$m = 4 \times 4 = 16$ equal payments to the student with interest at $i = 0.04 / 4 = 0.01$ per quarter.

Since $10,000 is the value of the account at the start of the term (and the amount the student "loaned" his account), $PV = \$10,000$. Substituting into formula (2):

$$(2) \quad PV = \frac{PMT(1-(1+i)^{-m})}{i} \quad \text{becomes} \quad \$10,000 = \frac{PMT(1-(1+0.01)^{-16})}{0.01}$$

To solve for PMT multiply both sides by 0.01: $\$10,000 \times 0.01 = PMT(1-(1+0.01)^{-16})$

Then divide both sides by the coefficient of PMT: $\dfrac{\$10,000 \times 0.01}{(1-(1+0.01)^{-16})} = PMT$

Calculating, $PMT = \dfrac{\$10,000 \times 0.01}{\left(1-(1.01)^{-16}\right)} = \$679.45$.

As with other loans, the amount of interest equals the total of the payments, less the principal paid off. Here that is $16 \times \$679.45 - \$10,000 = \$871.20$.

Calculating the Answer:													
With (-) key:	10000	X	.01	÷	(	1	-	1.01	^	(-)	16	)	=
With +/- key:	10000	X	.01	÷	(	1	-	1.01	^	16	+/-	)	=

In general, to solve formula (2): $PV = PMT\left(\dfrac{1-(1+i)^{-m}}{i}\right)$ for PMT we multiply both sides of each

equation by the reciprocal of the fraction on the right side. This yields:

$$(4) \quad PMT = \frac{PV \times i}{\left(1-(1+i)^{-m}\right)} = \quad \textbf{Periodic Payment needed to pay off amortized loan amount of } PV$$

When you use formulas (3) and/or (4) it is important to first analyze the problem to decide whether the problem involves a known future accumulation (a value to be accumulated at the end of the sequence of payments) or a known present value (a value at the start of the sequence of payments that is repaid by the sequence of payments). This will help you decide which formula to use.

Example 3 A student will buy a car priced at $6500 by paying $1000 down and paying off the remaining debt by making monthly payments at 6.9% interest for two years.
(a) What should his monthly payment be if the first payment is at the end of the first month?
(b) How much total interest would he pay?

Solution (a) This situation is similar to Examples 3 and 4 in Section 2.2. In particular, the cash value price of the car = the down payment + the PV of the loan payments. So $\$6500 = \$1000 + PV$, or $PV = \$5500 =$ loan principal. Here is the appropriate time line.

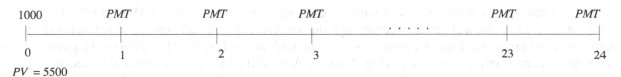

$PV = 5500$

From the information given, $i = 0.069 \div 12 = 0.00575$ is the interest rate per month, and there will be $m = 2 \times 12 = 24$ payments. We use formula (4) because we know PV:

$$PMT = \frac{5500 \times 0.00575}{\left(1-(1.00575)^{-24}\right)} = \$246.00.$$

(b) As in Section 2.2, Total Interest = $m \times PMT - PV = 24 \times \$246 - \$5500 = \$404.$

Quiz Yourself (Answers at the end of this section, before the problems.)

1. A family wants to accumulate \$40,000 over the next 15 years by making equal monthly payments into a savings account paying 4.5% compounded monthly. If the first payment is made at the end of the first month, what should their monthly deposit amount be? How much total interest will they earn?

2. A man buys a car priced at \$25,000 by trading in his car and making monthly payments for 4 years at 6% compounded monthly. If the dealership will give him \$6000 for his trade-in, what will his monthly payment be? How much total interest will he pay?

Installment Loans: The Add-On Interest Method

Some finance companies make loans that are **not amortized**. Short-term loans that are not amortized are called **Installment Loans**. With installment loans the **Add-On Interest Method** is often used to determine the monthly payment. With this method we determine the amount $I = Prt$ of **simple interest** that the original principal P would earn over the term of the loan. The monthly payment is then found by dividing $P + I$, the original principal plus the total interest, by the number of monthly payments.

Monthly Payment of Installment Loan using the Add-on Interest Method

$$\frac{\text{monthly}}{\text{payment}} = \frac{P+I}{m} \quad \text{where} \quad \begin{cases} P \text{ is the principal of the loan,} \\ I = Prt \text{ is the amount of Simple Interest,} \\ \text{and } m \text{ is the number of monthly payments} \end{cases}$$

<u>Example 4</u> Suppose you purchase a new computer for \$960. You may finance the purchase by a loan for one year at an annual interest rate of 15%.

(a) What will be your monthly payment using the Add-On Interest Method? How much interest would you pay using this method?

(b) What would be your monthly payment if the loan is amortized? How much interest would you pay using this method?

<u>Solution:</u> (a) With the Add-On Interest Method, over 1 year the amount of simple interest on \$960 at 15% will be

$$I = Prt = \$960 \times 0.15 \times 1 = \$144.00$$

Adding this to the purchase price of \$960, we have \$960 + \$144 = \$1104, which is the amount of money that must be repaid in the 12 monthly payments. So

Monthly payment = \$1104 $\div$ 12 = \$92.00.

The amount of interest is the I we previously calculated: $I = Prt = \$960 \times 0.15 \times 1 = \$144.00$

(b) If the loan is amortized, we use formula (4) with $i = 0.15 \div 12 = 0.0125$, $m = 12$, and $PV = \$960$.

$$PMT = \frac{\$960 \times 0.0125}{\left(1-(1.0125)^{-12}\right)} = \$86.65.$$

The amount of interest paid is $12 \times \$86.65 - \$960 = \$79.80$

Notice in Example 4 that the amount of interest paid using the Add-On Interest Method is higher than with amortization. This will be true even though the interest rates of two loans are stated as being the same. Somewhere on the finance contract you will be told the method used to calculate the payments and the total amount of interest you are paying. Also, the APR of the loan will be stated; this rate gives the true interest rate. We will not actually calculate the APR, as it is influenced by any fees or other charges. But the APR is much closer to the amortized loan rate than the Add-On Interest Method rate.

Be careful! With the Add-on Interest Method of installment loan payment calculation, you are actually paying a (usually much) higher interest rate than the stated simple interest rate.

Quiz Yourself: (Answer at the end of this section, before the problems.)

3. Suppose you purchase a new iPad for $630. You may finance the purchase by a loan for 9 months at an annual interest rate of 18%.
   (a) What will be your monthly payment using the Add-On Interest Method? How much interest would you pay using this method?
   (b) What would be your monthly payment if the loan is amortized? How much interest would you pay using this method?
   (c) Which loan is better for you?

Examples of More Complex Situations

Example 5 A machine shop must accumulate $12,000 during the next 10 years to replace certain of its machines. It has $2500 in a fund earning 3% compounded annually. Assuming the interest rate stays the same for the next ten years, what sum must the shop invest at the end of each year in this fund in order to have the $12,000 at the end of the ten years? How much interest will they have earned in the ten years?

Solution This situation in this problem is similar to that in Example 5 of Section 2.1 because the account starts with a lump sum already invested, and this sum is augmented by periodic payments. We must deal with the lump sum separately from the periodic payments. A timeline of the situation is:

The right-hand end of the time line indicates that:

[Future Accumulation of the sequence of payments the company makes]

+ [Future Value of the $2500 already in the fund] = $12,000.

The $2500 already in the fund will accumulate to $F = \$2500(1 + 0.03)^{10} = \$3359.79$ at the end of 10 years. So the future accumulation of the sequence of payments must provide the rest of the $12,000, which is $12,000 - $3359.79 = $8640.21. Using formula (3) to find *PMT* when *FA* = $8640.21, and using $i = 0.03$, and $m = 10$, we calculate:

$$PMT = \frac{8640.21 \times 0.03}{\left((1.03)^{10} - 1\right)} = \$753.69$$

So the machine shop must augment their current $2500 savings by depositing $753.69 at the end of each year into the fund to accumulate the total of $12,000.

The total amount that the shop has actually contributed in the ten years is

$$\$2500 + 10 \times \$753.69 = \$2500 + \$7536.90 = \$10,036.90$$

The rest of the $12,000 future accumulation, $12,000 - $10,036.90 = $1,963.10, is the interest they will have earned.

Example 6 Sam has $150,000 in a savings account when he retires, and it is earning 4.2% annual interest compounded monthly. He will make no further deposits, and wants to make a monthly withdrawal from the account for the next 12 years. Assuming the account continues to earn interest at the same rate, and his monthly withdrawals are all equal, what monthly withdrawal amount will result in the account being completely exhausted at the end of the 12 years?

Solution: Think of the situation as being that the bank has "borrowed" $150,000 of Sam's money, and will repay it to him by making equal monthly payments for the next 12 years at 4.2% compounded monthly. Thus $150,000 = PV$ (since it is an amount at the *start* of the payments), $m = 12 \times 12 = 144$, and $i = 0.042 / 12 = .0035$. Here is the time line:

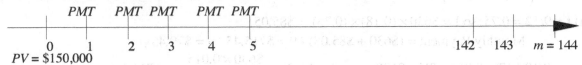

We must calculate PMT from PV, so we use formula (4): $PMT = \dfrac{\$150,000 \times 0.0035}{\left(1 - (1.0035)^{-144}\right)} = \$1327.91$

He receives a total of $144 \times \$1327.91 = \$191,219.04$. These payments repay his $150,000, so the rest is interest earned: Amount Interest $= 144 \times \$1327.91 - \$150,000 = \$41,219.04$.

Quiz Yourself: (Answers on next page.)

4. Rework Quiz Yourself problem 1 supposing you already had saved $10,000. How much should your monthly payment be now? How much total interest will you earn now?

5. You reach retirement and have managed to save $600,000. You predict it will earn 3.6% compounded monthly for the foreseeable future. You want to be able make monthly withdrawals from the account for the next 30 years. What monthly withdrawal amount will completely exhaust the funds at the end of the 30 years? How much interest will your money have earned in the 30 years?

Answers to Quiz Yourself

1. $FA = \$40,000$, $i = 0.045 / 12 = 0.00375$ $m = 15 \times 12 = 180$. $PMT = \dfrac{\$40,000 \times 0.00375}{\left((1.00375)^{180} - 1\right)} = \$156.00$

   Amount of Interest = $\$40,000 - 180 \times \$156 = \$11,920$.

2. $PV = \$25,000 - \$6,000 = \$19,000$ is the amount financed. $i = 0.06 / 12 = 0.005$ $m = 4 \times 12 = 48$.

   $PMT = \dfrac{\$19,000 \times 0.005}{\left(1 - (1.005)^{-48}\right)} = \$446.22$.   Amount of Interest = $48 \times \$446.22 - \$19,000 = \$2418.56$

3. (a) $t = 9/12 = 0.75$, so $I = \$630 \times (0.18) \times (0.75) = \$85.05$.

   Monthly Payment = $(\$630 + \$85.05) / 9 = \$715.45 / 9 = \$79.45$

   (b) $i = 0.18 / 12 = 0.015$, $PV = \$630$, $m = 9$ $PMT = \dfrac{\$630 \times 0.015}{\left(1 - (1.015)^{-9}\right)} = \$75.35$

   In (b), Amount of Interest = $9 \times \$75.35 - \$630 = \$48.15$

   (c) The monthly payment amount and interest amount are less with the amortized loan in (b). It is better for the consumer.

4. <u>Step 1</u> The $10,000 already saved will grow to $F = \$10000(1.00375)^{180} = \$19,615.55$ in 15 years.

   <u>Step 2</u> The monthly deposits must accumulate to the difference between the $40,000 goal and the amount in (a): $FA = \$40,000 - \$19,615.55 = \$20,384.45$. Using the same i and m as in 1,

   $PMT = \dfrac{\$19615.55 \times 0.00375}{\left((1.00375)^{180} - 1\right)} = \$76.50$

   The amount of interest is the $40,000 final total less the $10,000 you started with and the sum of the deposits: Interest Amount = $\$40,000 - \$10,000 - 180 \times \$76.50 = \$16,230$.

5. This is like Example 6. $PV = \$600,000$ $i = 0.036 / 12 = 0.003$ $m = 30 \times 12 = 360$

   $PMT = \dfrac{\$600,000 \times 0.003}{\left(1 - (1.003)^{-360}\right)} = \$2727.87$

   Amount of Interest Earned = $360 \times \$2727.87 - \$600,000 = \$382,033.20$.

Problems for Section 2.3

Sharpen Your Skills: (Answers in back of text.)

1. Give the keystrokes to evaluate $\dfrac{\$20,000 \times 0.003}{\left((1.003)^{120} - 1\right)}$ and find its value.

2. Give the keystrokes to evaluate $\dfrac{\$9,000 \times 0.004}{\left(1 - (1.004)^{-40}\right)}$ and find its value.

3. Solve $\$15,000 = \dfrac{PMT\left(1 - (1 + 0.025)^{-72}\right)}{0.025}$ for *PMT*. Evaluate your answer to the nearest penny.

4. Solve $\$10,000 = \dfrac{PMT\left((1 + 0.013)^{120} - 1\right)}{0.013}$ for *PMT*. Evaluate your answer to the nearest penny.

Communicate the Concepts: (Answers in back of text.)

5. Explain how to find the monthly payment needed to accumulate a future value in an account earning compound interest.

6. Explain how to find the monthly payment on an amortized loan.

7. Explain how to find the monthly payment amount on an installment loan using the Add-On Interest Method.

8. Explain how to find the amount of a monthly withdrawal that will completely exhaust a sum of money over a given length of time if the money is in an account earning compound interest.

Apply Your Knowledge: (Answers to odd-numbered problems in back of text.) You are encouraged to draw a timeline and place the relevant data on it.

9. How much must a person invest at the end of each 3 months for the next 5 years into an account paying 4% compounded quarterly in order to accumulate $3500 at the end of that time? How much interest will have been earned?

10. A parent buys a piano costing $2950. She pays $250 down and agrees to make monthly payments, the first due in one month, for the next 2 years to pay off the remaining balance. If interest is at 9.9% compounded monthly,
    (a) Find her monthly amortized loan payment.   (b) Find the total amount of interest paid.
    (c) How do the answers to (a) and (b) change if the Add-On Interest Method (and 9.9% annual simple interest) is used?

11. In order to save $50,000 for college over the next seven years, equal semi-annual deposits are to be made at the end of each six months into a fund earning 5% compounded semi-annually. Find the amount of each semi-annual deposit. How much of the $50,000 saved is interest?

12. You are the proud parent of a new baby. You want to begin saving now for her college education. You estimate that you will need $80,000 when she reaches age 18.
    (a) What monthly savings deposit would you have to make in an account paying 6% annual interest compounded monthly in order to attain your goal when she turns 18?
    (b) How much total interest will your investments have earned?

13. A man wants to purchase a used car priced at $19,000 by trading in his old car that is worth $6200. The dealer offers a 3-year amortized loan with a rate of 4.2% compounded monthly.
    (a) What will be his monthly payment? (b) How much total interest will he pay?
    (c) How will the answers to (a) and (b) change if the Add-On Interest Method is used (and 4.2% is annual simple interest)?

14. A student buys a car priced at $18,500 by paying $2,000 down and paying off the remaining debt by making monthly amortized loan payments at 9.3% interest compounded monthly for four years.
    (a) What should his monthly payment be? (b) How much total interest will he pay?

15. A student receives $250 credit for her old computer when buying a newer model costing $1750. The store offers her an 18-month amortized loan at 12% compounded monthly.
    (a) What will be her monthly payment?   (b) How much total interest will she pay?
    (c) How will the answers to (a) and (b) change if the Add-On Interest Method is used (and 12% is annual simple interest)?

16. A dealer offers a buyer the following two options to pay for a $22,000 car. What monthly payment would each result in?
    (a) $1,500 cash back to be applied as a down payment (reducing the amount financed) with the balance financed with an amortized loan at 6.9% compounded monthly for three years.
    (b) an amortized loan on the full value of the car at 2.9% compounded monthly for three years.

17. Rework Problem 11, assuming you had already saved $10,000 when you began to make deposits into the account. Find the amount of each semi-annual deposit that is needed to achieve the $50,000 goal.

18. Rework Problem 12, assuming you had already saved $10,000 when you began to make deposits into the account. What monthly savings deposit would you have to make in an account paying 6% annual interest compounded monthly in order to attain your goal when she turns 18?

19. Jane wants to have $6000 to buy a used car when she graduates from college 4 years from now. As of today she has $923 saved for it in an account paying 5.4% annual interest compounded monthly. What monthly deposit must she make at the end of each month for the next 4 years in order to have a total of $6000 in her savings account? How much interest will she have earned?

20. On May 1, 2015, Bob had $3275.60 in a fund paying 6% compounded quarterly. By making equal quarterly deposits in the fund, the first on August 1, 2015, and the last on November 1, 2024, he wants to have $20,000 in the fund at that time. Find the amount of the required deposits. How much interest will he have earned? (Remember: Our formulas assume payments are made at the *ends* of payment intervals.)

21. At retirement, your savings account has $800,000 in it and is earning 6% compounded monthly. You plan to make equal monthly withdrawals at the end of each month for the next 20 years.
    (a) What monthly withdrawal for the next twenty years will completely exhaust the account if the account continues to earn 6% compounded monthly?
    (b) How much interest will your account have earned during the twenty years?

22. At retirement, your savings account has $500,000 in it and is earning 7.2% compounded monthly. You plan to make equal monthly withdrawals at the end of each month for the next 25 years.
    (a) What monthly withdrawal for the next twenty-five years will completely exhaust the account if the account continues to earn 7.2% compounded monthly?
    (b) How much interest will your account have earned during the twenty-five years?

Review Problems
23. If you make a deal to purchase a car by trading in your $3000 car, giving a $2500 down payment, and agreeing to a 5 year amortized loan at 5.4% compounded monthly with monthly payments of $260, what is the cash value of this deal?

24. You have $1200 in a savings account paying 3% annual interest compounded quarterly. If you deposit an additional $200 per quarter in the account for the next 8 years, what will be the value of the account at that time?

Section 2.4 Amortization Schedules

In Section 2.3 we saw how to determine the amount of the periodic payment *PMT* needed to pay off an amortized loan. Each of those payments has two parts, one that goes to pay the amount of interest owed at the time that payment is made, and the other that goes to repay part of the original principal of the loan. Although the periodic payment amount stays fixed, the way that payment is broken into principal and interest does not stay fixed! This feature is one way to distinguish an amortized loan from an Installment Loan. In an Installment (Add-on Method) Loan, the distribution between Principal and Interest stays the same for all payments.

Example 1 A student buys a $3000 computer. He takes out an amortized loan for the full amount at 18% annual interest compounded monthly, and repaid in 6 substantially equal monthly payments.
  (a) What monthly payment is required?
  (b) What part of each payment goes to interest? What part goes to repay the principal?
  What is the remaining balance after each monthly payment?

Solution: (a) Here we want to find *PMT* with *PV* = $3000. The interest rate per payment interval is i = 0.18 / 12 = 0.015 (because n = 12 is the number of compoundings per year if the payments are monthly.)   The number of payments is m = 6. Using formula (4) from Section 2.3,

$$PMT = \frac{\$3000 \times 0.015}{\left(1 - (1 + 0.015)^{-6}\right)} = \$526.58$$

(b) As each of the six monthly payments is made, part of the payment goes to pay interest on the current balance of the loan, and the rest goes to pay principal and thereby reduce that current balance. At the start of the loan the current balance is the amount of the original principal. The first payment includes interest on that current balance, which is calculated by

Interest on current balance at first payment = i × *Balance* = 0.015 × 3000 = $45.00.

The rest of the payment, or $526.58 – $45.00 = $481.58, goes to repay part of the principal. Deducting this repaid principal from the current balance gives a new current balance of

Current balance after first payment = $3000.00 – $481.58 = $2518.42.

If the loan were to be paid off at the time of the first payment, this current balance is the additional amount (in addition to the first payment) that would be required to pay off the loan. If not, we repeat the process at the time of the second payment:

Interest on current balance at second payment = 0.015 × $2518.42 = $37.78

Part of second payment going to repay principal = $526.58 – $37.78 = $488.80

Current balance after second payment = $2518.42 – $488.80 = $2029.62

If the loan were paid off at the time of the second payment, this is the additional amount that would be required. If not, the process is repeated at the time of the third payment. Repetition of this process continues until the loan is paid off. Actually, these calculations are usually made at the start of the loan and arranged in a table, called an **amortization schedule**, like the one on the next page. The last column of the table gives the additional amounts required to pay off the loan at the end of each of the six periods.

Amortization Schedule for Example 1

Period	(a) Current Balance at start of period	(b) Payment Amount	(c) Amount Interest paid	(d) Principal repaid	(e) Current Balance after payment
1	$3000.00	$526.58	$45.00	$481.58	$2518.42
2	$2518.42	$526.58	$37.78	$488.80	$2029.62
3	$2029.62	$526.58	$30.44	$496.14	$1533.48
4	$1533.48	$526.58	$23.00	$503.58	$1029.90
5	$1029.90	$526.58	$15.45	$511.13	$518.77
6	$518.77	$526.55	$7.78	$518.77	0
Totals:		$3159.45	$159.45	$3000.00	

The final payment amount is determined in a different manner from all the other payment amounts.
This is because the final payment amount <u>must</u> consist of the current balance plus the interest owed on
that balance. If we had done no rounding during our previous calculations, this would have been the same
as the other payment amounts. But when we round to the nearest penny, this often causes the final
payment amount to be slightly different from the others.

General Procedure for Constructing an Amortization Schedule:

Start with the principal as the *Current Balance*, and repeatedly perform these four steps until the final
   payment is reached:
(i) Write the *Current Balance* in column (a)
(ii) Calculate the *Interest Amount*: Multiply the *Current Balance* by i, and round the result to the
       nearest penny. Write this in column (c)
(iii) Calculate the *Principal Repaid*: Subtract the *Interest* from the *Payment*, and write this in column (d)
(iv) Calculate the new *Current Balance*: Subtract the *Principal Repaid* from the old *Current Balance*,
       and write this in column (e)
   For the <u>final</u> payment amount, calculate the *Interest Amount* as in ii). Then, **instead of steps (iii)
       and (iv)**, the <u>final</u> *Payment Amount* is the *Interest Amount* plus the *Current Balance*.

Although the calculated payment amount of $526.58 in Example 1 makes the 6 payments come out
approximately even, in fact the borrower is usually free to pay a larger amount at any payment. Any extra
amount paid goes to repay principal and reduce the current balance faster than in the amortization
schedule above. This in turn will cause the subsequent interest amounts to be less since they are calculated
as i times the current balance. The next example shows how this works.

Example 1 (Continued) Suppose the student in the previous example decides he can afford to pay $650
per month, still at 18% compounded monthly. Create an amortization schedule for his payments.

<u>Solution</u> We apply the process above. The monthly interest rate is still $i = 0.015$.

Period	Current Balance at start of period	Payment Amount	Amount Interest paid	Principal repaid	Current Balance after payment
1	$3000.00	$650.00	$45.00	$605.00	$2395.00
2	$2395.00	$650.00	$35.93	$614.07	$1780.93
3	$1780.93	$650.00	$26.71	$623.29	$1157.64
4	$1157.64	$650.00	$17.36	$632.64	$525.00
5	$525.00	$532.88	$7.88	$525.00	$0
Totals:		$3132.88	$132.88	$3000.00	

In period 1, Amount Interest = $0.015 \times \$3000 = \$45$; Principal repaid = $650 - $45 = $605; New current
balance = $3000 - $605 = $2395. In period 2, Amount Interest = $0.015 \times \$2395 = \$35.93$; Principal
repaid = $650 - $35.93 = $614.07; New current balance = $2395 - $614.07 = $1780.93. And so on. The
final payment (in Period 5) is found by adding the current balance and the interest owed on it.

With this payment amount it takes 4 payments of $650 per month and a final payment of $532.88 to pay off the loan. This last payment is significantly different from the other monthly payments, but is still calculated as the final current balance plus the interest due on that balance. The total interest paid is $26.57 less, and this occurs because the current balance decreases faster than in the previous amortization schedule. Also note that the totals still reflect the general principle that the total amount of interest paid equals the total of all the payments minus the original principal of the loan.

Example 1 (Concluded) Suppose, to pay for the computer, you took out a six-month $3000 *installment* loan that used the Add-On Interest Method at 18% simple interest. What would your monthly payment be? How is each payment split between interest paid and principal repaid?

Solution: You will have to pay $I = Prt = \$3000(0.18)(0.5) = \$270$ in total interest split over the six monthly payments. This means each monthly payment of ($3000 + $270) / 6 = $545 will consist of $3000 / 6 = $500 in principal and $270 / 6 = $45 in interest. These amounts stay constant throughout the six payments. After the first $545 payment you still owe $3000 - $500 = $2500; after the second $545 payment you owe $2500 - $500 = $2000, etc. The $270 in total interest you will pay will be almost double the $132.88 in total interest you pay with an amortized loan.

Quiz Yourself (Answers at the end of the section, before the problems.)
1. You take out a four-month loan at 9% annual interest to finance a $500 charge.
   (a) If the loan is amortized (and the rate compounded monthly), what will be your monthly payment? Make an amortization table. How much total interest would you pay?
   (b) Make an amortization table if you make a $200 payment at the end of each month (until the last payment) instead of the monthly payment calculated in (a). How much total interest would you pay?
   (c) If your loan uses the Add-On Interest Method (and the interest rate is simple interest), what would be your monthly payment? How is that payment split between principal and interest? How much total interest would you pay?

Paying Off a Credit Card

A debt owed on a credit card is a kind of loan that is different from an amortized loan because you are not required to pay it off in a fixed period of time. Instead you are required to make a minimum payment that usually covers the interest owed but little of the principal. In addition, you may make additional purchases with the card that can slow or even reverse your progress toward paying off the debt.

Example 2 Suppose you owe $1500 on a credit card charging 18% annual interest compounded monthly.
(a) If you want to pay off the debt in 1 year, and make no new purchases, what should your monthly payment be to accomplish this?
(b) Suppose you make this payment, but charge an additional $50 per month. What will your balance be after 4 months of payments and charges? Is your balance growing?
(c) Suppose you make the payment in (a), but charge an additional $120 per month. Will your balance increase or decrease from month to month?

Solution (a) Your monthly interest rate is $i = 0.18 / 12 = 0.015$, and $PV = \$1500, m = 12$ payments. To find your payment amount we use formula (4): $PMT = \dfrac{\$1500 \times 0.015}{\left(1 - (1.015)^{-12}\right)} = \$137.52$.

Your total interest is 12($137.52) - $1500 = $150.24

(b) Because of the additional charges we must use a variation of an amortization table to track the monthly balance. An example is shown on the next page. With this version the New balance = Old balance − Balance repaid + New purchases.

Period	Current Balance	Payment	Amt Interest	Balance Repaid	New Purchases	New Balance at end of period
1	$1500.00	$137.52	$22.50	$115.02	$50.00	$1434.98
2	$1434.98	$137.52	$21.52	$116.00	$50.00	$1368.98
3	$1368.98	$137.52	$20.53	$116.99	$50.00	$1301.99
4	$1301.99	$137.52	$19.53	$117.99	$50.00	$1234.00

After 4 months your balance will be $1234.00. This is more than without the purchases, but you will eventually pay off the debt.

(c) If you make a $137.52 payment, which may well be above the minimum the credit card asks for, but charge an additional $120, your first payment will still include $22.50 interest and $115.02 in principal paid. So your new balance after this first payment is:

New balance = old balance – Balance repaid + New purchases
= $1500 - $115.02 + $120 = $1504.98

The table below shows how the balance grows during the first 4 periods.

Period	Current Balance	Payment	Amt Interest	Balance Repaid	New Purchases	New Balance at end of period
1	$1500.00	$137.52	$22.50	$115.02	$120.00	$1504.98
2	$1504.98	$137.52	$22.57	$114.95	$120.00	$1520.03
3	$1520.03	$137.52	$22.80	$114.72	$120.00	$1525.31
4	$1525.31	$137.52	$22.88	$114.64	$120.00	$1540.67

In general, if your principal repaid is more than your amount of new purchases your next balance will be less than the current balance.

Quiz Yourself (Answers at the end of this section, before the problems.)
2. You owe $1200 on a credit card charging 12.9% annual interest compounded monthly.
  (a) What should your monthly payment be in order to pay it off in 6 months?
  (b) How interest is there in your first payment?
  (c) If you make the monthly payment and make new charges of $200 each month, will you eventually pay off the credit card?

Finding the Payoff Amount (Current Balance) of an Amortized Loan

The **current balance** at a particular point in an amortized loan is also referred to as the **payoff amount** at that point, because payment of that amount at that point in time will completely pay off the loan. One way to find the payoff amount after a certain number of payments is an amortization schedule as described above, but this method requires that you determine all the lines of the table down to the point of the payoff. We now discuss another method for finding the payoff amount.

Recall that in Example 1 a $3000 debt is paid off in 6 payments of $526.58. Suppose you have paid the first 4 payments. At that point your current balance (payoff amount) is what the remaining two payments will pay off, so the current balance is the present value of the 2 remaining payments. Using $PMT = 526.58$, $i = 0.015$, and $m = 2$ (the number of remaining payments) in formula (2) from Section 2.2, we have

$$PV = \$526.58 \frac{\left(1-(1.015)^{-2}\right)}{0.015} = \$1029.93$$

which is the same (except for 3 cents due to rounding the payment amounts) as the balance after the fourth payment in our amortization table. In general:

The _Payoff Amount_ of a loan _at a particular point in time_

is the current balance on the loan at that time. With an amortized loan the payoff amount
may be calculated as the present value of all payments on the loan that are <u>yet to be made</u>:

(5)   **Payoff Amount** = $PMT \dfrac{\left(1-(1+i)^{-k}\right)}{i}$, where k = number of <u>remaining</u> payments

---

Here is a time line showing the situation with k payments remaining:

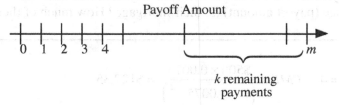

Payoff Amount

k remaining
payments

Example 3 A woman has an automobile loan for 5 years at 3.6% compounded monthly with monthly
payments of $455.91.
  (a) What was the original amount of the loan?
  (b) She has just paid her 35th payment. What is the payoff amount of the loan at this time?
  (c) Compare the interest amount in her first payment to that in her 36th payment.

  Solution: (a) The original amount of the loan is the L of the entire $m = 5(12) = 60$ payments of PMT
  = $455.91, with $i = 0.036 / 12 = 0.003$, so using formula (2) the original amount of the loan was

$$PV = \$455.91 \frac{\left(1-(1.003)^{-60}\right)}{0.003} = \$24{,}999.78$$

  (b) The payoff amount after 35 payments is the PV of the $k = 60 - 35 = 25$ payments remaining.

  Using formula (5): $PV = \$455.91 \dfrac{\left(1-(1.003)^{-25}\right)}{0.003} = \$10{,}964.99$.

  (c) At the time of her first payment she owes $i = 0.003$ times the original principal of the loan, as we
  saw in the amortization procedure, or $0.003 \times \$24{,}999.78 = \$75.00$ in interest. (The rest of the
  $455.91 first payment goes to repay principal.) At the time of her 36th payment she owes interest at
  the same rate, but now multiplied by her current balance of $10,964.99. So she owes $0.003 \times$
  $10,964.99 = $32.89 in interest. (Again, the rest of her 36th payment goes to repay principal.)

Example 4 A man has been making monthly payments on a 30-year mortgage at 6.9% for the last 8 years.
The loan amount of the mortgage was $120,000. How much is the current balance on his mortgage?

  Solution: First we need to determine his monthly payment. Using $PV = \$120{,}000$,
  $m = 30 \times 12 = 360$, and $i = 0.069 / 12 = 0.00575$ we use Formula (4) from Section 2.3 to calculate:

$$PMT = \frac{\$120{,}000 \times 0.00575}{(1-(1.00575)^{-360})} = \$790.32$$

  The current balance on his mortgage is then the payoff amount (present value) of the remaining
  payments. There are 22 years of payments remaining, or $k = 22 \times 12 = 264$ remaining payments.
  Using formula (5),

$$PV = \$790.32\frac{\left(1-1.00575^{-264}\right)}{0.00575} = \$107{,}194.25$$

So he has a current balance of \$107,194.25 on his mortgage. We can now see that he has only paid off \$120,000 - \$107,194.25 = \$12,805.75 in principal during the 8 years of payments made so far. The reason is that most of each of the first few payments is interest. For example, in his first payment the amount of interest was $0.00575 \times \$120,000 = \$690.00$, so only \$790.32 - \$690.00 = \$100.32 went to pay off the principal.

Quiz Yourself (Answer below)

3. Twelve years ago a couple took out a \$150,000 30-year mortgage at 6.9% compounded monthly.
   (a) What is their monthly payment? How much of their first payment was interest?
   (b) What is the current balance (payoff amount) on their mortgage? How much of their next payment will be interest?

Quiz Yourself Answers:

1. (a) $i = 0.09 / 12 = 0.0075$ $m = 4$ $PMT = \dfrac{\$500 \times 0.0075}{\left(1 - (1.0075)^{-4}\right)} = \$127.35$

Period	Current Balance at start of period	Payment Amount	Amt Interest paid	Principal repaid	Current Balance after payment
1	\$500.00	\$127.35	\$3.75	\$123.60	\$376.40
2	\$376.40	\$127.35	\$2.82	\$124.53	\$251.87
3	\$251.87	\$127.35	\$1.89	\$125.46	\$126.41
4	\$126.41	\$127.36	\$0.95	\$126.41	\$0.00
Totals:		\$509.41	\$9.41	\$500.00	

You pay a total of \$9.41 in interest. (Note: You may also calculate 4(\$127.35) - \$500 = \$9.40; but this is approximate. The \$0.01 difference is due to the rounding each month. \$9.41 is exact.)

(b)

Period	Current Balance at start of period	Payment Amount	Amt Interest paid	Principal repaid	Current Balance after payment
1	\$500.00	\$200.00	\$3.75	\$196.25	\$303.75
2	\$303.75	\$200.00	\$2.28	\$197.72	\$106.03
3	\$106.03	\$106.83	\$0.80	\$106.03	\$0.00
Totals:		\$506.83	\$6.83	\$500.00	

You only make 3 payments, with the last being \$106.83. Your total interest is \$6.83.

(c) With Add-On Interest $I = \$500(0.09)(4/12) = \$15.00$ total interest. Your monthly payment is (\$500 + \$15) / 4 = \$128.75. Each payment is \$500/4 = \$125 in principal and \$15/4 = \$3.75 interest.

2. (a) $i = 0.129 / 12 = 0.01075$ $m = 6$ $PMT = \dfrac{\$1200 \times 0.01075}{\left(1 - (1.01075)^{-6}\right)} = \$207.59$

(b) Interest in first payment = $0.01075(\$1200) = \$12.90$

(c) Principal repaid in first payment = \$207.59 - \$12.90 = \$194.69. If you make new charges of \$200 your next balance will be \$1200 - \$194.69 + \$200 = 1205.31, more than it was previously. You will not eventually pay off the card.

3. (a) $i = 0.069 / 12 = 0.00575$ $m = 12(30) = 360$ $PMT = \dfrac{\$150000 \times 0.00575}{\left(1 - (1.00575)^{-360}\right)} = \$987.90$

Interest in first payment = $0.00575(\$150,000) = \$862.50$

(b) After 12 years there are 18 remaining years of payments, which is 18(12) = 216 payments

Payoff Amount = PV of remaining payments = $\$987.90 \dfrac{\left(1 - (1.00575)^{-216}\right)}{0.00575} = \$122{,}012.49$

Interest in next payment = $0.00575(\$122.012.49) = \$701.57$.

Problems for Section 2.4

Sharpen Your skills: (Answers in back of text.)

1. An amortized loan of $700 for 8 months at 9% interest has monthly payments of $90.48. Complete the first two lines of an amortization table for this loan.

Period	Current Balance at start of period	Payment Amount	Amount Interest paid	Principal repaid	Balance after payment
1					
2					

2. An amortized loan of $4800 for 15 months at 10.5% interest has monthly payments of $342.86. Complete the first two lines of an amortization table for this loan.

Period	Current Balance at start of period	Payment Amount	Amount Interest paid	Principal repaid	Balance after payment
1					
2					

3. What is the monthly payment of a $1400 Installment Loan for 8 months at 9% simple interest using the Add-On Interest Method? How is the payment split between principal and interest?

4. What is the monthly payment of a $2400 Installment Loan for 15 months at 10.5% simple interest using the Add-On Interest Method? How is the payment split between principal and interest?

5. What is the balance remaining after 5 payments on the loan in Problem 1 above?

6. What is the balance remaining after 11 payments on the loan in Problem 2 above?

7. Suppose you have a $400 balance on a credit card charging 18% interest. If you make a $35 payment and charge $30 in new items, what will be your balance next month?

8. What would be your new balance in problem 7 if you made a $120 payment and had $110 in new charges?

Communicate the Concepts: (Answers in back of text.)

9. Explain how to find the amount of interest in the next payment on an amortized loan.

10. Explain how to find the total amount of interest in a loan that uses the Add-On Interest Method.

11. Explain two ways to determine the current balance on an amortized loan.

12. Explain how to find the balance next month on your credit card if you know the interest rate, the amount of your previous payment, and the amount of your new charges.

Apply Your Knowledge: (Answers to odd-numbered problems in back of text.)

13. Suppose you buy a stereo for $950, and pay it off with an amortized loan with four substantially equal monthly payments at 12% annual interest compounded monthly.
    (a) What is the periodic interest rate?   (b) What initial payment is required?
    (c) Create an amortization schedule for this loan.

Period	Balance at start of period	Payment Amount	Amount Interest Paid	Principal repaid	Current Balance after payment
1					
2					
3					
4					

    (d) What is the final payment amount?

14. After using your computer for a year or so, you decide to upgrade to a better system. A friend buys the old computer for $500, and you use this for a down payment on a new system that costs $2995. You finance the balance through the dealer in a sequence of four substantially equal monthly payments, and the dealer charges 15% annual interest compounded monthly.
    (a) What is the periodic interest rate?
    (b) What initial payment is required?
    (c) Create an amortization schedule for this loan.

Period	Current Balance at start of period	Payment Amount	Amount Interest Paid	Principal repaid	Current Balance after payment
1					
2					
3					
4					

    (d) What is the final payment amount?

15. A business borrows $6,000 from a bank that charges 7% interest compounded semi-annually. The business is to repay the loan with an amortized loan having 4 approximately equal payments, one at the end of every six month period, for the two years.
    (a) What is the periodic interest rate?
    (b) What initial payment is required?
    (c) Create an amortization schedule for this loan.

Period	Current Balance at start of period	Payment Amount	Amount Interest paid	Principal repaid	Current Balance after payment
1					
2					
3					
4					

    (d) What is the final payment amount?

16. A business borrows $10,000 from a bank that charges 9% interest compounded quarterly. The loan is to be repaid in 8 approximately equal payments at the end of each quarter for the next two years.
    (a) What is the periodic interest rate?   (b) What initial payment is required?
    (c) Create an amortization schedule for this loan. (d) What is the final payment amount?

Period	Current Balance at start of period	Payment Amount	Amount Interest paid	Principal repaid	Current Balance after payment
1					
2					
3					
4					
5					
6					
7					
8					

17. You have a $2500 debt you owe on a credit card that charges 18% annual interest compounded monthly. If you make no new purchases with the card, what monthly payment would you need to make to pay off the debt in 1 year? How much total interest would you pay?

18. You have a $2500 debt you owe on a credit card that charges 21% annual interest compounded monthly. If you make no new purchases with the card, what monthly payment would you need to make to pay off the debt in 3 years? How much total interest would you pay?

19. You owe $2000 on a credit card that charges 21% annual interest compounded monthly.
    (a) If you make no new purchases, what monthly payment amount would pay off the debt in 1 year of approximately equal payments?
    (b) Suppose you actually make a payment of $200 per month, but also make $50 per month in new purchases. What will your balance be after 4 months? Will your balance be lower than at the start?

Period	Current Balance	Payment	Amt Interest	Balance Repaid	New Purchases	New Balance at end of period
1	$2000.00	$200.00			$50.00	
2		$200.00			$50.00	
3		$200.00			$50.00	
4		$200.00			$50.00	

(c) Suppose you make a $200 payment the first month, but charge $175 in new purchases. Will your next balance be larger or smaller than your original $2000 debt?

20. You owe $3000 on a credit card that charges 15% annual interest compounded monthly.
    (a) If you make no new purchases, what monthly payment amount would pay off the debt in 2 years of approximately equal payments?
    (b) Suppose you actually make a payment of $150 per month, but also make $50 per month in new purchases. What will your balance be after 4 months? Will your balance be lower than at the start?

Period	Current Balance	Payment	Amt Interest	Balance Repaid	New Purchases	New Balance at end of period
1	$3000.00	$150.00			$50.00	
2		$150.00			$50.00	
3		$150.00			$50.00	
4		$150.00			$50.00	

(c) Suppose you make a $150 payment the first month, but charge $125 in new purchases. Will your next balance be larger or smaller than your original $3000 debt?

21. John is making monthly payments of $342.15 on his five-year car loan at 6.9% compounded monthly.
    (a) What was the original value of the loan?
    (b) What part of his first payment was interest? What part went to pay off the principal?
    (c) If he just made the 23rd monthly payment, what is his current payoff amount?
    (d) What part of the 24th monthly payment is interest? What part goes to repay the principal?

22. Jim is making monthly payments of $345.68 on a four-year car loan at 9% compounded monthly.
    (a) What was the original value of the loan?
    (b) What part of his first payment is interest? What part goes to pay off the principal?
    (c) If he just made the 32nd monthly payment, what is his current payoff amount?
    (d) What part of the 33rd monthly payment is interest? What part goes to repay the principal?

23. A couple have a 15-year home mortgage of $90,000 at 6.6% compounded monthly.
    (a) What is their monthly payment on the mortgage?
    (b) They have just completed 5 years of payments. What is the payoff amount on their mortgage?

24. A woman has 30-year home mortgage of $150,000 at 6.9% compounded monthly.
    (a) What is her monthly payment on the mortgage?
    (b) If she has just completed 10 years of payments, what is the payoff amount on her mortgage?

25. Reconsider the loan discussed in Problem 15. Suppose instead of the payment amount found in the problem, which makes the fourth payment amount about the same as the others, you decide you can afford to pay $1800 per payment. Create an amortization schedule for the loan using this payment amount. (Recall the interest rate was 7% compounded semi-annually and the principal was $6000.) How many payments does it take to pay off the loan? What is the amount of the last payment? How much interest do you save with this new payment amount?

Period	Balance at start of period	Payment Amount	Amount Interest Paid	Principal repaid	Balance after payment
1	$6000.00	$1800.00			
2					
3					
4					

26. Reconsider the loan discussed in Problem 16. Suppose instead of the payment amount found in the problem, which makes eighth payment amount about the same as the others, you decide you can afford to pay $1500 per payment. Create an amortization schedule for the loan using this payment amount. (Recall the interest rate was 9% compounded quarterly and the principal was $10,000.) How many payments does it take to pay off the loan? What is the amount of the last payment? How much interest do you save with this new payment amount?

Period	Balance at start of period	Payment Amount	Amount Interest Paid	Principal repaid	Balance after payment
1	10,000.00	1500.00			
2					
3					
4					
5					
6					
7					
8					

Review Problems

27. A man has $15,000 in a savings account paying 3% compounded monthly. He wants to accumulate a total of $25,000 five years from now. What monthly deposit does he need to make into the account at the end of each month to achieve this? How much interest will he have earned?

28. Your company offers you a retirement pension of $4,000 per month for 20 years, with the first payment made today. If money is worth 2.4% compounded monthly, what is the cash value today of this pension?

Section 2.5 Home Mortgages

For many people the largest financial decision they will make is a home mortgage. In this section we will apply the methods from the previous sections to evaluate a mortgage. We will discuss methods for choosing among various mortgage options and a way to decide whether to refinance.

Example 1 Suppose you decide to purchase a home with a selling price of $115,000 by paying 20% down and financing the remaining balance with monthly payments over 30 years at 7.2% interest, compounded monthly.
      (a) What is the amount you will finance?
      (b) What will be your monthly payment? How much interest is in your first payment?
      (c) What is the total amount of interest you will pay if you make the 30 years of payments?

Solution (a) The down payment is 20% of $115,000, or $23,000. So the amount to be financed is the other 80% of $115,000, or $92,000.
(b) From the information given we see that the principal of the loan is $PV = \$92,000$, $i = 0.072 / 12 = 0.006$, and $m = 30 \times 12 = 360$ payments. Thus your monthly payment will be

$$PMT = \frac{\$92,000 \times 0.006}{\left(1 - (1.006)^{-360}\right)} = \$624.49$$

    As in Section 2.4 the interest in your first payment is $i \times PV = 0.006 \times \$92,000 = \$552.00$

(c) The total amount of interest paid during the 30 years is found as in Section 2.2. It is

    $Total\ Interest\ Paid = m \times PMT - PV = 360 \times \$624.49 - \$92,000 = \$132,816.40.$

(*Caution*: This is only an estimate of the total interest. It assumes the last payment is the same as the others, but as we saw in the previous section, that may not be true.)

The amount of interest involved in a home mortgage seems staggering to most people. Notice that the first payment of $624.49 includes interest of $0.006 \times 92,000 = \$552$, so only $624.49 - $552 = $72.49 is applied to the principal. The first payment is almost all interest! As the payments progress, the amount of interest paid per payment slowly decreases as the current balance slowly decreases, and the amount per payment applied to the principal increases.

Example 2 The bank offers the purchaser in Example 1 a 15-year loan at 6.9% compounded monthly.
      (a) What is the amount you will finance?
      (b) What will be your monthly payment? How much interest is in your first payment?
      (c) What is the total amount of interest you will pay if you make the 30 years of payments?

Solution: (a) The term and rate of the mortgage do not affect the down payment or amount to be financed. They do affect the monthly payment. So the loan amount is the same as above, $92,000.

(b) $i = 0.069 / 12 = 0.00575$, and $m = 15 \times 12 = 180$ payments. So the monthly payment is

$$PMT = \frac{\$92,000 \times 0.00575}{\left(1 - (1.00575)^{-180}\right)} = \$821.79$$

Notice the monthly payment is almost $200 larger with the 15-year loan than with the 30-year loan. The first payment of $821.79 includes interest of $0.00575 \times \$92,000 = \$529.00$, so $821.79 - $529.00 = $292.79 is being applied to the principal. This is $220.30 more principal in the first payment than with the 30-year loan.

(c) Total Interest = $180 \times \$821.79 - \$92,000 = \$55,922.20$. This is only about 40% as much total interest as was paid with the 30-year loan!

Example 3 The bank also offers the purchaser in Example 1 a 30-year loan at 6.9% compounded monthly, but this loan requires the payment of 2 "points" at the start of the loan. The purchaser does not have any additional funds with which to pay these "points", but the bank offers to "include them in the loan." How does this affect our calculations?

Solution Each "point" equals 1% of the value of the loan. The bank is actually offering to loan the purchaser additional funds so he can pay both the $92,000 toward the selling price of the house and the "points". At first it might seem that he needs to borrow an additional 2% of $92,000, or $1,840. This would make a total loan of $93,840. But then the points would be 2% of $93,840 = $1869.60, which is not 2% of $92,000 = $1840. So he needs to borrow even more. The easiest way to find the actual loan needed is to use algebra.

Let L be the actual amount he will borrow. This must include the $92,000 of the selling price, and the points, which are 2% of L. Thus $L = \$92,000 + 2\%$ of L. This means 98% of $L = \$92,000$.

$$\text{Solve:} \qquad 0.98L = \$92,000$$

$$L = \$92,000 \,/\, 0.98 = \$93,877.55$$

This is the PV of the loan needed. Now we find the payment using formula (4). Since $PV = \$93,877.55$, $i = 0.069 / 12 = 0.00575$, and $m = 30 \times 12 = 360$ payments, we calculate that

$$PMT = \frac{\$93,877.55 \times 0.00575}{\left(1 - (1.00575)^{-360}\right)} = \$618.28$$

The payment is slightly less than the $624.49 in Example 1. The total amount paid is $360 \times \$618.28 = \$222,580.80$, so the total interest is $\$222,580.80 - 93,877.55 = \$128,703.25$. This is also slightly less than for the loan in Example 1.

Technique for Finding a Loan Amount That Includes Points

If a buyer needs to make a loan that will include D to be used toward a house purchase, as well as pay p "points" on that loan, then the amount L of the loan must satisfy: $D + p\%$ of $L = L$. When D is known this may be solved for the loan amount L.

Here is a comparison of the important features in the loans discussed in Examples 1 - 3.

Example	Interest Rate	Amount Borrowed	Term of Loan	Monthly Payment	Total Interest
1	7.2%	$92,000.00	30 yrs	$624.49	$132,816.40
2	6.9%	$92,000.00	15 yrs	$821.79	$ 55,922.20
3	6.9%	$93,877.55	30 yrs	$618.28	$128,703.25

Caution: In our discussions above our monthly payments have included only principal and interest payments. Typically, homeowners also make escrow payments to cover property taxes and the homeowners insurance. These escrow payments are usually included in the monthly payment of the homeowner, but do not affect the balance or interest of the mortgage.

Quiz Yourself (Answers at the end of this section, before the problems.)
1. You will purchase a $250,000 house by putting 20% down and getting a mortgage for the rest. You are offered two options, a 30-year mortgage at 5.1% compounded monthly, or a 15-year mortgage at 4.2% compounded monthly. For each find:
   (a) the monthly payment and amount of interest in the first payment,
   (b) total amount of interest paid. How much interest would you save on the 15–year mortgage?
2. You are also offered a 30-year mortgage at 4.95% compounded monthly, provided you pay 1.5 points.
   (a) What loan amount would you need if you were to borrow enough to pay the $200,000 and the points as well?
   (b) What would be your monthly payment with this mortgage?

Example 4: Should You Refinance? Suppose you took the 15-year loan (in Example 2) at 6.9% compounded monthly, where the monthly payment was $821.79. Five years later mortgage rates fall to 6.45% compounded monthly, and you are considering refinancing your loan. (This means taking out a new loan at 6.45% that will pay off the current balance on the original loan.) However, there would be a total of $1000 in closing costs to make such a new loan. Should you refinance now?

Solution The choice is between (i) making 120 payments of $821.79 with the original mortgage, or (ii) taking out a new 10-year loan whose principal is the current payoff amount of the original loan. Because the $1000 in closing costs is like paying points, we will add it to the principal of the new loan (in much the same way we do points) to compare the two loans more fairly.

If you take out a new loan then you will finance an amount equal to the current balance (payoff amount) of the original loan, plus the $1000 closing costs. Using the method at the end of Section 2.4 we can calculate the payoff amount. There are $k = 120$ remaining payments of $PMT = \$821.79$ at $i = 0.069 / 12 = 0.00575$. So

$$\text{Payoff Amount on current loan} = \frac{\$821.79\left(1-1.00575^{-120}\right)}{0.00575} = \$71{,}092.95$$

We will finance $71,092.95 + $1000 in closing costs, so $72,092.95 is the *PV* of the new loan. The new loan will have 120 monthly payments at the new rate of $i = 0.0645 / 12 = 0.005375$ per month. Using formula (4) we calculate the monthly payment of the new loan to be

$$PMT = \frac{\$72{,}092.95 \times 0.005375}{\left(1-1.005375^{-120}\right)} = \$816.77$$

Refinancing will reduce your monthly payment $5.02 per month. This sounds good! But whether you should refinance depends on how long you will keep your loan. If you keep it the entire remaining 120 months, then the only consideration is the payment amounts, and you **should** refinance. However:

Example 4 (Continued) What if you only keep the new loan 3 years?
Solution In 3 years (36 payments) you will save $36 \times \$5.02 = \$180.72$ in monthly payments, and still have 7 years, or 84 more payments, left. Here are the payoff amounts on the two mortgages when there are 84 payments remaining:

$$\text{Payoff Amount of Original Mortgage at } i = 0.00575: \frac{\$821.79\left(1-1.00575^{-84}\right)}{0.00575} = \$54{,}626.33$$

$$\text{Payoff Amount of New Mortgage at } i = 0.005375: \frac{\$816.77\left(1-1.005375^{-84}\right)}{0.005375} = \$55{,}093.20$$

The situation after 3 years is: Although you have saved $180.72 in monthly payments with the new mortgage, you will owe $55,093.20 - $54,626.33 = $466.87 more in principal. In net you have lost $466.87 = $180.72 = $286.10   The reason you owe more principal with the new mortgage is the $1000 in closing cost you had to pay. This was added into the principal when you refinanced.

Example 4 (Continued) What if you keep the new loan 5 years?
Solution In 5 years (60 payments) you will save $60 \times \$5.02 = \$301.20$ in monthly payments, and still have 5 years, or 60 more payments, left. Here are the payoff amounts on the two mortgages when there are 60 payments remaining:

$$\text{Payoff Amount of Original Mortgage at } i = 0.00575: \frac{\$821.79\left(1-1.00575^{-60}\right)}{0.00575} = \$41{,}601.08$$

$$\text{Payoff Amount of New Mortgage at } i = 0.005375: \frac{\$816.77\left(1-1.005375^{-60}\right)}{0.005375} = \$41{,}794.04$$

So after 5 years you have saved $301.20 in monthly payments, but owe $41,794.04 - $41,601.08 = $192.96 more in principal. This means you would be $301.20 - $192.96 = $108.24 ahead in five years if you refinance now.

Quiz Yourself (Answers below.)

3. You took out the $200,000 30-year mortgage at 5.1% compounded monthly in problem 1. It is now 10 years later, and mortgage rates are now 4.5%. It would cost $2500 in closing costs to refinance, and if you refinance you will borrow enough to pay the closing costs and your current balance. Your new loan will have as many payments as your current mortgage has remaining. If you plan to stay in the house another 3 years, should you refinance? Would that answer change if you only stayed 2 years?

Quiz Yourself Answers

1. (a) 20% of $250,000 = $50,000 down, so loan amount = $250,000 - $50,000 = $200,000.

30-year: $i = 0.051 / 12 = 0.00425$ $m = 12(30) = 360$ payments $PMT = \dfrac{\$200{,}000 \times 0.00425}{\left(1-(1.00425)^{-360}\right)} = \$1085.90$

Interest in first payment: $0.00425(\$200{,}000) = \$850.00$
Total Interest $= 360(\$1085.90) - \$200{,}000 = \$190{,}924.00$

15-year: $i = 0.042 / 12 = 0.0035$ $m = 12(15) = 180$ payments $PMT = \dfrac{\$200{,}000 \times 0.0035}{\left(1-(1.0035)^{-180}\right)} = \$1499.50$

Interest in first payment $= 0.0035(\$200{,}000) = \$700.00$
(b) Total Interest $= 180(\$1499.50) - \$200{,}000 = \$69{,}910$ You save $121,014 in total interest.

2. (a) The 1.5 points will be based on the whole mortgage, not just the $200,000. If L is the loan amount:
Solve $L = \$200{,}000 + 0.015L$ $0.985L = \$200{,}000$ $L = \$200{,}000 / 0.985 = \$203{,}045.69$
This is the principal of the mortgage.

(b) $i = 0.0495 / 12 = 0.004125$ $m = 360$ $PMT = \dfrac{\$203{,}045.69 \times 0.004125}{\left(1-(1.004125)^{-360}\right)} = \$1083.80$

3. After 10 years there are 240 payments remaining. The current balance at that point is

$$\frac{\$1085.90\left(1-1.00425^{-240}\right)}{0.00425} = \$163{,}172.40.$$

If we add to this the $2500 in closing costs, the new loan amount will be $165,672.40. It will have 240 payments with $i = 0.045 / 12 = 0.00375$ So the payment is $PMT = \dfrac{\$165{,}672.40 \times 0.00375}{\left(1-(1.00375)^{-240}\right)} = \$1048.13$

If you stay 3 years, or 36 payments, you save $36(\$1085.90 - \$1048.13) = \$1359.72$ in monthly payments. But you will be behind on your balance after 3 years, when there are $240 - 36 = 204$ payments remaining. The payoff amounts on the original and the new (proposed) mortgage at that time are:

Payoff Amount of Original Mortgage at $i = 0.00425$: $\dfrac{\$1085.90\left(1-1.00425^{-204}\right)}{0.00425} = \$147{,}942.25$

Payoff Amount of New Mortgage at $i = 0.00375$: $\dfrac{\$1048.13\left(1-1.00375^{-204}\right)}{0.00375} = \$149{,}253.65$

Difference = $1311.40. Since you are ahead in monthly payment savings by a little more than you are behind in your balance ($1359.72 – 1311.40 = $48.32), you should refinance.
If you stayed 2 years you would save $24(\$1085.90 - \$1048.13) = \$906.48$ in monthly payments. There will be $240 – 24 = 216$ payments left after 2 years. The payoff amounts at that time are:

Original Mortgage at $i = 0.00425$: $\dfrac{\$1085.90\left(1-1.00425^{-216}\right)}{0.00425} = \$153{,}279.41$

New Mortgage at $i = 0.00375$: $\dfrac{\$1048.13\left(1-1.00375^{-216}\right)}{0.00375} = \$154{,}974.40$

Difference = $1694.99, which is more than your $906.48 savings in payments. Don't refinance.

Problems for Section 2.5

Apply Your Knowledge: (Answers to odd-numbered problems in back of text.)

1. A purchaser is buying a $176,000 house and putting 25% down. The bank is offering a 20-year loan at 7.5% compounded monthly, with no points.
    (a) What is the loan amount?
    (b) What will the monthly payment amount be?
    (c) What is the (approximate) total amount of interest paid during the term of the loan?
    (d) What part of the first payment is interest? What part is principal?

2. A purchaser is buying a $130,000 house and putting 15% down. The bank is offering a 30-year loan at 7.74% compounded monthly, with no points.
    (a) What is the loan amount?
    (b) What will the monthly payment amount be?
    (c) What is the (approximate) total amount of interest paid during the term of the loan?
    (d) What part of the first payment is interest? What part is principal?

3. The homebuyer in Problem 1 is also being offered a 20-year loan at 7.26% compounded monthly, with 2 points. Assume the buyer borrows the money to pay the points as part of the loan.
    (a) What is the loan amount?
    (b) What will the monthly payment amount be?
    (c) What is the (approximate) total amount of interest paid during the term of the loan?
    (d) What part of the first payment is interest? What part is principal?

4. The homebuyer in Problem 2 is also being offered a 30-year loan at 7.5% compounded monthly, with 1.5 points. Assume the buyer borrows the money to pay the points as part of the loan.
    (a) What is the loan amount?
    (b) What will the monthly payment amount be?
    (c) What is the (approximate) total amount of interest paid during the term of the loan?
    (d) What part of the first payment is interest? What part is principal?

5. Suppose you took out the loan in Problem 1 six years ago. Now mortgage rates have fallen to 7.05% compounded monthly, but it will cost $2500 in closing costs to obtain the new loan.
    (a) What is the payoff amount of your current loan?
    (b) If you refinanced with a new 14-year loan, adding the closing costs into the principal of the new loan, what would be your new monthly payment? If you expect to make the entire 14 years of payments should you refinance? Justify your answer.
    (c) Suppose you expect to sell the house after 5 years.
        (i) How much would you save in monthly payments during the 5 years?
        (ii) What will be the payoff amounts of the old and new mortgages after 5 years?
        (iii) Using your answers to (i) and (ii), should you refinance? Justify your answer.

6. Suppose you took out the loan in Problem 2 ten years ago. Now mortgage rates have fallen to 7.5% compounded monthly, but it will cost $1500 in closing costs to obtain the new loan.
    (a) What is the payoff amount of your current loan?
    (b) If you refinanced with a new 20-year loan, adding the closing costs into the principal of the new loan, what would be your new monthly payment? If you expect to make the 20 years of payments should you refinance?
    (c) Suppose you expect to sell the house after 4 years.
        (i) How much would you save in monthly payments during the 4 years?
        (ii) What will be the payoff amounts of the old and new mortgages after 4 years?
        (iii) Using your answers to (i) and (ii), should you refinance? Justify your answer.

7. Suppose you took out a $150,000 30-year mortgage five years ago at 7.8% compounded monthly. Your monthly payment is $1079.81. Now mortgage rates have fallen to 6.9% compounded monthly, but it will cost $2000 in closing costs to obtain the new loan.
    (a) What is the payoff amount of your current loan?
    (b) If you refinanced with a new 25-year loan at 6.9%, adding the closing costs into the principal of the new loan, what would be your new monthly payment? If you expect to make the 25 years of payments should you refinance?
    (c) Suppose you expect to sell the house after 5 years.
      (i) How much would you save in monthly payments during the 5 years?
      (ii) What will be the payoff amounts of the old and new mortgages after 5 years?
      (iii) Using your answers to (i) and (ii), should you refinance? Justify your answer.

8. Suppose you took out a $250,000 30-year mortgage ten years ago at 6.9% compounded monthly. Your monthly payment is $1626.48. Now mortgage rates have fallen to 5.7% compounded monthly, but it will cost $3000 in closing costs to obtain the new loan.
    (a) What is the payoff amount of your current loan?
    (b) If you refinanced with a new 20-year loan, adding the closing costs into the principal of the new loan, what would be your new monthly payment? If you expect to make the entire 20 years of payments should you refinance?
    (c) Suppose you expect to sell the house after 5 years.
      (i) How much would you save in monthly payments during the 5 years?
      (ii) What will be the payoff amounts of the old and new mortgages after 5 years?
      (iii) Using your answers to (i) and (ii), should you refinance? Justify your answer.

9. Suppose you took out a $200,000 30-year mortgage eight years ago at 5.1% compounded monthly. Your monthly payment is $1085.90. Now mortgage rates have fallen to 4.5% compounded monthly, but it will cost $2500 in closing costs to obtain the new loan.
    (a) What is the payoff amount of your current loan?
    (b) If you refinanced with a new 22-year loan, adding the closing costs into the principal of the new loan, what would be your new monthly payment? If you expect to make the entire 20 years of payments should you refinance?
    (c) Suppose you expect to sell the house after 5 years.
      (i) How much would you save in monthly payments during the 5 years?
      (ii) What will be the payoff amounts of the old and new mortgages after 5 years?
      (iii) Using your answers to (i) and (ii), should you refinance? Justify your answer.

Communicate the Concepts: (Answers in back of text.)
10. Explain how to decide whether to refinance your mortgage.

11. Explain how to find the loan amount L of a mortgage if you will finance $D out of the price of the house and you will pay p points for the loan.

Section 2.6 Finding the Number of Payments

If you make an extra payment on your mortgage, that extra amount goes to reduce your current balance. We now consider the problem of determining how long it will take to pay off the mortgage if you make this extra payment each month. Here is an example.

Example 1 John takes out a 30 year mortgage for $80,000 at 7.2% compounded monthly. His monthly payment is $543.03. He decides to pay an additional $100 each month until the loan is repaid. How long will it take for him to repay the loan in this fashion?

Solution: Essentially, John has set up a contract (with himself) to pay $643.03 per month on a loan having present value $80,000. We want to find the number of payments needed to pay off such a loan. We saw in Section 2.4 how to create an amortization table in this situation, but we now develop a method for calculating the number of payments without such a table.

In this problem we know $PV = \$80,000$, $PMT = \$643.03$, and $i = 0.072 / 12 = 0.006$, but we do not know the number of payments m. So we substitute these values in formula (2) and solve for m:

$$\$80,000 = \$643.03\left(\frac{1-(1.006)^{-m}}{0.006}\right)$$

Multiply both sides by 0.006 and divide by $643.03:

$$\frac{80000 \times 0.006}{643.03} = 1 - 1.006^{-m}$$

Subtract 1 from both sides:

$$\frac{80000 \times 0.006}{643.03} - 1 = -1.006^{-m}$$

Multiply both sides by -1:

$$1 - \frac{80000 \times 0.006}{643.03} = 1.006^{-m}$$

Since the unknown m is an exponent,

we apply logarithms:

$$\log\left(1 - \frac{80000 \times 0.006}{643.03}\right) = -m\log(1.006)$$

Finally, divide by $-\log(1.006)$:

$$m = -\log\left(1 - \frac{80000 \times 0.006}{643.03}\right) \div \log(1.006)$$

Evaluating this on your calculator gives $m = 229.3949689$. This means it will take 229 payments of $643.03, and a 230th payment of approximately $0.3949689 \times \$643.03 = \$235.98$. Since the payments are monthly those 230 payments take $230 / 12 = 19.1666$ years, or 19 years and $0.16666 \times 12 =$ two months.

Calculating the Answer: In the discussion above we left the evaluation of all of our calculations to the very last step. Doing this avoids problems with rounding or re-entering partial answers as we go along, as we discussed in Chapter 1. But doing so also makes us evaluate a very forbidding looking expression at the end. The exact keystrokes to evaluate this on your calculator depend on how your calculator evaluates logarithms and how you enter negative numbers. Here are ways to evaluate the expression above on some calculators:

(-) log (1 - 80000 × .006 ÷ 643.03) ÷ log (1.006) =

(1 - 80000 × .006 ÷ 643.03) log ÷ 1.006 log +/- =

If these calculations look too daunting, it is possible to make an intermediate calculation and use your ANS key:

Step 1: Evaluate the expression inside the first log:

1 - 80000 × .006 ÷ 643.03 =   gives   0.25353405

Step 2: Evaluate the original expression using the ANS key:

(-) log (ANS) ÷ log (1.006) =   gives   229.3949689

Example 1 Continued: How much interest (approximately) would John save if he makes the extra $100 per month payments?

Solution At $543.03 per month for 360 months John's total payments are approximately $360 \times \$543.03 = \$195{,}490.80$. At $643.03 per month for 229.3949689 months John's total payments are approximately $229.3949689 \times \$643.03 = \$147{,}507.85$. In both scenarios he pays back the total principal, so the difference between the totals of the payments must be the difference between the total interest paid with the two mortgages. So $195,490.80 - $147,507.85 = $47,982.95 is the total interest he would save by making the extra $100 per month payments.

> **When comparing two mortgages that have the same original principal, the total interest saved equals the difference in the totals of the payments made.**

General Formula for Number of Required Payments to Pay Off a Debt

By going through the same steps as in Example 1 we can solve formula (2) for m and obtain:

> **The number m of payments required to pay off a debt of PV at a periodic rate of i by making m payments of PMT dollars each is given by:**
>
> $$(6) \qquad m = -\log\left(1 - \frac{PV \times i}{PMT}\right) \div \log(1+i)$$
>
> <u>**When making this calculation, the fractional part of m means the last payment should be that fractional part of a whole payment to pay of the debt.**</u>

Example 2: Suppose you owe $2500 on a credit card that charges 18% annual interest compounded monthly. You can only afford to make monthly payment of $100 per month. How long will it take to pay off the credit card? How much interest will you have paid?

Solution Here $PV = \$2500$, $i = 0.18 / 12 = 0.015$, and $PMT = \$100$. Using formula (6):

$$m = -\log\left(1 - \frac{2500 \times 0.015}{100}\right) \div \log(1.015) = -\log(0.625) \div \log(1.015) = 31.57 \text{ payments.}$$

So it will take 31 payments of $100 and a final payment of about $(.57)(\$100) = \$57$. The total interest paid will be about $31.57(\$100) - \$2500 = \$657.00$

Example 3: A retiree has managed to save $300,000 that is in an account paying 5.4% compounded monthly. If the retiree withdraws $2,500 per month, how long will it be until the account is exhausted?

Solution: This problem is similar to Example 6 in Section 2.3, except that there we knew the number of payments but not the payment amount, whereas here we know the payment amount but not the number of payments. Here is a time line of the situation:

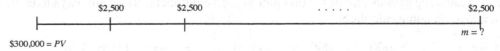

In essence, the bank has "borrowed" the retiree's $300,000 and is "repaying" it at $2,500 per month. Thus $300,000 = PV$. We need to determine how long it will take the bank to "repay" the entire amount, so m is our unknown. Since $i = 0.054 / 12 = .0045$, we can use formula (6) to find m:

$$m = -\log\left(1 - \frac{300000 \times 0.0045}{2500}\right) \div \log(1.0045) = -\log(0.46) \div \log(1.0045) = 172.95,$$

or almost 173 monthly payments. The account will be used up in 14 years, 5 months, with a last payment of about $0.95 \times (\$2500) = \$2375$.

Quiz Yourself (Answers at the end of this section, before the problems.)
1. You take out a $150,000 30-year mortgage at 5.7% compounded monthly.
   (a) What is your monthly payment?
   (b) If you make a $1050 payment each month instead of the monthly payment in (a), how long (in years and months) will it take to pay off the mortgage? How large will the last payment need to be?
   (c) How much interest will you save over the life of the loan if you make the $1050 payment rather than the payment in (a)?
2. Suppose you have managed to save $650,000 when you retire, and it is in an account paying 4.5% annual interest compounded monthly. If you withdraw $4,000 each month, how long, in years and months, will it be until you have completely exhausted the account?

Example 4: Suppose you take out a $110,000 mortgage for 30 years at 6% annual interest compounded monthly. How long will it be until your payoff amount is $50,000?

Solution   One solution method would be to create an amortization table. But we can also make use of formula (6). Here is a timeline of the situation.

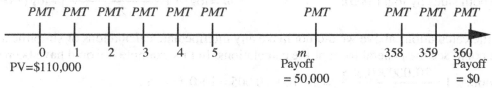

Step 1   We first determine the monthly payment on the mortgage using formula (4).
Use $i = 0.06 / 12 = 0.005$, $m = 360$, $PV = \$110,000$. This gives

$$PMT = \frac{\$110,000 \times 0.005}{\left(1 - (1.005)^{-360}\right)} = \$659.51$$

Step 2   Now we use formula (6) to determine the number m of monthly payments of $659.51 at $i = 0.005$ per month that are necessary to pay off a PV of $50,000.

$$m = -\log\left(1 - \frac{50,000 \times .005}{659.51}\right) \div \log(1.005) = -\log(0.620930691) \div \log(1.005) \approx 95.545$$

Step 3   At $659.51 per month it will take 95.545 payments to pay off the last $50,000 of the mortgage. This means it takes the first $360 - 95.545 = 264.5$ payments to reduce the balance from $110,000 to $50,000. This represents a time period of about $264/12 = 22$ years, with an additional payment reducing the payoff to just below $50,000. (You are not allowed to make a partial payment on your mortgage unless it is the last payment.)

Conclusion: It will take a little over 22 years for the payoff amount to reach $50,000.

Finding The Number of Payments Required to Accumulate a Future Value

Example 5: Susan can save $200 per month and will invest it into an account paying 6% annual interest compounded monthly. Her goal is to have $20,000 to purchase a car. How many monthly deposits will she have to make in order to reach her goal?

Solution   This situation is like the situation we discussed in Section 2.1, except that here we know the $FA = \$20,000$ but not the number of payments m. Here is a time line of the situation.

In this example the monthly interest rate is $i = 0.06/12 = 0.005$. We fill the values of the variables into

formula (1) and solve for m:

$$\$20,000 = \$200 \frac{\left((1+0.005)^m - 1\right)}{0.005}$$

Divide by $PMT = \$200$:

$$\frac{20,000}{200} = \frac{\left((1.005)^m - 1\right)}{0.005}$$

Multiply by $i = 0.005$ and simplify:

$$\frac{20,000 \times 0.005}{200} = \left((1.005)^m - 1\right)$$

Add 1 to both sides:

$$1 + \frac{20,000 \times 0.005}{200} = (1.005)^m$$

Take logs of both sides:

$$\log\left(1 + \frac{20,000 \times 0.005}{200}\right) = m\log(1.005)$$

Divide both sides by $\log(1.005)$:

$$m = \log\left(1 + \frac{20,000 \times 0.005}{200}\right) \div \log(1.005)$$

In the calculations above we did not make any intermediate calculations or simplifications so that we could see the general form of the calculations. In this example it would have been easier to simplify $1 + \dfrac{20,000 \times 0.005}{200} = 1 + 100 \times 0.005 = 1 + 0.5 = 1.5$.

Thus $m = \log(1.5) \div \log(1.005) = 81.29558$ payments. So it will take her 81 deposits of \$200 and a last deposit of $0.29558 \times \$200 = \$59.12$ to reach her goal of \$20,000.

General Formula for Number of Payments Required to Accumulate a Future Value

By going through the same steps as in Example 5 we can solve formula (1) for m and obtain:

The number m of payments of PMT dollars each required to accumulate FA by making payments into an account earning a periodic rate of i is given by

$$(7) \qquad m = \log\left(1 + \frac{FA \times i}{PMT}\right) \div \log(1 + i)$$

<u>When making this calculation, the fractional part of m means the last payment should be that part of a whole payment to accumulate a total of FA.</u>

Example 6: Frank plans to deposit \$325 per month into his retirement account that pays 5.4% annual interest compounded monthly. If he does so, and the account continues to pay interest at the current rate, how long will it be until his account has a value of \$1,000,000? About how large should the last deposit be to reach \$1,000,000? How much total interest will he have earned?

Solution: Since the \$1 million will be accumulated it is the FA of his \$325 monthly deposits. The monthly interest rate is $i = 0.054 / 12 = 0.0045$. Inserting these into formula (7) we have:

$$m = \log\left(1 + \frac{1,000,000 \times 0.0045}{325}\right) \div \log(1.0045) = 600.8458236$$

The 601 monthly payments required to reach at least \$1,000,000 convert to 50 years and 1 month of monthly payments. (!) The last payment will only need to be about $0.8458236 \times \$325 = \$274.89$.

His total interest will be \$1,000,0000 - 600.8458236×\$325 = \$804,725.11 (!)

Calculating the Answer: Here are ways to evaluate the expression above on some calculators:

log (1 + 1000000 × .0045 ÷ 325) ÷ log (1.0045) =

(1 + 1000000 × .0045 ÷ 325) log ÷ 1.0045 log =

If these calculations look too daunting, it is possible to make an intermediate calculation of the expression inside the log in the numerator, and use your ANS key:

Step 1: Evaluate the expression inside the log in the numerator:

1 + 1000000 × .0045 ÷ 325 =   gives 14.84615385

Step 2: Evaluate the original expression using the ANS key for the value of the expression in the first parentheses: (using ANS avoids retyping 14.84615385)

log (ANS) ÷ log (1.0045) =   gives 600.8458236

Quiz Yourself (Answer below.)

3. A couple begins depositing $200 each month into an account paying 5.1% annual interest compounded monthly. Their goal is to have $80,000 for their child's education. How long (in years and months) will it be until they accumulate $80,000? About how much will the last payment need to be? About how much total interest will they have earned?

Quiz Yourself Answers

1. (a) $i = 0.057 / 12 = 0.00475$ $\$150,000 = PV$ By formula (3), $PMT = \dfrac{\$150000 \times 0.00475}{\left(1 - 1.00475^{-360}\right)} = \$870.60$

(b) If $PMT = \$1050$. Using formula (6): $m = -\log\left(1 - \dfrac{150000 \times 0.00475}{1050}\right) \div \log(1.00475) \approx$

239.51.... months. It will take 240 payments, or 20 years, 0 months, with the last payment being about 0.51($1050) = $535.50.

(c) Total Interest savings = difference in total payments = 360($870.60) – 239.51($1050) = $61,930.60

2. $i = 0.045 / 12 = 0.00375$ $\$650,000 = PV$ $PMT = \$4000$. Using formula (6):

$m = -\log\left(1 - \dfrac{650000 \times 0.00375}{4000}\right) \div \log(1.00375) \approx 251.1383$ There will be 252 payments, or 21

years, 0 months of payments, with the last payment being about .1383($4000) = $553.20.

3. $i = 0.051 / 12 = 0.00425$ $PMT = \$200$ $FA = \$80,000$. Using formula (7):

$m = \log\left(1 + \dfrac{80,000 \times 0.00425}{200}\right) \div \log(1.00425) = 234.20257....$

It takes 235 months, or 19 years, 7 months. The last payment will only need to be about
$0.20257 \times (\$200) = \$40.51$

They will have earned about $80,000 – 234.20257×$200 = $33,159.49 in total interest.

Problems for Section 2.6

Sharpen Your Skills: (Answers in back of text.)

1. Give the keystrokes to evaluate this expression, and find its value:

$$-\log\left(1-\frac{20000\times 0.004}{450}\right)\div\log(1.004)$$

2. Give the keystrokes to evaluate this expression, and find its value:

$$\log\left(1+\frac{8,000\times 0.005}{150}\right)\div\log\left(1.005\right)$$

Communicate the Concepts: (Answers in back of text.)

3. If you are given a choice between two mortgages, how can you determine which will cost you less in interest, and also how much that one will save in interest?

4. Explain why the value of m determined in Section 1.6 must be a whole number, but the fractional parts of the values of m determined by formulas (6) and (7) in this section have meaning.

Apply Your Knowledge: (Answers to odd-numbered problems in back of text.)

5. Suppose you take out a \$134,000 mortgage at 5.7% annual interest compounded monthly for 30 years. The monthly payments are \$777.74 each. If you make an extra payment of \$75 each month,
   (a) How long (in years and months) will it take until you pay off the mortgage? About what will your last payment need to be?
   (b) Approximately how much total interest will you save by making the extra payment each month?

6. Suppose you take out a \$160,000 mortgage at 5.1% annual interest compounded monthly for 15 years. The monthly payments are \$1273.62 each. If you make an extra payment of \$125 each month,
   (a) How long (in years and months) will it take until you pay off the mortgage? About what will your last payment need to be?
   (b) Approximately how much total interest will you save by making the extra payment each month?

7. Suppose you owe \$1500 on a credit card that charges 16.5% interest compounded monthly. You will not make any new purchases, but you can only afford to make a \$30 monthly payment on this debt.
   (a) What part of your first \$30 payment at the end of the first month goes for interest, and what part goes to repay part of the debt?
   (b) How many monthly payments of \$30 will it take to pay off the debt? How long is that in years and months? About how much will the last payment need to be? How much interest will have been paid when the debt is paid off?

8. Suppose you owe \$2500 on a credit card that charges 21% interest compounded monthly. You will not make any new purchases, but you can only afford to make a \$50 monthly payment on this debt.
   (a) What part of your first \$50 payment at the end of the first month goes for interest, and what part goes to repay part of the debt?
   (b) How many monthly payments of \$50 will it take to pay off the debt? How long is that in years and months? About how much will the last payment need to be? How much interest will have been paid when the debt is paid off?

9. Your parents retire at age 65 with $900,000 in their retirement account, which pays 7.2% annual interest compounded monthly. They estimate that they will need $4500 per month to live on. However, since their retirement account is not tax-free, they will need to withdraw $6500 per month from their retirement account each month in order to have $4500 after taxes. If they continue to make such withdrawals, how long (in years and months) will their retirement account last? About how much will the last withdrawal be?

10. A person retires with $550,000 in their retirement account, which pays 4.8% annual interest compounded monthly. If they withdraw $3500 each month and the account continues to pay the current rate of interest, how long (in years and months) will it be before the account is completely exhausted? About how much will the last withdrawal be?

11. Consider the original $134,000 mortgage in Problem 5 above. It was at 5.7% annual interest compounded monthly for 30 years, with monthly payments of $777.74 each. How long (in years and months) will it be after the start of the mortgage until the balance on the mortgages drops below $100,000?

12. Consider the original $160,000 mortgage in Problem 6 above. It was at 5.1% annual interest compounded monthly for 15 years, with monthly payments of $1273.62 each. How long (in years and months) will it be after the start of the mortgage until the balance on the mortgage drops below $100,000?

13. A worker can save $200 per month in an account paying 6.3% annual interest compounded monthly. How long (in years and months) will it be from the time she begins making deposits until the value of the account reaches $300,000? About how much will the last payment need to be? When she reaches her goal what part of the value of her account is interest?

14. John wants to save for a new (to him) car, rather than take out a loan. He thinks the car will cost $15,000, and that he can save $250 per month in an account paying 3% annual interest compounded monthly. How many monthly deposits will be required until he has enough savings to purchase the car? About how much will the last deposit need to be? At the end of that number of months, how much interest will his account have earned?

15. A couple have $1,000,000 in their retirement account, which pays 6.6% annual interest compounded monthly. They want to withdraw $5500 per month. If they do so, how long will it be until their retirement account is exhausted? (Hint: If something unusual happens, consider the amount of interest in the first payment and the implications of that amount.)

16. Suppose you take out a $200,000 mortgage at 4.2% annual interest compounded monthly for 30 years. The monthly payments are $978.03 each. If you make an extra payment of $100 each month,
   (a) How long (in years and months) will it take until you pay off the mortgage? About what will your last payment need to be?
   (b) Approximately how much total interest will you save by making the extra payment each month?

17. A person retires with $750,000 in their retirement account, which pays 4.5% annual interest compounded monthly. If they withdraw $4000 each month and the account continues to pay the current rate of interest, how long (in years and months) will it be before the account is completely exhausted? About how much will the last withdrawal be?

18. Suppose you owe $1200 on a credit card that charges 21% interest compounded monthly. You will not make any new purchases, but you can only afford to make a $30 monthly payment on this debt.
(a) What part of your first $30 payment at the end of the first month goes for interest, and what part goes to repay part of the debt?
(b) How many monthly payments of $30 will it take to pay off the debt? How long is that in years and months? About how much will the last payment need to be? How much interest will have been paid when the debt is paid off?

19. Consider the original $200,000 mortgage in Problem 16 above. It was at 4.2% annual interest compounded monthly for 30 years, with monthly payments are $978.03 each. How long (in years and months) will it be after the start of the mortgage until the balance on the mortgages drops below $150,000?

20. At age 21 you start saving $200 per month in an account that pays 3% interest compounded monthly. How old will you be when you account's value reaches $400,000?

Challenge Problems: *: (Answers in back of text.)

21. Suppose your goal is to accumulate $500,000 for retirement. You have access to an account that pays 6% annual interest compounded monthly, and it will continue to do so indefinitely. You are now 25 years old, and you want to have that $500,000 when you reach age 65. You begin now to make a $400 deposit each month into the account. Find the smallest number of monthly deposits you need to make starting now so that, if you leave the deposits to accumulate interest in the account from when you quit making deposits until you reach 65, you will have the $500,000 you seek at that time. (This problem cannot be done by any of the formulas in this section directly, but rather by using the algebraic techniques used to develop those formulas.)

22. Suppose your goal is to accumulate $500,000 for retirement. You have access to an account that pays 6% annual interest compounded monthly, and it will continue to do so indefinitely. You now have $20,000 saved in the account. If you begin now to make a $400 deposit each month into the account, how long will it be until you have accumulated $500,000? (This problem cannot be done by any of the formulas in this section directly, but rather by using the algebraic techniques used to develop those formulas.)

Section 2.7 Saving for Retirement

Along with the home mortgages discussed in the previous section, the other big financial decision you will make is about saving for retirement. In this section we will discuss the relative effects of the variables involved, and also the effects of some of the tax-saving opportunities offered by the government.

I. When saving for retirement, which is most important, the length of time you save, your interest rate, or the amount you save each year?

Example 1: From age 22 to age 34 Sam deposits $1000 per year in a savings account paying 6% annual compound interest. He then quits making deposits, and leaves the money to continue earning interest until he reaches age 65. Sarah starts later, at age 47, and deposits $3000 per year in an account paying the same rate until she reaches age 65. Which one of them will have accumulated a larger savings when he/she reaches age 65?

Solution We calculate the value of Sam's savings in a manner similar to Example 4 of Section 2.1. First we find the value just after he makes the last deposit. At that point he will have made 34 - 22 = 12 yearly deposits, so the value at that point is

$$FA = \$1000\frac{(1.06^{12}-1)}{0.06} = \$16,869.94$$

This lump sum is then left in the account for 65 - 34 = 31 compoundings, so the value when he reaches age 65 will be

$$F = \$16,869.94(1.06)^{31} = \$102,705.89$$

When Sarah reaches age 65 she has just made the last of 65 - 47 = 18 deposits of $3000 at the same interest rate, so the value of her account will be

$$FA = \$3000\frac{(1.06^{18}-1)}{0.06} = \$92,716.96$$

Notice that although Sarah deposited three times as much money each year as Sam, and made deposits for half again as many years as he did, she still did not have as much accumulated at age 65. The reason is that Sam made his deposits at an early age, when the account had many years to grow, but Sarah's deposits were made near retirement age.

Example 2 Consider a person who makes deposits of $1000 per year for 20 years into a savings account paying 5% annual compound interest. If the person could double one (and only one) of those variables (amount, time, or rate), which doubling has the largest effect on the value of the account?

Solution According to formula (1) the value of the account after those 20 years will be

$$FA = \$1000\frac{(1.05^{20}-1)}{0.05} = \$33,065.95$$

Let's investigate the effect of doubling each variable:
(i) Suppose you deposit twice as much each year, or $2000, while keeping the interest rate and the number of payments the same as they were before. The value of your account will be doubled:

$$FA = \$2000\frac{(1.05^{20}-1)}{0.05} = \$66,131.91$$

(ii) Suppose instead you manage to find an investment paying twice the original interest rate, or 10%. Keeping the payment amount and number of payments what they originally were, the value of your account would be

$$FA = \$1000\frac{(1.10^{20}-1)}{0.10} = \$57,275.00$$

(iii) Suppose instead you made twice as many of the original payments at the original interest rate. This means you make deposits for 40 years. Keeping the payment amount and interest rate what they originally were, the value of your account will be

$$FA = \$1000\frac{(1.05^{40}-1)}{0.05} = \$120,799.77$$

From the three calculations above we see that doubling the number of investments (and thus the length of time over which they are made) had more effect that doubling the payment amount or interest rate over the original length of time. In fact, doubling the length of time (and thus the number of payments) almost quadruples the final value!

Conclusion 1:   Beginning <u>early</u> to save for retirement is the most important factor in the value you accumulate!

II. The Effects of Taxes on Retirement Savings

When you decide to begin saving for your retirement you must decide the tax structure of your account. We will investigate three standard situations, a regular savings account, a Traditional Individual Retirement Account (IRA), and a Roth IRA.

Example 3: Consider an investor who invests $2000 at the end of each year for 30 years in an account paying 7% annual compound interest. Suppose the investor is in the 28% income tax bracket. (This means that any additional salary, or savings for retirement, will be taxed at a rate of 28%.) What will be the <u>after-tax</u> value of the account if it is set up as (i) a regular savings account, (ii) a Traditional Individual Retirement Account (IRA), or (iii) a Roth IRA

Solution (i) If you use a regular savings account, then each $2000 of your salary you set aside to invest would be taxed at 28% <u>before</u> it is invested. This means you will have to pay 28% of the $2000 in taxes, leaving 72%, or $(0.72)\times(\$2000) = \$1440$, to actually be invested each year. Also, each year's interest at 7% is also taxed at 28%, leaving a true interest rate of $(0.72)\times(7\%) = 5.04\%$. After 30 years, the value of the account would be

$$FA = \$1440\frac{(1.0504^{30}-1)}{0.0504} = \$96,331.71$$

Since you have already paid taxes on all this money, any withdrawal of these funds will not incur any additional taxes, so your actual value is <u>$96,331.71</u>.

(ii) With a Traditional IRA the tax on your deposits and the interest they earn are *deferred* until you make withdrawals from the account at retirement. So the entire $2000 of your savings is deposited and earns the actual interest rate of 7%. So the future value of the deposits would be

$$FA = \$2000\frac{(1.07^{30}-1)}{0.07} = \$188,921.57$$

However, any withdrawals from a Traditional IRA <u>are</u> subject to taxes at the time of the withdrawal. (This is the deferred tax on the original deposits and interest.) Assuming a 28% tax bracket, any withdrawals from the account lose 28% of their value to taxes. So your account is really only worth 72% of $188,921.57, or <u>$136,023.53</u>. Comparing this to the result of (i), the after-tax value of this Traditional IRA's is about 40% more than the after-tax value of the regular savings account!

(iii) With a Roth IRA your deposits are taxed as in a regular savings account, so only $1440 of each $2000 is available for deposit. But neither the interest you earn nor your withdrawals at retirement are ever subject to taxes. So you earn interest at the stated 7% rate, and you accumulate

$$FA = \$2000\frac{(1.07^{30}-1)}{0.07} = \underline{\$136,023.53}.$$

Since your withdrawals at retirement are not taxed, this is the actual value of your account. Notice that in this case it is the same as the value of the Traditional IRA.

Conclusion 2: Both Traditional and Roth IRAs produce significantly larger after-tax account values for retirement savings than regular savings accounts.

Example 4: In Example 3 the after-tax values accumulated by the Traditional IRA and the Roth IRA were the same. How would the values of accounts be changed if the investor were only in the 15% tax bracket when the deposits were made and interest was earned, but was still in the 28% tax bracket when withdrawals are made at retirement?

Solution: With a Traditional IRA the deposits and interest are tax deferred, so changing the tax rate at the time these are made and earned does not affect the after-tax value accumulated. But the after-tax value of the Roth IRA is affected, because its deposits are taxed. At the 15% tax rate each $2000 set aside for retirement would still have 85% of it, or $1700, available for deposit in the Roth IRA. These deposits earn interest at the same 7% rate as before, because interest is tax-free in a Roth IRA. So the value of the account would be

$$FA = \$1700\frac{(1.07^{30}-1)}{0.07} = \$160{,}583.34$$

In this case the Roth IRA produces a higher account value than the Traditional IRA.

Conclusion 3: If retirement savings deposits are made at a lower tax rate than the rate at which withdrawals would be taxed, a Roth IRA will produce a larger after-tax retirement savings account value than a Traditional IRA.

Example 5: Suppose the investor in Example 3 will be in the 28% tax bracket when deposits are made and interest earned, but will be in the 15% tax bracket when withdrawals are made at retirement. How would the after-tax values of the Traditional IRA and the Roth IRA be affected?

Solution: The after-tax value of the Roth IRA would still be $136,023.53, because deposits are still taxed at the 28% rate (and interest and retirement withdrawals are still tax-free). However the after-tax value of the Traditional IRA is now affected. The $2000 deposits are still tax deferred and the entire amount may be invested, and the interest is still tax deferred so the rate is the stated 7%. So as calculated in Example 3, the nominal value of the account will be $188,921.57. Withdrawals from this are now taxed at only 15%, so 85% of the nominal value is actually available, or $160,583.33. So in this case the Traditional IRA produces a higher after-tax value than the Roth IRA!

Conclusion 4: If retirement savings deposits are made at a higher tax rate than the rate at which withdrawals would be taxed, a Traditional IRA will produce a larger after-tax retirement savings account value than a Roth IRA.

Problems for Section 2.7
(Answers to odd-numbered problems in back of text.)

1. From age 20 to age 28 Frank deposits $300 per quarter in a savings account paying 6.2% annual interest compounded quarterly. He then quits making deposits, and leaves the money to continue earning interest until he reaches age 65. Fran starts later, at age 52, and deposits $800 per quarter in an account paying the same rate. How much will each of them will have accumulated when he/she reaches age 65? (Ignore the effects of taxes.) Do your calculations support the first conclusion of this section? Explain.

2. John deposits $100 per month from age 25 to age 35 in a regular savings account. He fails to make further deposits, but the money continues to earn interest. Jane waits to begin making deposits until she reaches age 50. She then deposits $300 per month from age 50 to age 65 in a similar account. Both accounts pay 6.6% annual interest compounded monthly. What is the value of each account when the person reaches age 65? (Ignore the effects of taxes.) Do your calculations support the first conclusion of this section? Explain.

3. Consider a person who makes a $1500 per year deposit for 25 years in a savings account paying 6% annual compound interest. Find the value of the account accumulated after the 25 years. (Ignore the effect of taxes.) Then find the value of the account if the person (a) raises the amount saved to $2000 per year or (b) raises the interest rate to 8% annual compound interest. Which has a larger effect on that value of the account?

4. Consider a person who deposits $150 per month for 20 years in an account paying 5.4% annual interest compounded monthly. Find the value of the account accumulated after the 20 years. (Ignore the effect of taxes.) Then find the value of the account if the person (a) raises the number of years in which deposits are made to 25, or (b) raises the interest rate to 6.6% annual interest compound monthly. Which has a larger effect on that value of the account?

5. Consider an investor who invests $200 at the end of each month for 20 years in an account paying 6.15% interest compounded monthly and then retires. Suppose the investor is in the 15% income tax bracket when both deposits and withdrawals are made and interest is earned. Find the after-tax value of the account if it is set up as:
    (a) A regular savings account;
    (b) A Traditional IRA;
    (c) A Roth IRA.

6. Consider an investor who invests $500 at the end of each quarter for 25 years in an account paying 6.4% annual interest compounded quarterly and then retires. Suppose the investor is in the 32% income tax bracket when both deposits and withdrawals are made and interest is earned. Find the after-tax value of the account if it is set up as:
    (a) A regular savings account;
    (b) A Traditional IRA;
    (c) A Roth IRA.

7. Rework Problem 5 if the investor is in the 32% income tax bracket when deposits are made and interest is earned, but is in the 15% bracket when withdrawals are made in retirement. Explain how your calculations support one of the conclusions of this section.

8. Rework Problem 6 if the investor is in the 32% income tax bracket when deposits are made and interest is earned, but is in the 28% bracket when withdrawals are made in retirement. Explain how your calculations support one of the conclusions of this section.

9. Rework Problem 5 if the investor is in the 15% income tax bracket when deposits are made and interest is earned, but is in the 32% bracket when withdrawals are made in retirement. Explain how your calculations support one of the conclusions of this section.

10. Rework Problem 6 if the investor is in the 28% income tax bracket when deposits are made and interest is earned, but is in the 32% bracket when withdrawals are made in retirement. Explain how your calculations support one of the conclusions of this section.

Section 2.8 Overview and Review Problems for Chapter 2

2.1: In this section we learned how to compute the **future accumulation** of a sequence of equal payments at equal time periods and made at the ends of the payment intervals, which is denoted FA. This is the sum of the future values of the individual payments, just after the last payment is made, and is found by:

(1) $$FA = PMT \frac{\left((1+i)^m - 1\right)}{i}$$ **Future Value of a Sequence of Payments (just after the last payment is made)**

where FA = the future accumulation of the sequence of payments, that is, the sum of the future values of the payments just after the last payment is made

i = interest rate per interest period $\quad PMT$ = the periodic payment amount.

m = total number of interest periods = number of payment intervals = total number of payments,

If the payments are made into a savings account, then the **total amount of interest that will have been earned is** $\quad I = FA - m \times PMT$

2.2: In this section we developed the formula for the **present value** of the same sequence of payments:

(2) $$PV = PMT \frac{\left(1 - (1+i)^{-m}\right)}{i}$$ **Present Value of a Sequence of Payments (Principal of Amortized Loan Paid Off by the Payments)**

Here PV is the sum of the present values of the payments, m is the number of payments, and i is the periodic interest rate. PV is the principal of an amortized loan that will be paid off by the sequence of payments.

The **total amount of interest you will pay** over the term of the amortized loan is the difference between the total of all the payments and the principal PV: $\quad I = m \times PMT - PV$.

If you are negotiating a deal involving a down payment or trade-in, remember:

$$Cash\ Value = \begin{array}{c} Present\ Value\ of \\ Periodic\ Payments \end{array} + \begin{array}{c} Down\ Payment \\ (if\ any) \end{array} + \begin{array}{c} Trade\text{-}in \\ (if\ any) \end{array}$$

2.3: In this section we developed the formulas for finding the periodic payment amount needed to pay off a loan or accumulate a sum. The formulas are

(3) $$PMT = \frac{FA \times i}{\left((1+i)^m - 1\right)} =$$ **Periodic Payment needed to accumulate future accumulation of FA**

(4) $$PMT = \frac{PV \times i}{\left(1 - (1+i)^{-m}\right)} =$$ **Periodic Payment needed to pay off amortized loan amount of PV**

To determine which of the formulas to use, you must decide whether you are given the value at the beginning of the time interval (present value; formula (3)) or at the end of the time interval (future accumulation; formula (4)). To find the monthly payment on an amortized loan, use the formula (4) since the loan amount is the PV and PMT is the monthly payment.

We also learned about the **Add-On Interest Method** which is used on **Installment Loans:**

$$\begin{array}{c} monthly \\ payment \end{array} = \frac{P + I}{m} \quad where \quad \begin{cases} P \text{ is the principal of the loan,} \\ I = Prt \text{ is the amount of Simple Interest,} \\ and\ m \text{ is the number of monthly payments} \end{cases}$$

2.4: In this section we learned how to set up an **amortization** schedule:
Make 5 columns that will contain the *Current Balance*, *Payment Amount*, *Interest Due*, *Principal Paid*, and the *New Balance*. Start with the principal as the *Current Balance*, and repeatedly perform these five steps until the final payment is reached:

(i)   Write the *current balance* in the first column. After the first time period, the *current balance* will be the same as the *new balance* from the previous period.

(ii) Write the *payment amount* in the second column (see below for final payment).

(iii) Calculate the *interest*: Multiply the *current Balance* by the periodic interest rate i, and round the result to the nearest penny. Write this in the interest column.

(iv) Calculate the *principal paid*: Subtract the *interest* from the *payment*. Write this in column four.

(v) Calculate the *new balance*: Subtract the *principal paid* from the *current balance*, and write this in the last column.

When you get to the last line, to find the final payment, calculate the *interest* as in iii). Then the final *payment* is the *interest* plus the *current balance*.

We also learned that **the payoff amount (outstanding balance) of an amortized loan just after a payment has been made is the present value of all payments yet to be made:**

$$(5) \qquad \textbf{Payoff Amount} = PMT\frac{\left(1-\left(1+i\right)^{-k}\right)}{i}, \textbf{where} \quad k = \textbf{number of remaining payments}$$

2.5: In this section we learned how to analyze a home mortgage, what points are, a way to decide whether to refinance a mortgage.

1) The **total interest paid** on a home mortgage is the product of the payment amount times the number of payments, less the loan amount: $I = m \times PMT - PV$

2) **Points** on a loan are a percentage of the loan amount paid by the borrower, i.e. 1 point is 1% of the loan. To find the loan amount L necessary to pay both the dollar amount D of the house price to be financed as well as p points on the loan, solve $L = D + p\%$ of L for L.

2.6: In this section we learned how to find the effect on a mortgage of an additional amount paid each month, and how to find the number of payments of size *PMT* required to pay off an amortized loan amount or exhaust an account in a given amount of time.

To find the number of payments m required to pay off a loan by making a payment *PMT* each month, or the number of withdrawals required to completely exhaust an account that is earning interest, use the formula

$$(6) \quad m = -\log\left(1-\frac{PV\times i}{PMT}\right)+\log\left(1+i\right)$$

PV is the current value of the amortized loan (account) i is the interest rate per period

To find the number of payments m required to accumulate a certain future accumulation by making a certain payment each month, use the formula

$$(7) \quad m = \log\left(1+\frac{FA\times i}{PMT}\right)+\log\left(1+i\right)$$

In both formula (6) and (7), the fractional part of m gives the fraction of a final payment needed.

To decide whether to refinance at a certain point in a mortgage,

(i) calculate the payoff amount of the current mortgage at this time.

(ii) use this plus any closing costs as the principal of a mortgage at the new rate, of length equal to the number of remaining payments on the current loan. Find the monthly payment of the new loan.

(iii) If you plan to keep the new mortgage for k more payments, determine the total of k payments of the old mortgage versus the total of k payments on the new mortgage. Compare these savings to the difference of the payoff amounts of the two mortgages after k payments have been made. (Usually the new mortgage will save on payments but lose on payoff amount.)

2.7: In this section we investigated which of the variables time, interest rate, or deposit amount, had the largest effect on the value of a retirement savings account, and decided that the length of time the investments had to accumulate interest had the largest effect. We also investigated how Traditional IRAs and Roth IRAs work, and decided that each can increase the after-tax value of retirement savings. If the investor is at a higher income tax rate when making deposits into the account than when making withdrawals in retirement from the account, a Traditional IRA produces a larger after-tax value than a Roth IRA. But if the investor is at a higher income tax rate when making withdrawals in retirement from the account than when making deposits into the account, a Roth IRA produces a larger after-tax value than a Traditional IRA.

Review Problems for Chapter 2 (Answers in back of text.)

1. Suppose you buy a computer for $4000 and pay it off using an amortized loan with a sequence of five substantially equal monthly payments at 9% annual interest compounded monthly.
   (a) What initial payment is required?
   (b) Create an amortization schedule for the loan, and find the final payment.
   (c) How much total interest would she pay?
   (d) If the loan were an Installment Loan at 9% simple interest, what would the monthly payment be? How much interest would she pay?

2. A mother is depositing $25 monthly into a fund earning 6.6% compounded monthly. This money is to be used for her granddaughter's college education. If she makes deposits beginning one month after her granddaughter turns 4 years old, and makes the last deposit on her 18th birthday, how much money will she have available for college 9 months after her 18th birthday? How much interest will her investments have earned?

3. You just won the Illinois Lottery for $40 million! This will be paid to you in 20 annual installments of $2 million, the first today. What is the cash value of this prize today if money is worth:
   (a) 3% (b) 6%

4. Lisa has a home equity loan for $13,500 for 10 years at 8.1% compounded monthly.
   (a) What is her monthly payment?
   (b) If she makes the monthly payment in a) for the next 10 years, how much total interest will she pay?
   (c) What will be the payoff amount of her loan after 36 payments?
   (d) Suppose she increases her monthly payment by $100 (beginning with the first payment). When will the loan be completely paid off? About how much will her last payment need to be?
   (e) How much total interest will she pay if she makes the extra $100 monthly payment?

5. A company wants to have $20,000 ten years from now by making equal quarterly payments into an account that pays 7% annual interest compounded quarterly.
   (a) What quarterly payment is required to accumulate the desired $20,000?
   (b) Rework (a), assuming that the company already has $6,000 in the account.

6. A man will receive a pension consisting of a $2300 payment at the start of each month for the next 27 years. Figuring interest at 3.3% compounded monthly, what is the cash value of his pension today?

7. Compare the amounts you will have at age 65 under each of these scenarios. In each you make annual deposits into an investment paying 10% annual interest compounded annually.
   (a) You invest $2200 per year from age 18 to 25, then make no further investments.
   (b) You invest $2200 per year from age 30 to 65.

8. A worker can save $150 per month in an account paying 4.8% annual interest compounded monthly.
   (a) How long (in years and months) will it be from the time the worker begins making deposits until the value of the account reaches at least $250,000?
   (b) About how much will the last payment need to be to reach $250,000?
   (c) When $250,000 is reached, what part of the value of the account is interest?

9. You put $5000 down on a new car and finance the balance with $400 per month payments for four years at 5.7% compounded monthly. What was the cash value of the car? How much total interest are you paying on this deal?

10. A purchaser is buying a $140,000 house and putting 20% down. The bank offers a 30-year amortized loan at 8.1% compounded monthly, with 1.5 points.
    (a) If the amount you borrow includes the points, what amount of money will be borrowed?
    (b) What is the monthly payment?
    (c) How much of the first payment is interest paid? How much is principal repaid?
    (d) What is the (approximate) total interest paid during the term of the loan?
    (e) What will be the balance remaining after 10 years (120 payments)?
    (f) How long (in years and months) from the start of the loan will it be until the balance falls below
        $80,000?

11. A worker has $250,000 in a retirement account that is tax-free and pays interest at the rate of 4.2% compounded monthly. Assuming that rate doesn't change,
    (a) She wants to determine a fixed amount that she can withdraw from the account every month for the next 20 years. What fixed amount will completely use up the account at the end of 20 years?
    (b) She wants to consider withdrawing $3000 every month. If she does so, how long will it be before the account is completely exhausted? About how much will the last payment be?

12. Suppose you invest $3000 at the end of each year for 15 years in an IRA paying 7.5% annual compound interest. Suppose the investor is in the 32% income tax bracket when both deposits are made and interest is earned, but is in the 15% income tax bracket when withdrawals are made. Find the after-tax value of the account if it is set up as
    (a) a Traditional IRA;
    (b) a regular savings account;
    (c) a Roth IRA.

Chapter 3   Linear Programming

Managers of businesses are often concerned with maximizing the total profit or minimizing the total cost of their products. They must decide how to allocate their resources among the products they make, how many of each product to make, and what the price of each product should be. As they make these decisions they operate under certain constraints, such as the amount of materials available, the amount of labor available, and perhaps required production limits. Although such decisions can be made by trial and error, or based on "experience", a good company will analyze the problem in an organized manner, often using Linear Programming.

Our study of Linear Programming will begin with problems that are small enough to do by hand using basic algebra and graphing, and then progress to larger problems that are best solved using special software on a computer. In both situations the manager's major role is to identify that a linear programming approach is applicable and translate the verbal or written description into mathematical language. This mathematical description can then be used to obtain a mathematical solution to the problem, either by hand or by using the software. Finally, that mathematical solution is interpreted and evaluated in the original problem.

A Historical Perspective

Although the basic mathematical ideas for Linear Programming had been known previously, a technique for solving large-scale problems depended on the invention of the computer. After World War II applied mathematicians were concerned with how best to locate military supplies and personnel. These were actually large linear programming problems. In 1947 George Dantzig (shown at right) developed the simplex algorithm (see Section 3.3) which could be easily implemented on a computer and which allowed a linear programming problem of large size to be solved efficiently. Dantzig's original example was to find the best assignment of 70 people to 70 jobs. The number of possible assignments exceeds the number of particles in the observable universe. However, it takes only a moment to find the optimum solution by posing the problem as a linear programming problem and applying the simplex algorithm. The theory behind linear programming produces a drastically reduced number of possible solutions that must be checked to find the best one. Numerous modifications and adaptations of the simplex algorithm have been made since then, allowing linear programming techniques to be applied to a wide variety of problems.

Linda A. Cicero/Stanford News Service

Linear programming has changed the way businesses make decisions. A predictable procedure based on objective data has replaced guesswork and intuition. Linear programming has saved businesses billions of dollars, and it is estimated that about 75% of all computer time used by businesses is used on solving linear programming problems. Oil refineries use it to decide how to mix gasolines, airlines use it to route planes and crews, large farms use it to plan crop production, and phone companies use it to design telephone networks.

Section 3.1   Translating a Linear Programming Problem into Mathematics

To solve a linear programming problem we must recognize that this technique is applicable, and translate the English description of the problem into mathematical language. We will discuss this recognition and translation process while we consider the following problem.

Example 1 Cardinal Furniture Cardinal Furniture Company produces chairs and tables. To produce a chair the company uses 3 yards of fabric, 2 board-feet of lumber, and 30 minutes of assembly workers' time. To produce a table the company uses 4 board-feet of lumber and 15 minutes of assembly workers' time. The company wants to plan how many chairs and tables to make so as to maximize their profit. The company knows that each chair will yield a $60 profit and each table will yield a $50 profit. On Monday there are 1500 yards of fabric, 3000 board-feet of lumber, and 300 hours of assembly workers' time available. How many chairs and tables should be produced on Monday in order to give the largest possible profit?

At first this may look like a typical algebra word problem. However, if you read the problem carefully you notice some differences:
1) There seem to be many possibilities for the numbers of chairs and tables to make, from none at all to hundreds of each.
2) But our choices are restricted by the amounts of fabric, lumber, and assembly workers' time available, so there are limits to how many chairs and tables we can make.
3) Instead of trying to find just one solution, we want to find the "best" solution, where "best" here means most profitable.

These conditions are typical of a linear programming problem. In addition, in order to be a linear programming problem the problem must satisfy proportionality. This property states that the number of each type of product that can be made is proportional to the amount of resources available. That is, if we had twice as much of each resource (fabric, lumber, workers' time), then we could make twice as many of each type of product (chairs and tables). Proportionality must also be true about the profit; if we make twice as many of each type of product, then we will earn twice as much profit. (Thus no price discounts for large volume purchases.) Finally, linear programming problems are usually about dealing with an immediate problem, not about a long-term solution. Next week there may be a different amount of the resources available, or the profits may change due to new prices, etc.

Mathematical Formulation of Example 1: To translate the Cardinal Furniture Problem into mathematical language we first have to introduce variables. Those variables are the answers to the question "How many..." or "How much ..." in the word problem. In the Cardinal Furniture Problem we are asked "How many chairs and tables should be produced on Monday?" so we let
   x = the number of chairs to be made on Monday
   y = the number of tables to be made on Monday
(It may seem strange to write down "the number of ...", but we will see that on some problems it is very important to have the units for the variables clearly identified. *Get in the habit of writing down the units*.)

These variables are called the *production variables*. A *production policy* is a set of values of the production variables. When there are two production variables it is written (x, y). The *objective* of the problem is to find the production policy that will yield the largest profit while using up no more than the available resources. So we need to have a formula which will calculate the profit in terms of the values of the production policy. In this problem there is a $60 profit on each chair made and a profit of $50 on each table made. So the formula for the total **profit** P (also called the **objective function**) is:
   $P = \$60x + \$50y$, which is to be maximized (i. e. made as large as possible.)

Now we need to formulate all the limits (or constraints) imposed by the availability of "resources". (Here "resources" refers to anything which may influence or limit how much of each "product" can be produced.) To help us do this we will set up a "**product-resource chart**", with <u>one row for each resource and one column for each product</u> (i.e. each production variable). In the final column we will list the amount of each resource available.

	In each chair	In each table	Total Amount available
fabric	3 yards	0	1500 yards
lumber	2 bd-ft	4 bd-ft	3000 bd-ft
Workers' time	30 minutes	15 minutes	300 hours

For example, the entry "4 bd-ft" represents the fact that each table requires 4 board-feet of lumber, and the "0" reflects the fact that each table requires no fabric. Also, *it is important that each resource have all the numbers on its row written in the same units*. In this problem this is already true for the first two rows. In the last row we need to have all the numbers in minutes or all the numbers in hours. Arbitrarily, we choose to convert all the numbers to minutes. Since 1 hour equals 60 minutes, we multiply the 300 hours of workers' time available by 60 minutes per hour, and find that there are 18,000 minutes of time available. This results in the chart we actually use:

	In each chair	In each table	Total Amount available
fabric	3 yards	0	1500 yards
lumber	2 bd-ft	4 bd-ft	3000 bd-ft
Workers' time	30 minutes	15 minutes	300 x 60 = 18,000 minutes

If we make x chairs, we will use 3 yards of fabric in each, or $3x$ yards of fabric in all. If we make y tables, we use no fabric at all. So for our production policy of (x, y), a total of $3x + 0y$ yards of fabric will be used. This total amount must not exceed the amount of fabric available, 1500 yards. In mathematical language, this means.

$$3x \leq 1500 \text{ yards of fabric}$$

Similarly, our production policy of (x, y) will use 2 board-feet of lumber for each of the x chairs and 4 board-feet of lumber for each of the y tables, and the total used cannot exceed the 3000 board-feet of fabric available. Thus

$$2x + 4y \leq 3000 \text{ board-feet of lumber}$$

Finally, the amount of workers' time that our production policy will use is $30x + 15y$ minutes, and this must not exceed the 18,000 minutes available:

$$30x + 15y \leq 18,000 \text{ minutes workers' time}$$

The three inequalities above are called **resource constraints**. They describe mathematically how the amounts of resources available constrain how many of each product we can make.

There is another type of constraint which is not explicitly stated in the problem but which is nevertheless important. Since it is impossible to make a negative number of any product, each of our production variables must be nonnegative. These are the **non-negativity** or **minimum constraints**: $x \geq 0, y \geq 0$.

We have now obtained the **mathematical formulation of the Cardinal Furniture problem**:

Let x = the number of chairs made on Monday, y = number of tables made on Monday.
Maximize   Profit: $P = \$60x + \$50y$
Given these constraints: $3x \quad\quad\ \leq\ 1500$ yards of fabric
$\qquad\qquad\qquad\qquad\qquad 2x +\ \ 4y \leq 3000$ board-feet of lumber
$\qquad\qquad\qquad\qquad\ 30x + 15y \leq\ 18,000$ minutes workers' time
$\qquad\qquad\qquad\qquad\qquad x \geq 0, y \geq 0$

> ### Obtaining the Mathematical Formulation of a Linear Programming Problem
> 1. **Read** the problem carefully.
> 2. Identify the "**products**" to be made and the "**resources**" from which they are to be made. (Be careful about the **units** involved.) Define the **production variables**, which are the number of units of each product to be made.
> 3. Write down the **objective function**, which gives the thing to be maximized, usually profit P, in terms of the production variables.
> 4. Write down a chart with one column for each "product" and one row for each "resource". In the chart list the amount of each resource needed for 1 unit of each product. Add an extra column at the right containing the amount of each resource available.
> 5. Use the chart to write the **constraints** in terms of the production variables. These often are of the form "the amount of this resource used to produce our unknown amounts of the products is ≤ the amount of the resource available". Remember to include the non-negativity constraints!

Feasibility and Slack

A production policy (x, y) is called feasible if the values for x and y satisfy all the constraints of the problem. (When there are only two such variables, we refer to these values as determining a **feasible point** (x, y).) What are some feasible production policies for the Cardinal Furniture Example? An obvious one is to make no chairs or tables at all, so that $x = 0$ and $y = 0$, but this would result in a profit of $P = 60(0) + 50(0) = 0$. We hope we can make more profit than that! This would leave all of each resource unused. **The amount of a resource that is unused by a particular feasible production policy is called the slack in that constraint for that production policy**.

In general, if we are given a production policy, like $x = 500$ chairs, $y = 300$ tables, we can test whether it is feasible by testing algebraically whether it satisfies each constraint:

Constraint	Test With $x = 500, y = 300$	True?
$3x \leq 1500$	Is $3(500) \leq 1500$?	Yes, $1500 \leq 1500$
$2x + 4y \leq 3000$	Is $2(500) + 4(300) \leq 3000$?	Yes, $2200 \leq 3000$
$30x + 15y \leq 18{,}000$	Is $30(500) + 15(300) \leq 18{,}000$?	No, $15{,}000 + 4500 > 18{,}000$

Because the production policy (500, 300) fails one of the constraints it is **not feasible**. In particular, it would require 19,500 minutes of workers' time, but only 18,000 minutes are available.

Let's lower the number of chairs to 300, and test whether $x = 300$, $y = 300$ is feasible:

Constraint	With $x = 300, y = 300$	True?
$3x \leq 1500$	Is $3(300) \leq 1500$?	Yes, $900 \leq 1500$
$2x + 4y \leq 3000$	Is $2(300) + 4(300) \leq 3000$?	Yes, $1800 \leq 3000$
$30x + 15y \leq 18{,}000$	Is $30(300) + 15(300) \leq 18{,}000$?	Yes, $9000 + 4500 \leq 18{,}000$

Our work shows that the production policy $x = 300$ chairs, $y = 300$ tables is feasible.

Is it the best production policy, as measured by the profit function $P = \$60x + \$50y$? It produces a profit of $P = \$60(300) + 50(300) = \$33{,}000$. But from the first constraint we see that there are 1500 yards of fabric available, but only 900 would be used, so there is are 600 yards of unused fabric in the first constraint; this the slack in this constraint. There is a slack of $3000 - 1800 = 1200$ bd-ft of unused lumber in the second constraint, and a slack of $18000 - (9000 + 4500) = 4500$ hours of unused workers' time in the last constraint. This policy can't make the largest possible profit, because there is more of every resource available (slack in every constraint). We should be able to make more chairs and tables from the available resources, and thus make more profit.

Quiz Yourself: (Answer at the end of this Section, before the Problems.)
1. Test whether $x = 400$ chairs, $y = 400$ tables is feasible in the Cardinal Furniture Example. If it is feasible, find the slack in each constraint.

Constraint	With $x = 400, y = 400$	True?	Slack
$3x \leq 1500$			
$2x + 4y \leq 3000$			
$30x + 15y \leq 18{,}000$			

Your work on the Quiz Yourself above should find that (400, 400) is feasible, and uses up all of the workers' time available (the third constraint). The slack in this constraint is 0. So we can't increase either x or y any further without violating that constraint. Is this the best production policy? We will see in the next section that it is not; we can increase y while decreasing x to achieve a larger profit while not violating the constraints. But for now, we can make this conclusion:

> The best production policy of a linear programming problem must use up all of at least one of the resources, (or equivalently, have at least one slack amount of 0), otherwise we could just make more of all the products to get more profit.

Example 2: Cardinal Fruits Cardinal Fruits sells two assortments of fruit. The Legend assortment contains 4 apples, 4 grapefruit, 9 oranges, and 2 kiwis, and <u>sells</u> for $28.95. The Supreme assortment contains 12 apples, 4 grapefruit, 4 oranges, and no kiwis, and <u>sells</u> for $23.95. Each apple costs the company $0.20, each grapefruit costs $0.25, each orange costs $0.30, and each kiwi costs $0.50. This week the company has available 9600 apples, 4000 grapefruit, 7200 oranges, and 1400 kiwis. Assuming they can sell all the assortments they can make, how many of each type assortment should Cardinal Fruits make this week in order to maximize their profit?

Formulation: Steps 1, 2: Cardinal Fruits is making two kinds of fruit assortments out of 4 kinds of fruit. They want to know how many of each type assortment to make to maximize profit. The products are the Legend assortment and the Supreme assortment; the resources are the four kinds of fruit used to make the assortments. Our production variables are:

   Let x = number of Legend assortments made, y = number of Supreme assortments made.

Step 3: In this problem we are not given the profit on either of the assortments. Instead we must use a fundamental rule of business:

Profit on item = its selling price - cost of resources needed to make item

So the profit on one Legend Assortment is its price, $28.95, less the cost of 4 apples, 4 grapefruit, 9 oranges, and 2 kiwis. This is $28.95 - 4(\$0.20) - 4(\$0.25) - 9(\$0.30) - 2(\$0.50) = \$23.45$. Similarly the profit on one Supreme is $23.95 - 12(\$0.20) - 4(\$0.25) - 4(\$0.30) = \$19.35$. If the company makes x Legend and y Supreme assortments, the total profit will be

   $P = \$23.45x + \$19.35y$

Step 4: A product-resource chart would be:

	In each Legend	**In each Supreme**	**Total Available**
Apples	4	12	9600
Grapefruit	4	4	4000
Oranges	9	4	7200
Kiwis	2	0	1400

Example 2 (continued) <u>Step 5</u>: Using the chart, the first constraint is that making x Legends takes $4x$ apples, and making y Supremes takes $12y$ apples, and the total of these must be no more than the 7600 apples available: $4x + 12y \leq 9600$ apples

In a similar fashion the other constraints are:

$$4x + 4y \leq 4000 \text{ grapefruit}$$
$$9x + 4y \leq 7200 \text{ oranges}$$
$$2x \quad\quad \leq 1400 \text{ kiwis}$$
$$x \geq 0, \ y \geq 0$$

<u>Mathematical Formulation:</u>

Let x = number of Legend assortments made, y = number of Supreme assortments made.

Maximize $P = \$23.45x + \$19.35y$

Subject to: $4x + 12y \leq 9600$ apples

$\quad\quad\quad\quad\quad 4x + 4y \leq 4000$ grapefruit

$\quad\quad\quad\quad\quad 9x + 4y \leq 7200$ oranges

$\quad\quad\quad\quad\quad 2x \quad\quad \leq 1400$ kiwis

$\quad\quad\quad\quad\quad x \geq 0, \ y \geq 0$

Quiz Yourself (Answer at the end of this Section, before the Problems.)

2. A coffee salesman sells two blends of coffee, Bold and Brisk. Each pound of Bold consists of 10 ounces of Arabica beans and 6 ounces of Robusta beans, and sells for $12. Each pound of Brisk consists of 5 ounces of Arabica beans, 6 ounces of Robusta beans, and 5 ounces of Kona beans, and sells for $10. Today he has 62.5 pounds of Arabica, 56.25 pounds of Robusta, and 37.5 pounds of Kona beans. How much of each blend should he make to yield as large a revenue as possible. (Assume he can sell all he makes of both blends.)

(a) Formulate this problem mathematically by going through the 5 steps on page 146.

(b) Is it feasible for the coffee salesman to make 40 pounds of Bold and 120 pounds of Brisk? Why or why not? If it is feasible, how much slack is there is each constraint?

(c) Is it feasible for the coffee salesman to make 50 pounds of Bold and 100 pounds of Brisk? Why or why not? If it is feasible, how much slack is there is each constraint?

Example 3: Crop Allocation A farmer has 100 acres on which to plant two crops: corn and wheat. Each acre of corn will take 2 workdays to cultivate, and each acre of wheat will take 4 work-days. There are 300 work-days available for cultivation. Each acre of corn yields 40 bushels, and each acre of wheat yields 24 bushels, but there are only storage facilities for 3,600 bushels of grain. The farmer makes a profit of $3.60 per bushel for corn and $3.50 per bushel on wheat. How many acres of corn and how many acres of wheat should the farmer plant to maximize his net profit? Is it feasible for the farmer to plant 40 acres of corn and 60 acres of wheat? If so, what is the slack in each constraint?

<u>Formulation:</u> <u>Steps 1, 2:</u> The products are corn and wheat; the resources are work-days, storage facilities, and land (!). Notice that although the profit per bushel is given, we are asked to find the number of <u>acres</u> of each crop to plant. This determines the units of our production variables:

$\quad$ Let C = number of acres of corn to be planted

$\quad\quad\quad W$ = number of acres of wheat to be planted

<u>Step 3:</u> The farmer wants to maximize his net profit. *Be careful in writing the profit function.* The profits stated in the problem are *per bushel*, but our variables C and W are in *acres*. So we need to use the number of bushels produced by one acre of each grain. One acre of corn produces 40 bushels which earn a net profit of $3.60 each, so one acre of corn earns a net profit of ($3.60)(40) = $144. Similarly one acre of wheat yields 24 bushels, each with a profit of $3.50, so one acre of wheat earns a net profit of ($3.50) (24) = $84. This means that C acres of corn and W acres of wheat will earn a net profit of

$$P = \$144C + \$84W$$

Example 3 (continued) Step 4: What constrains how many acres of corn and wheat the farmer can plant? One constraint is that he only has 100 acres available, so

$C + W \leq 100$ acres   (Not $C + W = 100$; he doesn't *have* to use all the acres available.)

The farmer is also constrained by the 300 work-days available for cultivation, and the storage facilities for only 3600 bushels of grain. A complete product-resource chart looks like:

	Per Acre of Corn	Per Acre of Wheat	Available
Acres of land	1	1	100
Work-days	2	4	300
Storage facilities	40 bushels	24 bushels	3600 bushels

If the farmer plants C acres of corn, it will take 2 work-days per acre, or $2C$ work-days for cultivation. Similarly it will take $4W$ work-days to cultivate W acres of wheat. So the work-days constraint is

$2C + 4W \leq 300$ work-days.

Since C acres of corn will produce $40C$ bushels of corn, and W acres of wheat will produce $24W$ bushels of wheat. So C and W are constrained by

$40C + 24W \leq 3600$ bushels storage

Finally, the values of C and W must be nonnegative: $C \geq 0, W \geq 0$

Mathematical formulation:

      Let C be the number of acres of corn to be planted, and
        W be the number of acres of wheat to be planted.

Maximize $P = \$144C + 84W$

Subject to $C + W \leq 100$ acres

                     $2C + 4W \leq 300$ work-days

                     $40C + 24W \leq 3{,}600$ bushels storage

                     $C \geq 0, W \geq 0$

To test whether it is feasible to plant 40 acres of corn and 60 acres of wheat, test the constraints:

                 $40 + 60 \leq 100$ acres ? True

                 $2(40) + 4(60) = 80 + 240 \leq 300$? False.

Since the work-days constraint is false, there are not enough work-days to plant 40 acres of corn and 60 acres of wheat. It is not feasible. There is a slack of 0 in the first constraint: $40 + 60 = 100$.)

Example 4: Arts and Crafts Shop An arts and crafts shop makes flower arrangements, baskets, and centerpieces. The costs of the materials (of which the shop has all it needs) are the same for each, but they require specialized skill from each of the three workers. An arrangement requires 2 minutes by Joan, 6 minutes by Beth, and 4 minutes by Carol. A basket requires 6 minutes by Joan, 10 minutes by Beth, and 8 minutes by Carol. A centerpiece requires 10 minutes by Joan, 8 minutes by Beth, and 16 minutes by Carol. The shop makes a profit of $10 on each arrangement, $25 on each basket, and $35 on each centerpiece. This month Joan is scheduled to work 80 hours, but Beth and Carol will work 200 hours each. How many arrangements, baskets, and centerpieces should the shop make this month to maximize its profit? (Assume they can sell all the items they make.) Is it feasible for the Shop to make 300 arrangements, 250 baskets, and 250 centerpieces? If it is, how much slack is there in each constraint?

Formulation: This is an example of a problem with more than two production variables. Reading from the next-to-last sentence, the production variables should be:

      Let x = number of arrangements to make
         y = number of baskets to make
         z = number of centerpieces to make.

Using the given profit on each arrangement, the total profit is: $P = \$10x + \$25y + \$35z$.

Example 4 (continued) Here is a mixture chart showing the amount of each worker's time going into each product:

	Arrangements (x)	**Baskets (y)**	**Centerpieces (z)**	**Available**
Joan	2 minutes each	6 minutes each	10 minutes each	80 hours
Beth	6 minutes each	10 minutes each	8 minutes each	200 hours
Carol	4 minutes each	8 minutes each	16 minutes each	200 hours

Notice that the limit on each workers time is expressed in hours, but the time she spends on each item is in minutes. It is easiest to convert hours to minutes, so we do that.

Joan spends $2x$ minutes on the x arrangements, $6y$ minutes on the y baskets, and $10z$ minutes on the z centerpieces. The sum of these must be less than or equal to the 80 hours = 4800 minutes she can work.

Beth spends $6x$ minutes on the x arrangements, $10y$ minutes on the y baskets, and $8z$ minutes on the z centerpieces. The sum of these must be less than or equal to the 200 hours = 12,000 minutes she can work.

Carol spends $4x$ minutes on the x arrangements, $8y$ minutes on the y baskets, and $16z$ minutes on the z centerpieces. The sum of these must be less than or equal to the 200 hours = 12,000 minutes she can work.

In mathematical notation these read:

$$2x + 6y + 10z \le 4{,}800 \text{ minutes of Joan's time}$$
$$6x + 10y + 8z \le 12{,}000 \text{ minutes of Beth's time}$$
$$4x + 8y + 16z \le 12{,}000 \text{ minutes of Carol's time}$$

Of course, we still have: $x \ge 0, y \ge 0, z \ge 0$.

Mathematical Formulation:

Let x = number of arrangements to make, y = number of baskets to make,
z = number of centerpieces to make.

Maximize $P = \$10x + \$25y + \$35z$

Subject to: $2x + 6y + 10z \le 4{,}800$ minutes of Joan's time
$6x + 10y + 8z \le 12{,}000$ minutes of Beth's time
$4x + 8y + 16z \le 12{,}000$ minutes of Carol's time
$x \ge 0, y \ge 0, z \ge 0$.

Is it feasible to make 300 arrangements, 250 baskets, and 250 centerpieces? Test each constraint:

$2(300) + 6(250) + 10(250) = 600 + 1500 + 2500 \le 4{,}800$? True
Slack: $4{,}800 - (600 + 1500 + 2500) = 200$ unused minutes of Joan's time.
$6(300) + 10(250) + 8(250) = 1800 + 2500 + 2000 \le 12{,}000$? True
Slack: $12{,}000 - (1800 + 2500 + 2000) = 5{,}700$ unused minutes of Beth's time.
$4(300) + 8(250) + 16(250) = 1200 + 2000 + 4000 \le 12{,}000$? True
Slack: $12{,}000 - (1200 + 2000 + 4000) = 4{,}800$ unused minutes of Carol's time.

Since all are true, it is feasible to make 300 arrangements, 250 baskets, and 250 centerpieces.

Quiz Yourself: (Answer on the next page)

3. Cardinal Candy has 1000 pounds of chocolate, 200 pounds of nuts, and 160 pounds of caramel pieces available. A box of the Bobby Petrino mix uses 3 pounds of chocolate, 1 pound of nuts, 1 pound of caramel pieces, and sells for $27. A box of the Rick Pitino mix uses 2 pounds of chocolate, 2 pounds of nuts, 1 pound of caramel pieces, and sells for $23. A box of the Charlie Strong mix uses 4 pounds of chocolate, 0.5 pounds of nuts 0.5 pounds of caramel pieces, and sells for $27. Each pound of chocolate cost $5, each pound of nuts cost $2, and each pound of caramel cost $4. How many boxes of each type of mix should Cardinal Candy make to maximize their *profit* (revenue – cost), assuming they can sell all the boxes they make?

   (a) Formulate this problem mathematically by going through the 5 steps on page 184.
   (b) Is it feasible for the company to make 50 boxes of Bobby Petrino, 60 boxes of Rick Pitino, and 60 boxes of Charlie Strong mix? Why or why not? If it is, what is the slack in each constraint?

Answers to Quiz Yourself:

1. Test whether (400, 400) is feasible:

Constraint	With $x = 400, y = 400$	True?	Slack
$3x \leq 1500$	$3(400) \leq 1500$?	Yes, $1200 \leq 1500$	300
$2x + 4y \leq 3000$	$2(400) + 4(400) \leq 3000$?	Yes, $800 + 1600 \leq 3000$	600
$30x + 15y \leq 18,000$	$30(400) + 15(400) \leq 18,000$?	Yes, $12,000 + 6,000 \leq 18,000$	0

This policy is feasible. There is a slack of 0 in the last constraint because none of the hours are unused.

2. The products are the two blends, Bold and Brisk. The resources are the three types of beans. Let:
   x = number of pounds of Bold
   y = number of pounds of Brisk
   Revenue = $\$12x + \$10y$
The product resource chart is:

	Per pound of Bold	Per pound of Brisk	Available
Arabica	10 ounces	5 ounces	62.5 pounds x 16 = 1000 ounces
Robusta	6 ounces	6 ounces	56.25 pounds x 16 = 900 ounces
Kona	0	5 ounces	37.5 pounds x 16 = 600 ounces

We must convert pounds to ounces (or vice versa), which is done by multiplying the number of pounds by 16, as shown in the last column above.

The number of ounces of Arabica beans used in x pounds of Bold and y pounds of Brisk is $10x + 5y$; this must be less than or equal to the 1000 ounces available: $10x + 5y \leq 1000$ ounces of Arabica.

Similarly $6x + 6y$ ounces of Robusta are used, and this must be $\leq$ the 900 ounces available
   $5y$ ounces of Kona are used, and this must be $\leq$ the 600 ounces available
(a) Mathematical Formulation: Maximize: Revenue = $\$12x + \$10y$
   Subject to: $10x + 5y \leq 1000$ ounces Arabica
   $6x + 6y \leq 900$ ounces Robusta
   $5y \leq 600$ ounces Kona
   $x \geq 0, y \geq 0$ (Don't forget the non-negativity conditions!)
(b) Is (40, 120) feasible? Test it in each constraint:
   $10(40) + 5(120) = 400 + 600 \leq 1000$? True   Slack: 0
   $6(40) + 6(120) = 240 + 720 \leq 900$? False
No need to check last constraint; there is not enough Robusta for this production policy.
(c) Is (50, 100) feasible? Test it in each constraint:
   $10(50) + 5(100) = 500 + 500 \leq 1000$? True   Slack: 0 unused pounds of Arabica
   $6(50) + 6(100) = 300 + 600 \leq 900$? True   Slack: 0 unused pounds of Robusta
   $5(100) \leq 600$? True   Slack: 100 unused pounds of Kona
Also $50 \geq 0$ and $100 \geq 0$, so this policy is feasible.

3. The products are the three types of boxes of candy; the resources are chocolate, nuts and caramel
   pieces. Let: x = number of boxes of Bobby Petrino mix,
   y = number of boxes of Rick Pitino mix,
   z = number of boxes of Charlie Strong mix.

To find the profit on each box we must subtract the costs of its ingredients from its selling price.
   Bobby Petrino box: cost = $3(\$5) + 1(\$2) + 1(4) = \$21$. Profit = $\$27 - \$21 = \$6$ per box
   Rick Pitino box: cost = $2(\$5) + 2(\$2) + 1(\$4) = \$18$. Profit = $\$23 - \$18 = \$5$ per box
   Charlie Strong box: cost = $4(\$5) + 0.5(\$2) + 0.5(\$4) = \$23$. Profit = $\$27 - \$23 = \$4$ per box

We are asked to maximize profit, so we write a formula for profit in terms of $x, y,$ and z:
   $P = \$6x + \$5y + \$4z$

Quiz Yourself Answers (3. continued)

Here is a product-resource chart:

	Per box of BP	Per Box of RP	Per box of CS	Available
chocolate	3 pounds	2 pounds	4 pounds	1000 pounds
nuts	1 pound	2 pounds	0.5 pounds	200 pounds
caramel	1 pound	1 pound	0.5 pounds	160 pounds

Chocolate constraint: $3x + 2y + 4z \leq 1000$ pounds available
Nuts Constraint: $1x + 2y + 0.5z \leq 200$ pounds available
Caramel constraint: $1x + 1y + 0.5z \leq 160$ pounds available
Non-negativity: $x \geq 0, y \geq 0, z \geq 0$

(a) Mathematical Formulation:
    Maximize: $P = \$6x + \$5y + \$4z$
    Subject to: $3x + 2y + 4z \leq 1000$ pounds of chocolate available
                  $1x + 2y + 0.5z \leq 200$ pounds of nuts available
                  $1x + 1y + 0.5z \leq 160$ pounds of caramel available
                  $x \geq 0, y \geq 0, z \geq 0$

(b) Test $(50, 60, 60)$ in the constraints:
        $3(50) + 2(60) + 4(60) = 150 + 120 + 240 = 510$; Is this ≤ 1000 ? True
        Slack: $1000 - (510) = 490$ unused pounds of chocolate
        $1(50) + 2(60) + 0.5(60) = 50 + 120 + 30 = 200$; Is this ≤ 200 ? True
        Slack: $200 - (200) = 0$ unused pounds of nuts ("no slack")
        $1(50) + 1(60) + 0.5(60) = 50 + 60 + 30 = 140$; Is this ≤ 160 ? True
        Slack: $160 - (140) = 20$ unused pounds of caramel.

Yes, it is feasible to make 50 boxes of Bobby Petrino mix, 60 boxes of Rick Pitino mix, and 60 boxes of Charlie Strong mix.

Problems for Section 3.1

Sharpen Your Skills (Answers in back of text.)

In Problems 1 and 2 use the given variables to translate the statements into constraints.

1. Let P be the number of gallons of premium gasoline and R be the number of gallons of regular gasoline a refinery produces in a month.
   (a) Each gallon of premium takes 0.7 gallons of high-octane fuel, and each gallon of regular takes 0.4 gallons of high-octane fuel, and there are 250,000 gallons of high-octane fuel available.

   (b) The refinery can produce at most 100,000 gallons of regular gasoline in a month.

2. Let T be the number of tables and C be the number of chairs that a furniture manufacturer will make this week.
   (a) The manufacturer can make at most 30 chairs this week.

   (b) Each table takes 4 hours of labor, and each chair takes 5 hours of labor. There are 240 hours of labor available this week.

In Problems 3 and 4 decide whether each of the given points is feasible for the given system of constraints. If the point is feasible, give the slack in each constraint.

3. Constraints:
$$20x + 50y \le 600$$
$$40x + 30y \le 800$$
$$35x \qquad \le 400$$
$$x, y \ge 0$$
Points: (a) $(15, 6)$

4. Constraints:
$$250x + 400y \le 32{,}500$$
$$350x + 200y \le 28{,}000$$
$$500y \le 25{,}000$$
$$x, y \ge 0$$
Points: (a) $(60, 40)$

(b) $(10, 8)$

(b) $(50, 50)$

Communicate the Concepts: (Answers in back of text.)

5. Describe how to decide whether a given set of values for the production variables is feasible for a system of constraints involving those variables.

6. What is meant by the "slack" in a constraint for a given set of values of the production variables?

7. What are the "non-negativity" constraints on a linear programming problem?

8. What is the "objective function" of a linear programming problem?

Apply Your Knowledge: (Answers to odd-numbered problems in back of text.)

Obtain a mathematical formulation for each linear programming problem below. Follow the steps outlined in the text. Define all the variables, give their units, and label each constraint (inequality) with the name and units of the resource that causes the constraint. Answer any questions about feasibility and slack.

9. A refinery mixes high-octane and low-octane fuels to make regular and premium gasoline. One gallon of regular is produced by mixing 3/4 gallon of low-octane and 1/4 gallon of high-octane fuel. One gallon of premium is produced by mixing 1/2 gallon of low octane and 1/2 gallon of high-octane fuel. The refinery makes $0.20 profit on regular and $0.30 profit on premium. The refinery has 50,000 gallons of high-octane and 60,000 gallons of low-octane available today. Formulate mathematically the problem of determining how many gallons of each type of gasoline the refinery should make today to maximize its profit. Is it feasible to make 70,000 gallons of regular and 40,000 gallons of premium gasoline today? If so, what is the slack in each constraint?

Solution:

Production variables: Profit Function:

Product-Resource Chart: Constraints:

Feasibility Test: Slack?

10. John makes regular and deluxe birdhouses. A store has contracted to purchase his birdhouses, up to 8 regular and up to 6 deluxe each day. He will work on them up to 9 hours a day, but it will take him 3/4 hour to make a regular birdhouse and 1 hour to make a deluxe birdhouse. He makes a $10 profit on each regular birdhouse and $16 profit on each deluxe birdhouse. Formulate mathematically the problem of determining how many of each type he should make per day to maximize his profit. Is it feasible for him to make 6 regular and 5 deluxe birdhouses in one day? If so, what is the slack in each constraint?

Solution:

Production variables: Profit Function:

Product-Resource Chart: Constraints:

Feasibility Test: Slack?

11. Kentucky Weavers make shawls and afghans. They spin yarn, dye yarn, and weave yarn for each. A shawl requires 1 hour of spinning, 1 hour of dyeing, and 1 hour of weaving. An afghan requires 2 hours of spinning, 1 hour of dyeing, and 6 hours of weaving. In a week, there are at most 14 spinning hours, 11 dyeing hours, and 30 weaving hours available. Formulate mathematically the problem of determining how many shawls and how many afghans Kentucky Weavers should make in one week to maximize profit if a shawl bring a profit of $25 and an afghan brings a profit of $40. Is it feasible for them to make 6 shawls and 4 afghans in one week? If so, what is the slack in each constraint?

Solution:

Production variables: Profit Function:

Product-Resource Chart: Constraints:

Feasibility Test: Slack?

12. Michigan Polar Products makes downhill and cross-country skis. A pair of downhill skis requires 2 man-hours for cutting, 1 man-hour for shaping, and 3 man-hours for finishing, while a pair of cross-country skis requires 2 man-hours for cutting, 2 man-hours for shaping, and 1 man-hour for finishing. Each day the company has available 140 man-hours for cutting, 120 man-hours for shaping and 150 man-hours for finishing. How many pairs of each type of ski should the company manufacture each day in order to maximize profit if a pair of downhill skis yields a profit of $10 and a pair of cross-country skis yields a profit of $8? Is it feasible to make 50 downhill and 20 cross-country skis? If so, what is the slack in each constraint?

Solution:

Production variables: Profit Function:

Product-Resource Chart: Constraints:

Feasibility Test: Slack?

13. A company produces two kinds of tents, Standard and Deluxe. Each Standard tent takes 2 hours of cutting and assembly, 2 yards of fabric, and 2 hours of finishing. Each Deluxe tent takes 1 hour of cutting and assembly, 2 yards of fabric, and 3 hours of finishing. This week they have 420 hours of cutting and assembly time, 500 yards of fabric, and 660 hours of finishing time available. The company makes $30 on each Standard tent and $50 on each Deluxe tent. Formulate mathematically the problem of determining how many of each type tent should the company make this week to maximize their profit. Is it feasible to make 100 Standard and 150 Deluxe tents? If so, what is the slack in each constraint?

Solution:

   Production variables: Profit Function:

   Product-Resource Chart: Constraints:

   Feasibility Test: Slack?

14. A bottler uses pineapple, orange, and grapefruit juice to make two juice mixtures, orange-pineapple and orange-grapefruit. The mixtures are sold in quart bottles, and the bottler makes a profit of $0.50 per bottle on orange-pineapple and $0.40 per bottle on orange-grapefruit. Each juice mixture is made by mixing equal amounts of the two juices in its name. Today there are 250 gallons of orange juice, 175 gallons of pineapple juice, and 100 gallons of grapefruit juice available. Formulate mathematically the problem of determining how many *quart bottles* of each juice mixture the bottler should produce today to maximize profit. (1 gallon = 4 quarts)

Solution:

   Production variables: Profit Function:

   Product-Resource Chart: Constraints:

15. Cardinal Candy makes a Rick Pitino mix and a Bobby Petrino mix. A box of the Rick Pitino mix takes 0.4 pounds of chocolate, 0.2 pounds of nuts, and 0.4 pounds of fruit, and sells for $12.95. A box of the Bobby Petrino mix takes 0.2 pounds of chocolate, 0.2 pounds of nuts, and 0.6 pounds of fruit, and sells for $9.95. Chocolate costs $6.00 per pound, nuts cost $4.00 per pound, and fruit costs $3.00 per pound. This week Cardinal Candy has 44 pounds of chocolate, 26 pounds of nuts, and 72 pounds of fruit.

(a) How much profit does Cardinal Candy make on a box of each type of candy mix?

(b) Formulate the problem of finding the number of each type of candy mix Cardinal Candy should make to maximize their profit. (Assume they can sell all they make.)

(c) Is it feasible to make 60 boxes of Rick Pitino and 70 boxes of Bobby Petrino? If so, what is the slack in each constraint?

Solution:

Production variables:

Profit on a box of Rick Pitino:

Profit on a box of Bobby Petrino:

Profit Function:

Product-Resource Chart: Constraints:

Feasibility Test: Slack?

16. A farmer owns a 200-acre farm, and plans to plant oats and/or soybeans on all or part of that land. Oats require 4 pounds of seed per acre, and soybeans require 5 pounds of seed per acre. He can purchase at most 920 pounds of seed. Oats require 3 workdays per acre, and soybeans require 2 workdays per acre. There are a maximum of 570 workdays available. The farmer will make a profit of $150 per acre on oats and $200 per acre on soybeans. Formulate mathematically the problem of determining how many acres of each crop he should plant to maximize his profit. Is it feasible for the farmer to plant 70 acres of oats and 130 acres of soybeans? If so, what is the slack in each constraint?

Solution:

Production variables:

Profit Function:

Product-Resource Chart: Constraints:

Feasibility Test: Slack?

17. A company makes three types of tables. The first type takes 1 hour of assembly, 2 hours of painting, and 1 hour of finishing, and earns a profit of $40. The second type takes 2 hours of assembly, 1 hour of painting, and 3 hours of finishing, and earns a profit of $50. The third type takes 3 hours of assembly, 2 hours of painting, and 1 hour of finishing, and earns a profit of $90. This week there are 500 hours of assembly time, 400 hours of painting time, and 600 hours of finishing time available. Formulate mathematically the problem of determining how many of each type table the company should make this week to maximize profit. Is it feasible for the company to make 100 of each type of table this week? If so, what is the slack in each constraint?

Solution:

   Production variables:

   Profit Function:

   Product-Resource Chart: Constraints:

   Feasibility Test: Slack?

18. A nut company sells three mixes, Regular, Deluxe, and Supreme, with a profit of $4 per pound on Regular and Deluxe mixes and a profit of $6 per pound on Supreme mix. The Regular mix is 50% peanuts, 30% cashews, and 20% hazelnuts. The Deluxe mix is 30% peanuts, 40% cashews, and 30% hazelnuts. The Supreme mix is 20% peanuts, 40% cashews, and 40% hazelnuts. Formulate mathematically the problem of determining how many pounds of each type of mix the company should make from 800 pounds of peanuts, 400 pounds of cashews, and 295 pounds of hazelnuts in order to maximize their profit.

Solution:

   Production variables:

   Profit Function:

   Product-Resource Chart: Constraints:

19. The Filled Jacket Company makes three kinds of jackets, cotton-filled (C), wool-filled (W), and down-filled (D). Each involves 50 minutes of sewing, but it takes 8 minutes to stuff a C, 9 minutes to stuff a W, and 6 minutes to stuff a D. The factory has available 225 pounds of wool and 135 pounds of down each week, as well as all the cotton it needs. Each jacket takes 12 ounces of its type of filling. The factory has 666 and 2/3 hours sewing time available and 80 hours and 4 minutes of stuffing time available per week, and makes $24 on each C jacket, $32 on each W jacket, and $36 on each D jacket. Formulate mathematically the problem of determining how many of each type jacket the company should make from these resources to maximize profit? (Be sure to convert hours to minutes and pounds to ounces.)

20. Louisville Paint mixes custom colors from 3 base pigments (red, yellow, and blue) by adding them to white paint. They have a total of 600 ounces of red, 300 ounces of yellow, and 200 ounces of blue pigment available per week. Each gallon of white paint costs $6.00, and each ounce of pigment costs $1.00. The mixtures are:
   1) Green - sells for $17.00 per gallon, requires 3 oz blue and 4 oz yellow
   2) Purple - sells for $18.00 per gallon, requires 5 oz red and 2 oz blue
   3) Pink - sells for $12.00 per gallon, requires 3 oz red only
   4) Orange - sells for $13.00, requires 4 oz yellow and 1 oz red
   Assume each gallon of a custom color requires a gallon of white and the pigments listed above.
   a) What is the profit per gallon for each of the custom colors?
   b) Formulate mathematically the problem of determining how many gallons of the custom colors they should make each week to maximize profit given the pigment constraints.

Section 3.2 Solving a Linear Programming Problem Graphically

A linear programming problem that has only two production variables can be solved graphically. This process takes a sequence of several steps, but the steps are always the same. The process starts by obtaining a graph of all the feasible points, called the **feasible region**.

The following discussion assumes that the two variables in the problem are named x and y. On some problems you may want to use other names for your variables, such as W and C. In that case one of your variables must be considered the "first" variable and the other the "second" variable for the purposes of graphing. So if W were chosen as your first variable, then it would be plotted along the horizontal axis, and C along the vertical axis, and your points will be of the form (W, C).

Graphing a Linear Inequality

Each constraint that we encounter will be of the form
  $ax + by \le c$, where a, b, and c are constants that may be zero.

This is called a *linear inequality*. Note that the set of solutions of the linear *inequality* includes the solutions to the linear *equation* $ax + by = c$. In a previous mathematics course you should have learned that the graph of a linear equation is always a *straight line* (hence the name "linear" equation). We will graph the line by using the fact that *two points determine a straight line*. The simplest two points to obtain are the points where the line crosses the axes. (Occasionally a line only crosses one of the axes, but more about that later.)

Consider the line $2x + 5y = 10$. The points on the y-axis of a coordinate system are the points for which the first (x-) coordinate is zero. So to obtain the point where our line crosses the y-axis we set x equal to zero in this equation, and solve for y:

  Set $x = 0$; Solve $2(0) + 5y = 10$,   so $5y = 10$,   and $y = 2$.

This means the point $(0, 2)$ is where our line crosses the y-axis. If we set $y = 0$ in our original equation and solve for x, we will find the point where our line crosses the x-axis:

  Set $y = 0$; Solve $2x + 5(0) = 10$,   so $2x = 10$,   and $x = 5$.

This means the point $(5, 0)$ is where our line crosses the x-axis. Now we plot these two points, which are called the **intercepts** of the line. To plot $(0, 2)$ we start at the origin $(0, 0)$ and move 0 units horizontally and 2 units vertically (along the y-axis). To plot $(5, 0)$ we start at the origin $(0, 0)$ and move 5 units horizontally (along the x-axis) and 0 units vertically. Finally we draw the straight line through the two points, as shown in Figure 3.1. The intercepts of the line are usually listed in a table beside the graph.

You should use always use graph paper and choose a scale on each axis that allows for all the intercepts to be plotted. Also, we will concentrate on the part of the graph in the first quadrant, where $x \ge 0$ and $y \ge 0$, because these non-negativity constraints will be present in all our linear programming problems.

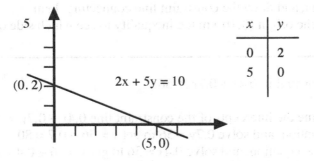

Figure 3.1   Table of intercepts and graph of $2x + 5y = 10$

So what is the graph of an inequality (constraint) like $2x + 5y \leq 10$? Because the "$\leq$" sign includes "=", the graph includes the line we just plotted, which is called the ***constraint line***. Let's try some other points not on the constraint line to test whether they satisfy the inequality:

Point	Substitution in $2x + 5y \leq 10$	True or False?	Relation to line
$(1, 5)$	$2(1) + 5(5) \leq 10$?	False	Above
$(1, 1)$	$2(1) + 5(1) \leq 10$?	True	Below
$(0, 0)$	$2(0) + 5(0) \leq 10$?	True	Below
$(2, 2)$	$2(2) + 5(2) \leq 10$?	False	Above

Notice that all the "True" points lie on one side of the constraint line, and all the "False" points lie on the other. This will always be the case. (You should make up other points, substitute them in the equation, and convince yourself that this is always true.) Our conclusion is:

The graph of a linear *inequality* (<u>constraint</u>) consists of the graph of the associated linear *equality* (<u>constraint line</u>) as well as all the points on one side of the constraint line.

Which side of the constraint line is part of the graph? To find out, proceed as we did above. Choose a test point not on the line (the origin is simplest if it is not on the line), substitute it into the inequality, and decide whether the test point satisfies the inequality. If the test point is "True", the graph includes the side of the line on which the point lies. If the test point is "False", the graph includes the other side of the line. In the case of our example $2x + 5y \leq 10$ above, the origin make the inequality true and it lies below the line. So the graph includes the line and the region below it. We show this by shading the part of the plane below the line, as in Figure 3.2.

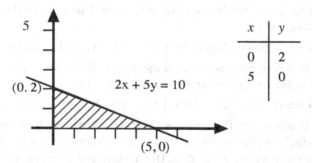

Figure 3.2 Graph of $2x + 5y \leq 10$ in First Quadrant

Steps for graphing a linear inequality in which two variables are present:

1. Determine the two intercepts by setting one variable equal to 0 and solving for the other variable, then setting the other variable to 0 and solving for the first variable.
2. Plot the two intercepts, and draw the constraint line connecting them.
3. Test a point (usually the origin $(0, 0)$) in the inequality to see which side of the constraint line should be included.

<u>Example 3.5</u> Graph the constraint $0.4x + 0.7y \leq 56$.

<u>Solution</u>: <u>Step 1</u>: Determine the intercepts of the constraint line $0.4x + 0.7y = 56$.
   We set $x = 0$ in the equation, and solve $0.7y = 56$ to get $y = 56 \div 0.7 = 80$.
   Then we set $y = 0$ in the equation, and solve $0.4x = 56$ to get $x = 56 \div 0.4 = 140$.
      So the intercepts of the constraint line are $(0, 80)$ and $(140, 0)$.

<u>Step 2:</u> Graph the intercepts and draw the line through them as shown below. (See Figure 3.3.)

<u>Step 3:</u> Test $(0, 0)$ in the inequality to determine which side of the constraint line to include. Substituting $(0, 0)$ into the constraint gives $0 \leq 56$, which is true, so we want to include the side of the constraint line containing the origin. Figure 3.3 shows the shaded region in the first quadrant that is the graph of $0.4x + 0.7y \leq 56$

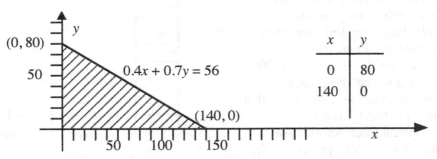

x	y
0	80
140	0

Figure 3.3 Graph of $0.4x + 0.7y \leq 56$ in First Quadrant

Quiz Yourself: 1. Graph the constraints $3x + 2y \leq 18, x \geq 0, y \geq 0$.

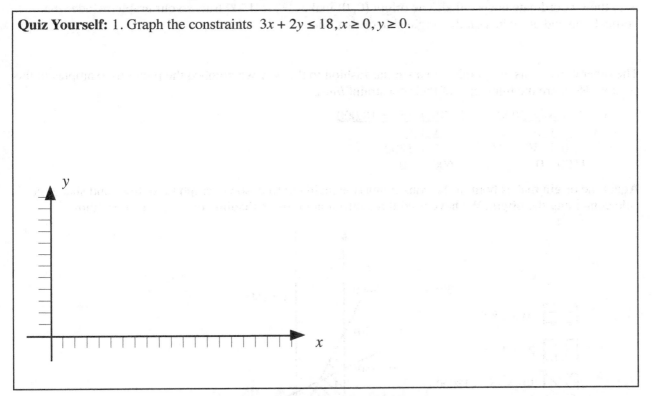

Graphing a Feasible Region

Example 3.6 Recall the mathematical formulation of the Cardinal Furniture Problem (Example 3.1):
Let x and y be the number of chairs and tables to be made, respectively.

Maximize   Profit: $P = \$60x + \$50y$
Given these constraints: (1) $3x \qquad \leq 1500$ yards of fabric
                              (2) $2x + 4y \leq 3000$ board-feet of lumber
                              (3) $30x + 15y \leq 18{,}000$ minutes workers' time
                                   $x \geq 0, y \geq 0$

The **feasible region** is the graph of all the points (x, y) that satisfy **all** the constraints. So the feasible region consists of the points **common** to the graphs of the linear inequalities listed. The nonnegativity constraints imply that our region lies in the first quadrant.

The first constraint, $3x \leq 1500$, is different from the ones we previously graphed, because one of the variables is "missing". This does not mean the variable must be zero; it means that the inequality imposes no constraint on the value of the missing variable. When we graph the associated constraint line $3x = 1500$ by finding its intercepts, we find the x-intercept to be $(500, 0)$. But when we set $x = 0$ in $3x = 1500$ (to find the y-intercept) we get the equation $0 = 1500$, which has no solution. This means that the constraint line $3x = 1500$ has no y-intercept; it is a vertical line! Another way to see this is to realize that $x = 500$ prescribes the first coordinate of all points on the line to be 500,

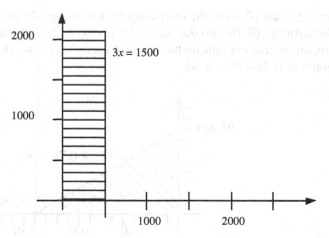

Figure 3.4 Graph of $3x \leq 1500$ in First Quadrant

with the y-coordinate unspecified. The origin $(0, 0)$ makes $3x \leq 1500$ true, so our graph includes the vertical line and all points on the origin side of that line:

The other constraints are graphed in a similar fashion to the way we graphed the previous examples in this section. Here are the intercepts of their constraint *lines*:

(2) $\underline{2x + 4y = 3000}$

x	y
0	750
1500	0

(3) $\underline{30x + 15y = 18,000}$

x	y
0	1200
600	0

Again the origin makes both of the constraints (inequalities) true, so we graph these lines and shade the side containing the origin. We have used three different kinds of shading, one for each constraint.

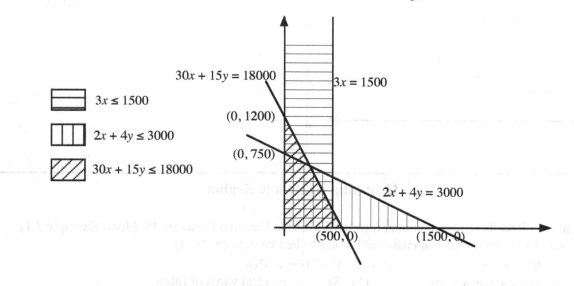

Figure 3.5 Graph of the Three Constraints in the Cardinal Furniture Problem

The feasible region is the region common to the graphs of the three constraints shown in Figure 3.5; that is, the feasible region is the region shaded with all three types of shading. Figure 3.6 below shows just the feasible region itself shaded.

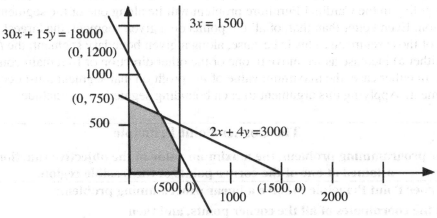

$30x + 15y = 18000$

$(0, 1200)$

$3x = 1500$

$(0, 750)$

$2x + 4y = 3000$

$(500, 0)$ $(1500, 0)$

Figure 3.6 Feasible Region for Cardinal Furniture Problem

Tips for Graphing a Feasible Region

1. Always use a piece of graph paper. (A copy of the graph paper provided at the end of the problems for this section works fine.) It may be hard to visually identify the corner points if the graph is not precise and accurate.
2. Before you begin to graph determine the intercepts of all the constraint lines that must be graphed. Then choose a scale (which <u>must</u> start at zero!) for each axis that allows these intercepts to be graphed comfortably on the axis.
3. Any constraint that has only a y term will have a horizontal constraint line; any constraint that has only an x term will have a vertical constraint line.

Quiz Yourself: 2. Graph the system of constraints $3x + 2y \leq 18$
$$2x + 4y \leq 26$$
$$x \geq 0, y \geq 0.$$

(You graphed the first constraint in Quiz Yourself 1.)

There are usually many feasible points in a feasible region. That is, there are many feasible courses of action with the resources that are available. How can we choose the one that gives the largest profit? Recall our conclusion from Section 3.1 that *the best production policy must use up all of at least one of the resources, otherwise we could just make more of all the products to get more profit*. This says that the best production policy in the Cardinal Furniture problem will lie along one of the segments that bound the feasible region. Even better than that, of all the points on a given segment, the largest profit occurs at one of the ends of those segments. This is because, along a given boundary segment, the *linear* profit function must either a) increase as we move in one or the other direction or b) remain constant along the entire segment. In either case, the maximum value of the profit on that segment must occur at one of the ends of the segment. Applying this argument to each bounding segment, we conclude:

The Corner Point Principle

In a linear programming problem, the maximum value of the objective function is always attained at one of the corner points of the feasible region.

To use the Corner Point Principle to solve a linear programming problem:

    1) **Find the coordinates of all the corner points, and then**
    2) **Use the objective function to pick the best one as our solution.**

Application of the Corner Point Principle to solve the Cardinal Furniture Problem: We now do the two steps above for the Cardinal Furniture Problem. Here again are the constraints for this problem, and the graph of its feasible region:

Constraints:

    (1) $3x \le 1500$

    (2) $2x + 4y \le 3000$

    (3) $30x + 15y \le 18000$

    $x \ge 0, y \ge 0$

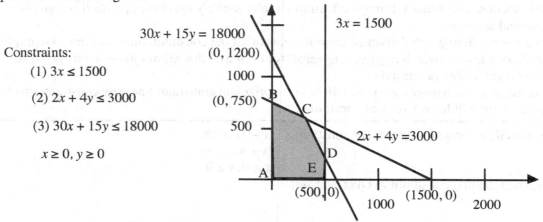

Figure 3.6 Constraints and Feasible Region for Cardinal Furniture Problem

Step 1: Find the coordinates of the corner points. By looking at the feasible region we see it has five corner points, labeled A, B, C, D, and E in Figure 3.6.
    A is the origin (0, 0).
    B and E are intercepts of constraint lines. (We actually found them when we graphed the lines!)
        B is where $2x + 4y = 3000$ crosses the y-axis, so B is (0, 750), and
        E is where $3x = 1500$ crosses the x-axis, so E is (500, 0).
(However, notice that not all intercepts of constraint lines are corner points. For example, (0, 1200) is the y-intercept of $30x + 15y = 18000$, but it is not a corner point because it is not feasible; it does not satisfy $2x + 4y \le 3000$.)

Each of the other two corners C and D is a point where two constraint lines cross.
    D is where line (1): $3x = 1500$
        crosses line (3): $30x + 15y = 18000$.

Application of the Corner Point Principle to solve the Cardinal Furniture Problem (Continued)

The coordinates of D must solve *both* equations. The first equation gives $x = 500$. If we substitute this into the second equation and solve for y, we obtain:

$30(500) + 15y = 18000$, so $15y = 3000$, so $y = 200$.

That means D is (500, 200).

Corner C is the intersection of (2) $2x + 4y = 3000$
and (3) $30x + 15y = 18000$.

This corner is found by solving the equations *simultaneously*. In a previous math course you probably learned how to solve a system of two linear equations in two unknowns, and that is what is needed here. (For a review of these techniques see the Appendix at the end of this section.) The simplest way to do this here is to multiply (both sides of) one of the equations by a number so that the resulting equation has the same x-term or the same y-term as the other equation. (There may be more than one way to do this; any way that eliminates a variable is OK.) For the two equations (2) and (3) above, one way is to multiply both sides of $2x + 4y = 3000$ by 15 so that the x term becomes $30x$, which agrees with the x term in the other equation. This gives:

15 times (2): $30x + 60y = 45000$
(3): $30x + 15y = \underline{18000}$

Now subtract, eliminating x: $45y = 27000$,
so $y = 27000 / 45 = 600$.

Then substitute $y = 600$ back into either of the original equations, for example (2):

$2x + 4(600) = 3000$,
$2x + 2400 = 3000$,
$2x = 600$, $x = 300$.
So C is (300, 600).

[**Note**: *Not all intersections of constraint lines are corner points*. For example, the point where line (1): $3x = 1500$ crosses line (2): $2x + 4y = 3000$ is not a corner point of the feasible region. This is the point (500, 500), and it is on the wrong side of the other line (3): $30x + 15y = 18000$, because $30(500) + 15(500) = 22500 > 18000$.]

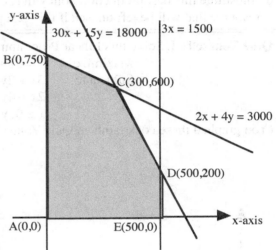

Figure 3.7 Feasible Region of the Cardinal Furniture Problem with Coordinates of Corner Points.

Step 2: Use the objective function to pick the best corner. The corner point that gives the best value of the profit function is the ultimate solution of this linear programming problem. Since the feasible region only has a few corner points, we make a chart showing the corner points and the value of P at each:

Corner Point	Value of $P = 60x + 50y$
A (0, 0)	0
B (0, 750)	$50(750) = 37500$
C (300, 600)	$60(300) + 50(600) = 48000$
D (500, 200)	$60(500) + 50(200) = 40000$
E (500, 0)	$60(500) = 30000$

Corner C(300, 600) yields the largest profit. So **the company should make 300 chairs and 600 tables from the resources it has available. This will yield a profit of $48,000.**

Using Slack to Determine the Unused Resources with the Optimal Solution

By substituting (300, 600) we find that the slack in the first (fabric) constraint of the Cardinal Furniture problem is $1500 - 3(300) = 600$. So there is 600 yards of fabric left unused. When we substitute (300, 600) in each of the other two resource constraints the slack is 0, so there is no lumber and no workers' time left unused if we make 300 chairs and 600 tables.

Solving a Linear Programming Problem by Graphing the Feasible Region
(Assumes the problem has only two production variables x and y)

1. For each constraint find the x- and y-intercepts of the associated constraint line. (If the constraint has no y term, the line is vertical; if it has no x term, the line is horizontal.) Use these values to determine the scales on your axes. Set up the axes with those scales.
2. For each constraint, graph the constraint line by using its intercepts. Then substitute a test point not on the line into the constraint to determine which side of the line is part of the graph. Indicate this side either by shading or by using arrows pointing to the proper side of the line.
3. The feasible region is the region in the first quadrant that is common to the graphs of all the constraints, i. e., that is on the proper side of each line. Shade this region.
4. Visually identify the corner points of the feasible region, and label them A, B, C, ... Find the coordinates of each corner point, using algebra where necessary.
5. Substitute each corner point into the profit function. The corner that produces the best value of the profit function gives the best production policy (x, y).
6. Substitute this best production policy in each resource constraint to determine the amount of each resource that will be left unused if this best production policy is followed.

Quiz Yourself: 3. Solve this Linear Programming Problem:

Maximize $P = 8x + 5y$
Subject to: $3x + 2y \le 18$
$2x + 4y \le 26$
$x \ge 0, y \ge 0.$

(You graphed these constraints in Quiz Yourself 2.)

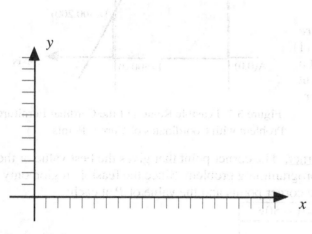

Corner Points:

Choose Best Corner Point:

Reflections on Our Work

Before considering another example, think about what happened as we went through the process of graphing the feasible region and selecting the best corner point. The objective function, $P = 60x + 50y$ in the Cardinal Furniture problem, was not used until the feasible region had been graphed and its corner points located. It was the system of constraints that determined the feasible region itself; the objective function was only used to choose the **best** one of the corner points. This is true in general:

> **In a Linear Programming Problem, the Feasible Region is determined by the system of constraints in the problem. Any problem with the same system of constraints will have the same feasible production policies, regardless of the profit function.**

> **In a Linear Programming Problem, the role of the objective function is to choose the "best" corner point of the feasible region.**

Application of the Corner Point Principle to solve the Cardinal Fruits Problem from Section 3.1

Recall the mathematical formulation of Example 2 in Section 3.1 concerning Cardinal Fruits:

Let x = number of Legend assortments made,
y = number of Supreme assortments made
Maximize $P = \$23.45x + \$19.35y$
Subject to: (1)$4x + 12y \le 9600$ apples
(2)$4x + 4y \le 4000$ grapefruit
(3)$9x + 4y \le 7200$ oranges
(4)$2x \quad\;\; \le 1400$ kiwis
$x \ge 0, \; y \ge 0$

Solution: Since the last constraint is missing its y term, its constraint line will be vertical. The intercepts of the other constraint lines are shown below. Each of these intercepts is found by setting a variable in the equation equal to 0, and solving for the other variable.

$4x + 12y = 9600$		$4x + 4y = 4000$		$9x + 4y = 7200$	
x	y	x	y	x	y
0	800	0	1000	0	1800
2400	0	1000	0	800	0

We have graphed these lines in Figure 3.8. Since the origin makes each constraint true, the feasible region is the region on the origin side of all four constraint lines. This region forms a six-sided polygon, and has six corners (vertices) that are identified by the letters A to F.

Corner A is the origin $(0, 0)$, corner B is the y-intercept of the first constraint, so B is (0, 800), and corner F is the x-intercept of constraint (4), so F is (700, 0). Corner E is where constraint lines (3) and (4) cross. Since the equation for line (4), $2x = 1400$, only has one variable, it is easily solved for that variable:

$2x = 1400$, so $x = 700$.

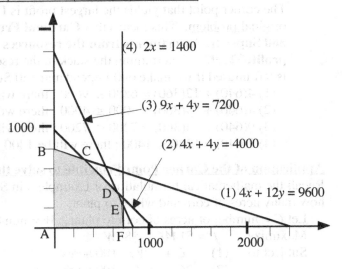

Figure 3.8 Graph of feasible region

Application of the Corner Point Principle to solve the Cardinal Fruits Problem (Continued)

We then substitute that into the equation for (3):

$$9(700) + 4y = 7200$$
$$6300 + 4y = 7200$$
subtract 6300: $4y = 900$
divide by 4: $y = 225$.   So E is (700, 225).

Corner D is where lines (2) and (3) cross, so we solve their equations simultaneously:

(2) $4x + 4y = 4000$
(3) $9x + 4y = 7200$

Subtract the first from the second:	$5x = 3200$
Divide by 5:	$x = 640$
Substitute into (2):	$4(640) + 4y = 4000$
Subtract $4(640) = 2560$:	$4y = 1440$
Divide by 4:	$y = 360$ So D is (640, 360)

Corner C is where lines (1) and (2) cross.

(1) $4x + 12y = 9600$
(2) $4x + 4y = 4000$

Subtracting (2) from (1) gives	$8y = 5600$, or $y = 700$.
Substituting this into (2) gives	$4x + 4(700) = 4000$
Subtract $4(700) = 2800$:	$4x = 1200$
Divide by 4:	$x = 300$. So C is (300, 700).

The chart below shows the value of the profit at each of these corner points.

Corner	Value of $P = \$23.45x + \$19.35y$
A(0, 0)	0
B(0, 800)	$15,480
C(300, 700)	$20,580
D(640, 360)	$21,974
E(700, 225)	$20,768.75
F(700, 0)	$16,415

The corner point that yields the largest profit is D(640, 360). <u>It is important to interpret this in the original problem.</u> This means that **Cardinal Fruits should make 640 Legend Assortments and 360 Supreme Assortments from the resources available. This will yield the maximum possible profit, $21,974.** Determining the slack in the resource constraints will tell us how much of each fruit is left unused if we make 640 Legend and 360 Supreme assortments:

(1) $4(640) + 12(360) = 6880 \le 9600$; there will be $9600 - 6880 = 2720$ apples left unused
(2) $4(640) + 4(360) = 4000 \le 4000$; there will be $4000 - 4000 = 0$ grapefruit left unused
(3) $9(640) + 4(360) = 7200 \le 7200$; there will be $7200 - 7200 = 0$ oranges left unused
(4) $2(640) = 1280 \le 1400$; there will be $1400 - 1280 = 120$ kiwis left unused.

Application of the Corner Point Principle to solve the Crop Allocation Problem from Section 3.1

Recall the mathematical formulation of Example 3 in Section 3.1 of the farmer who was trying to decide how many acres of corn and wheat to plant:

Let C = number of acres of corn to plant, W = number of acres of wheat to plant
Maximize $P = \$144C + \$84W$
Subject to   (1) $C + W \le 100$ acres
          (2) $2C + 4W \le 300$ work-days
          (3) $40C + 24W \le 3,600$ bushels storage
             $C \ge 0, W \ge 0$

<u>Application of the Corner Point Principle to solve the Crop Allocation Problem</u> (Continued)

Solution. Each of the constraint lines associated with these constraints has two intercepts, and each intercept is found by setting a variable equal to zero and solving for the other variable. The intercepts of (1) are clearly $(100, 0)$ and $(0, 100)$. The intercepts of the other constraint lines, and the graph of the feasible region, are shown in Figure 3.9.

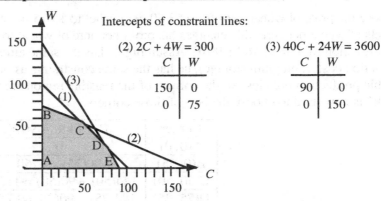

Intercepts of constraint lines:

(2) $2C + 4W = 300$

C	W
150	0
0	75

(3) $40C + 24W = 3600$

C	W
90	0
0	150

Figure 3.9 Feasible Region of Crop Allocation Problem

The region has five corners, which are labeled A, B, C, D, and E in Figure 3.9.

Corner A is the origin $(0, 0)$. Corner B is the W-intercept of line (2), so B is $(0, 75)$. Corner E is the C-intercept of line (3), so E is $(90, 0)$.

Corner C is where lines (1) and (2) meet, so it is the solution of

    (1) $C + W = 100$
    (2) $2C + 4W = 300$

To solve this system by elimination multiply equation (1) by 2, so the C-term becomes $2C$ as in equation (2). This will cause the elimination of C when we subtract:

    (2): $2C + 2W = 200$
100 times (1): <u>$2C + 4W = 300$</u>
Subtract: $-2W = -100$, so $W = -100 / -2 = 50$.

Substituting this back into (1) we get $C + 50 = 100$, so $C = 50$. Thus <u>corner C is $(50, 50)$</u>.

       (You should check that this agrees with the visual location of C in Figure 3.9.)

Corner D is where constraint lines (1) and (3) meet, so we solve

    (1) $C + W = 100$
    (3) $40C + 24W = 3600$

Multiply (1) by 24 and subtract the result from (3):

    (3) $40C + 24W = 3600$
24 times (1): <u>$24C + 24W = 2400$</u>
Subtract: $16C$ $= 1200$, so $C = 1200 \div 16 = 75$

Substitute into (1): $75 + W = 100$, so $W = 25$.   So <u>corner D is $(75, 25)$</u>.

Now that we have graphed the feasible region and located all its corner points we are ready to use the profit function to pick the best corner point as the best solution of the problem.

Corner	$P = 144C + 84W$
A$(0, 0)$	0
B$(0, 75)$	$84(75) = 6300$
C$(50, 50)$	$144(50) + 84(50) = 11{,}400$
D$(75, 25)$	$144(75) + 84(25) = 12{,}900$
E$(90, 0)$	$144(90) = 12{,}960$

According to this chart, **the best production policy is to plant 90 acres of corn and no acres of wheat, leaving the other 10 acres unused (fallow).** This may also be seen from finding the slack in each resource constraint: (1) $90 + 0 = 90 \le 100$; there are $100 - 90 = 10$ acres left unused

          (2) $2(90) + 4(0) = 180 \le 300$; there will be $300 - 180 =$ work-days left unused
          (3) $40(90) + 24(0) = 3{,}600 \le 3{,}600$; there will be 0 bushels storage left unused.

Sensitivity of the Profit Function

Suppose the price of wheat rises from \$3.50 per bushel to \$3.75 per bushel. Since the farmer gets 24 bushels of wheat per acre, this changes his profit per acre of wheat to \$3.75(24) = \$90 and changes the profit function to $P = \$144C + 90W$. Assuming he has the same amount of his resources (land, production costs, and grain storage), he has the same constraints as before, and hence has the same feasible production policies. So the corners of the feasible region are the same as before. But $P = \$144C + 90W$ is now used to choose the best of those corners:

Corner	$P = 144C + 90W$
A(0, 0)	0
B(0, 75)	90(75) = 6750
C(50, 50)	144(50) + 90(50) = 11,700
D(75, 25)	144(75) + 90(25) =13,050
E(90, 0)	144(90) = 12,960

Now it is more profitable to plant 75 acres of corn and 25 acres of wheat with the resources available. The small change in profit on wheat (\$0.25 per bushel) caused a significant change in how the acreage should be planted for maximum profit. When this happens we say that the solution is **sensitive to a small change in the profit function.** Of course, not all small changes will cause such a significant change in policy. For example, if the price of wheat had gone down \$0.25 per bushel instead of up \$0.25 per bushel, the best production policy would not have changed. However, knowing that such changes are possible is an important piece of information for the farmer before he commits his resources to a particular policy.

The Best Production Policy May Not Be Unique

It is possible for more than one feasible production policy to yield the largest profit. If the profit function in the Crop Allocation Problem had been $P = 120C + 72W$ then two corner points give the largest profit:

Corner	$P = 120C + 72W$
A(0, 0)	0
B(0, 75)	72(75) = 5400
C(50, 50)	120(50) + 72(50) = 9600
D(75, 25)	120(75) + 72(25) =10,800
E(90, 0)	120(90) = 10,800

From the chart we see that corner points D and E both yield the same maximum value of this profit function. Those two points lie on constraint line (3): $40C + 24W = 3600$. If we multiply that equation by 3 on both sides we get the equation $120C + 72W = 10,800$. The left hand side of this equation is the same as the profit function! This means that *any* point on constraint line (3) will yield a profit of \$10,800. In particular, any of the

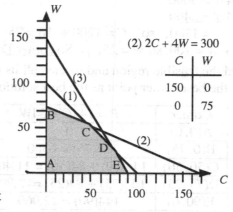

(2) $2C + 4W = 300$

C	W
150	0
0	75

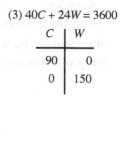

(3) $40C + 24W = 3600$

C	W
90	0
0	150

feasible points along (3) between corners D and E will also give a profit of \$10,800. In general:

Figure 3.9 Feasible Region Crop Allocation Problem

If two corner points of the feasible region both give the maximum value of the profit function, then any point on the segment joining those two points will also give the maximum value of the profit function.

Quiz Yourself: (Answer at the end of this section, before the Problems.)

4. Solve this problem: Let x = Number acres corn A, y = number acres soybeans to be planted

$$\text{Maximize} \quad P = 500x + 300y \text{ dollars}$$

Subject to:
  (1) $2x + y \le 30$ thousand pounds fertilizer
  (2) $3x + 4y \le 72$ hours labor
  (3) $\quad\;\; 2y \le 30$ hundred pounds seed
  $\quad\quad x \ge 0, y \ge 0$ \qquad\qquad Determine coordinates of Corner Points:

Choose best corner point: \qquad\qquad\qquad\qquad Determine slack in each constraint:

<u>Fill in the blanks to give the solution of the problem:</u> Plant _____ acres of corn and _____ acres of soybeans. This will yield the maximum profit of $_____. Doing so will cause there to be _____ pounds fertilizer, _____ hours labor, and _____ pounds seeds left unused.

Appendix: Finding The Intersection Point of Two Lines

The problem of finding the intersection point of two lines becomes the algebra problem of finding the ordered pair that is the simultaneous solution of the linear equations of the lines. In our problems those equations are always written in the form

$ax + by = c$

$dx + ey = f,$ where a, b, c, d, e, and f are constants.

There are two standard techniques for finding this ordered pair (x, y).

Method 1: Substitution

If one of the coefficients a, b, d, or e is zero, i. e. if one of the equation involves only one of the variables x and y, this is usually the easiest method. The method is to solve the equation involving only one variable to obtain the value of that variable, and then substitute that value into the other equation and solve for the value of the other variable. Here is an example:

(1) $5y = 20$ (The graph of this equation is a horizontal line; y is fixed.)

(2) $4x + 6y = 36$

Solution: (i) Solve (1) for y: $y = 4$

(ii) Then substitute this into the other equation: $4x + 6(4) = 36$

$$4x + 24 = 36$$

Subtract 24 from both sides: $4x\quad = 12, \quad$ so $x = 3$

The intersection point of the lines is $(3, 4)$.   (You should check that it solves both equations.)

Method 2: Elimination

If both equations involve both variables, elimination is usually the easiest method. The idea is to multiply one or both of the equations by constant(s) so that the resulting equations either have the x-terms or y-terms with the same coefficient. Then subtract one equation from the other, eliminating one of the variables. The result is then a situation similar to that in Method 1, so proceed as in that method. Here is an example.

(1) $4x + 5y = 48$

(2) $6x + 7y = 70$

Solution: Look for a common multiple of 4 and 6 (or a common multiple of 5 and 7, but that's larger); the simplest is 12. Multiply equation (1) by 3 and equation (2) by 2 so both x-terms become $12x$:

3 times (1): $12x + 15y = 144$

2 times (2): $\underline{12x + 14y = 140}$

Subtract: $y = \quad 4.$

Now substitute this back into one of the equations, say (1)

$$4x + 5(4) = 48$$

$$4x + 20 = 48$$

$$4x = 28, \quad \text{so } x = 7. \text{ The intersection point of the lines is } (7, 4).$$

Answers to Quiz Yourself:
1. Graph the constraints $3x + 2y \le 18$,
$$x \ge 0, y \ge 0.$$
The intercepts of the line $3x + 2y = 18$
are $(6, 0)$ and $(0, 9)$. The graph of $3x + 2y \le 18$, includes
the origin side of the line since $(0, 0)$ makes the inequality
true. The non-negativity constraints $x \ge 0$, $y \ge 0$ mean that
the graph should only include points in the first quadrant
(above the x-axis and to the right of the y-axis). The
solution is shown at right.

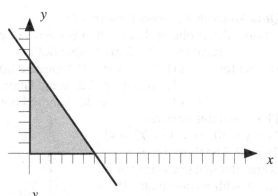

2. Graph the system of constraints $3x + 2y \le 18$
$$2x + 4y \le 26$$
$$x \ge 0, y \ge 0.$$
This system adds another constraint, $2x + 4y \le 26$, to
the graph in 1. above. This new constraint has
intercepts $(13, 0)$ and $(0, 6.5)$. The graph is shown at
right.

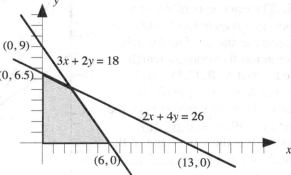

3. Maximize $P = 8x + 5y$
     Subject to: $3x + 2y \le 18$
$$2x + 4y \le 26$$
$$x \ge 0, y \ge 0.$$
The feasible region was graphed in 2. By looking at the graph we see that the corner points are $(0, 6.5)$,
$(6, 0)$ $(0, 0)$ and the point where the two constraint lines intersect. To find the coordinates of this point
solve the system consisting of the equations of the constraint lines:
$$3x + 2y = 18$$
$$2x + 4y = 26$$
To make the y-terms agree multiply the first equation by 2 (and carry down the second equation):
$$6x + 4y = 36$$
$$\underline{2x + 4y = 26}$$
Subtract: $4x \quad = 10$ So $x = 10/4 = 2.5$

Substitute this into either of the original equations (we chose the first) and solve for y:
$$3(2.5) + 2y = 18 \quad \text{so } 7.5 + 2y = 18 \quad \text{so } 2y = 10.5 \quad \text{so } y = 10.5/2 = 5.25$$
The fourth corner point is $(2.5, 5.25)$
[Check: Substitute in each equation: $3(2.5) + 2(5.25) = 7.5 + 10.5 = 18$ OK
$2(2.5) + 4(5.25) = 5 + 21 = 26$ OK]

By the Corner Point Principle one of those 4 points must give the maximum value of P:

Corner	$P = 8x + 5y$
$(0, 0)$	0
$(0, 6.5)$	$5(6.5) = 32.5$
$(6, 0)$	$8(6) = 48$
$(2.5, 5.25)$	$8(2.5) + 5(5.25) = 17 + 31.5 = 46.25$

The maximum value of P on this feasible region is 46.25, and this occurs at the point $(2.5, 5.25)$.

Quiz Yourself Answers (continued)

4. Solve this problem: Let x = number acres of corn, y = number acres of soybeans to be planted

Maximize $P = 500x + 300y$ dollars

Subject to: (1) $2x + y \le 30$ thousand pounds fertilizer

(2) $3x + 4y \le 72$ hours labor

(3) $2y \le 30$ hundred pounds seed $x \ge 0, y \ge 0$

The constraint lines are $2x + y = 30$, $3x + 4y = 72$, and $2y = 30$. The third line is a horizontal line consisting of all points with y-coordinate $30/2 = 15$. The intercepts of the other lines are given at right, and their graphs are shown. The feasible region has five corners which are labeled A, B, C, D, and E.

Corner A is the origin $(0, 0)$.

Corner B is the y-intercept of the line $2y = 30$, so B is $(0, 15)$.

Corner E is the x-intercept of the line $2x + y = 30$, so E is $(15, 0)$.

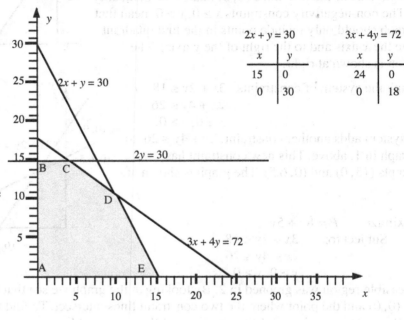

$2x + y = 30$	
x	y
15	0
0	30

$3x + 4y = 72$	
x	y
24	0
0	18

Corner C is the intersection of $2y = 30$ and $3x + 4y = 72$.

From the first equation $y = 15$. Substitute this into the second equation and solve:

$3x + 4(15) = 72$ $3x + 60 = 72$ $3x = 12$ $x = 4$ So corner C is $(4, 15)$.

Corner D is the intersection of two constraint lines:

$2x + y = 30$

$3x + 4y = 72$

To make the y-terms equal multiply the first term by 4 (and carry down the second equation):

$8x + 4y = 120$

$3x + 4y = 72$

Subtract: $5x \quad\quad = 48$ so $x = 48 / 5 = 9.6$

Substitute in the first equation: $2(9.6) + y = 30$ so $19.2 + y = 30$ so $y = 10.8$ Corner D is $(9.6, 10.8)$.

To find the corner at which P attains its maximum, calculate the value of P at each corner point:

Corner	$P = 500x + 300y$
A(0, 0)	0
E(15, 0)	500(15) = 7500
B(0, 15)	300(15) = 4500
C(4, 15)	500(4) + 300(15) = 6500
D(9.6, 10.8)	500(9.6) + 300(10.8) = 8040

The maximum value of P is 8040; it is attained at $x = 9.6$, $y = 10.8$. Since this point is the intersection of the constraint lines for (1) and (2), the slack in those constraints is 0.

The slack in constraint (3) is $30 - 2(10.8) = 8.4$.

Solution of the problem: Plant 9.6 acres of corn and 10.8 acres of soybeans. This will yield the maximum profit of $80,400. Doing so will cause there to be 0 pounds fertilizer, 0 hours labor, and 8.4 hundred pounds = 840 pounds of seeds left unused.

Problems for Section 3.2

Sharpen Your Skills (Answers in back of text.)

In Problems 1 - 4 graph the lines and find their point of intersection.

1. $5x + 2y = 40$
    $3y = 15$

Intercepts:

x	y		x	y

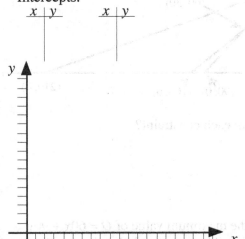

Intersection Point:

2. $6x + 4y = 48$
    $5x \quad\;\; = 30$

Intercepts:

x	y		x	y

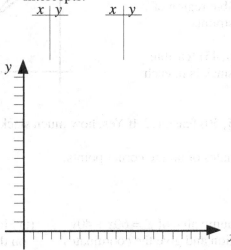

Intersection Point:

3. $3x + 4y = 24$
    $x + 2y = 10$

Intercepts:

x	y		x	y

Intersection Point:

4. $4x + 4y = 40$
    $2x + 6y = 42$

Intercepts:

x	y		x	y

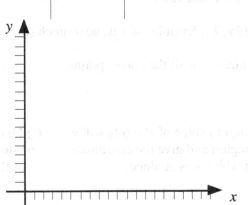

Intersection Point:

5. Sketched below are the graphs of the constraint lines associated with this system of constraints. The coordinates of the intercepts and intersections of the constraint lines are also given.

$$x + 3y \leq 210$$
$$x + \ y \leq \ 90$$
$$3x + 4y \leq 300$$
$$x \geq 0, y \geq 0$$

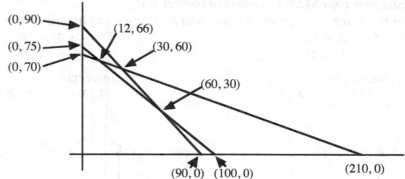

(a) Shade the feasible region of this system of constraints.

(b) Is the point $(40, 45)$ feasible? If Yes, how much slack is in each constraint?

(c) Is the point $(35, 50)$ feasible? If Yes, how much slack is in each constraint?

(d) List the coordinates of all the corner points.

(e) Find the maximum value of $P = 60x + 40y$ on this feasible region and give the coordinates of the point(s) at which it is attained.

(f) Find the maximum value of $Q = 60x + 90y$ on this feasible region and give the coordinates of the point(s) at which it is attained.

6. Sketched below are the graphs of the constraint lines associated with this system of constraints. The coordinates of the intersections of the constraint lines are also given.

$$x + 2y \leq \ 180$$
$$2x + 2y \leq \ 200$$
$$3x + 2y \leq \ 240$$
$$x \geq 0, y \geq 0$$

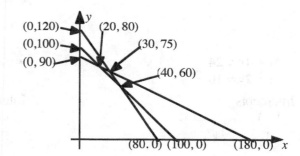

(a) Shade the feasible region of this system of constraints
(b) Is the point $(50, 40)$ feasible? If Yes, how much slack is in each constraint?

(c) Is the point $(35, 70)$ feasible? If Yes, how much slack is in each constraint?

(d) List the coordinates of all the corner points.

(e) Find the maximum value of $P = 60x + 40y$ on this feasible region and give the coordinates of the point(s) at which it is attained.

(f) Find the maximum value of $Q = 60x + 90y$ on this feasible region and give the coordinates of the point(s) at which it is attained.

Communicate the Concepts: (Answers in back of text.)

7. Explain how to graph a linear inequality (constraint).

8. What is the feasible region of a system of inequalities in two variables?

9. State the Corner Point Principle.

10. How is the Corner Point Principle used to solve a linear programming problem with two production variables?

11. If two linear programming problems have the same system of constraints, what can you conclude about the feasible regions of the two problems?

12. What role does the objective function play in the solution of a linear programming problem?

Apply Your Knowledge: (Answers to odd-numbered problems in back of text.)
In Problems 13 through 20 graph the feasible region of the corresponding system of inequalities. Label each line segment bounding the region with the number of the appropriate inequality, and determine the coordinates of every corner point of the feasible region.

13. (1) $3x + 4y \le 36$
     (2) $x + y \le 10$
         $x \ge 0, y \ge 0$

14. (1) $x + 2y \le 14$
     (2) $2x + 3y \le 24$
         $x \ge 0, y \ge 0$

Intercepts

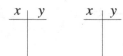

Intercepts

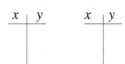

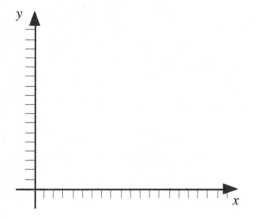

Corner points:

Corner points:

Graph these feasible regions. Label each line segment bounding the region with the number of the appropriate inequality, and determine the coordinates of every corner point of the feasible region.

15. (1) $2x + y \leq 22$
    (2) $x + y \leq 13$
    (3) $2x + 5y \leq 50$
        $x \geq 0, y \geq 0$

16. (1) $2x + y \leq 100$
    (2) $2x + 3y \leq 140$
    (3) $y \leq 40$
        $x \geq 0, y \geq 0$

Intercepts

x	y		x	y		x	y

Intercepts

x	y		x	y		x	y

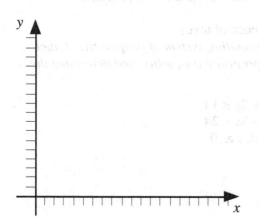

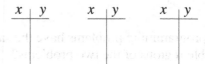

Corner points:

Corner points:

Graph these feasible regions. Label each line segment bounding the region with the number of the appropriate inequality, and determine the coordinates of every corner point of the feasible region.

17. (1) $x + 3y \le 30$
     (2) $3x + 4y \le 48$
     (3) $x + y \le 14$
     (4) $2x \quad \le 20$
        $x \ge 0, y \ge 0$

18. (1) $2x + y \le 30$
    (2) $x + y \le 20$
    (3) $3x + 5y \le 90$
    (4) $2x \quad \le 26$
        $x \ge 0, y \ge 0$

Intercepts

x	y

x	y

x	y

Intercepts

x	y

x	y

x	y

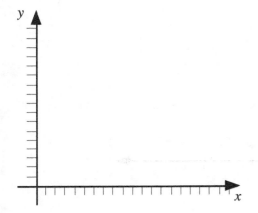

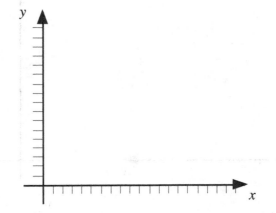

Corner points:

Corner points:

Graph these feasible regions. Label each line segment bounding the region with the number of the appropriate inequality, and determine the coordinates of every corner point of the feasible region.

19. (1) $x + 2y \le 38$
     (2) $2x + y \le 34$
     (3) $5x + 4y \le 100$
        $x \ge 0, y \ge 0$

20. (1) $x + y \le 14$
     (2) $x + 3y \le 30$
     (3) $5x + 3y \le 60$
        $x \ge 0, y \ge 0$

Intercepts

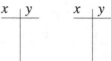

Intercepts

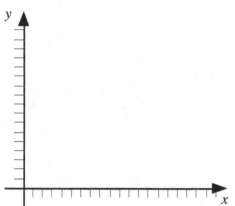

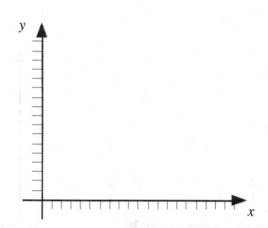

Corner points:

Corner points:

Use the results of Problems 13 - 20 and the Corner Point Principle to solve Problems 21 through 28.

21. Maximize these profit functions subject to the constraints in Problem 13:
    (a) $P = 5x + 6y$ (b) $P = 6x + 4y$

22. Maximize these profit functions subject to the constraints in Problem 14:
    (a) $P = 3x + 4y$ (b) $P = 2x + 5y$

23. Maximize these profit functions subject to the constraints in Problem 15:
    (a) $P = 3x + 4y$ (b) $P = 2x + 7y$

24. Maximize these profit functions subject to the constraints in Problem 16:
    (a) $P = 3x + 4y$ (b) $P = 3x + 5y$

25. Maximize these profit functions subject to the constraints in Problem 17:
    (a) $P = 8x + 11y$ (b) $P = 9x + 4y$

26. Maximize these profit functions subject to the constraints in Problem 18:
    (a) $P = 5x + 6y$ (b) $P = 4x + 7y$

27. Maximize these profit functions subject to the constraints in Problem 19. With one of the profit functions there is more than one corner point at which that profit function's value is as large as possible. Explain why this maximum value is attained at any point on the segment joining the two corner points.
    (a) $P = 8x + 6y$ (b) $P = 10x + 5y$

28. Maximize these profit functions subject to the constraints in Problem 20. With one of the profit functions there is more than one corner point at which that profit function's value is as large as possible. Explain why this maximum value is attained at any point on the segment joining the two corner points.
    (a) $P = 5x + 7y$ (b) $P = 10x + 6y$

In the rest of the Problems for this section, start with the given mathematical formulation of the listed problem from Section 3.1. Graph its feasible region, identify each corner point of the feasible region and find its coordinates, and use the Corner Point Principle to solve the problem. Complete the sentence below.

29. Problem 9 of Section 3.1.

R = # gallons of regular gasoline

P = # gallons of premium gasoline

Maximize $Profit = 0.20R + 0.30P$ Subject to:

(1) $0.75R + 0.5P \leq 60,000$ gallons low-octane

(2) $0.25R + 0.5P \leq 50,000$ gallons high-octane

$R \geq 0, P \geq 0$

Corner Points:

Intercepts

R	P		R	P

P

R

Choose Best Corner Point:

Solution: Make _____ gallons of _____ and _____ gallons of _____

This will earn a profit of _____. There will be _____ gallons of

low-octane and _____ gallons of high octane left unused.

Graph the feasible region, identify each corner point and find its coordinates, and use the Corner Point Principle to solve the problem. Complete the sentences below.

30. Problem 10 of Section 3.1. Let x = number of regular birdhouses

y = number of deluxe bird houses

Maximize $P = \$10x + \$16y$

Subject to: (1) $x \le 8$ regular birdhouses per day

(2) $y \le 6$ deluxe (max) per day

(3) $0.75x + 1y \le 9$ hours per day

$x \ge 0, y \ge 0$

Corner Points:

Intercepts

x	y		x	y

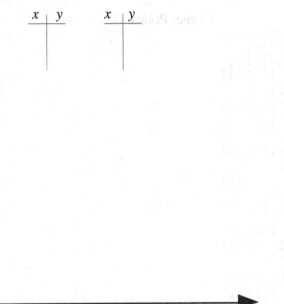

Choose Best Corner Point:

Solution: Make _____ regular birdhouses and _____ deluxe birdhouses.

This will earn a profit of _____.

There will be _____ hours per day left unused.

Graph the feasible region, identify each corner point and find its coordinates, and use the Corner Point Principle to solve the problem. Complete the sentence below.

31. Problem 11 of Section 3.1.

Let x = number of shawls to make, y = number of afghans to make.

Maximize $P = \$25x + \$40y$ Subject to:

(1) $x + 2y \leq 14$ hours spinning

(2) $x + \ y \leq 11$ hours dying

(3) $x + 6y \leq 30$ hours weaving

$\qquad x \geq 0, y \geq 0$

Intercepts:

Corner Points:

Corner Points: Best Corner Point:

Solution: Make _____ shawls and _____ afghans. This will earn a profit of _____.

There will be _____ hours of spinning, _____hours of dying, and

_____ hours of weaving left unused.

Graph the feasible region, identify each corner point and find its coordinates, and use the Corner Point Principle to solve the problem. Complete the sentence below.

32. Problem 12 of Section 3.1. Let x = number of pairs of downhill skis to be made
y = number of pairs of cross-country skis to be made
Maximize: $P = \$10x + \$8y$
Subject to: (1) $2x + 2y \leq 140$ man-hours of cutting time
(2) $x + 2y \leq 120$ man-hours of shaping time
(3) $3x + y \leq 150$ man-hours of finishing time
$x \geq 0, y \geq 0$

Intercepts:

Corner Points:

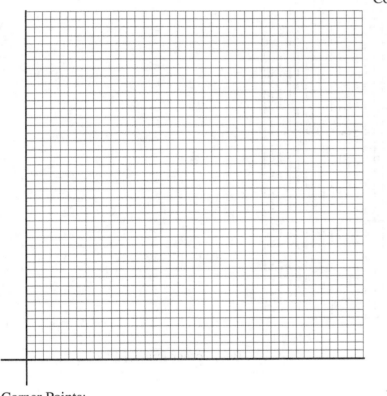

Corner Points:

Best Corner Point:

Solution: Make _____ downhill and _____ cross-country skis to earn a profit of _____.

There will be _____ man-hours of cutting time, _____ man-hours of shaping time, and

_____ man-hours of finishing time left unused.

Graph the feasible region, identify each corner point and find its coordinates, and use the Corner Point Principle to solve the problem. Complete the sentence below.

33. Problem 13 of Section 3.1. Let S = number of Standard tents, D = number of Deluxe tents to be made.

Maximize $P = \$30S + \$50D$

Subject to   (1) $2S + 1D \leq 420$ hours of cutting and assembly time

             (2) $2S + 2D \leq 500$ yards of fabric

             (3) $2S + 3D \leq 660$ hours of finishing time

                      $S \geq 0, D \geq 0$

Intercepts:

Corner Points:

Corner Points:

Best Corner Point:

<u>Solution</u>: Make _____ standard and _____ deluxe tents. This will earn a profit of

_____. There will be _____ hours of cutting and assembly, _____yards

of fabric, and _____hours of finishing time left unused.

Graph the feasible region, identify each corner point of the feasible region and find its coordinates, and use the Corner Point Principle to solve the problem. Complete the sentence below.

34. Problem 14 of Section 3.1.

Let x = # **1 qt** bottles of orange-pineapple, y = # **1 qt** bottles of orange-grapefruit

Maximize Profit P = $0.50x$ + $0.40y$

Subject to:

(1) $0.5x + 0.5y \leq 1000$ quarts orange juice

(2) $0.5x \leq 700$ quarts pineapple juice

(3) $0.5y \leq 400$ quarts grapefruit juice

$x \geq 0, y \geq 0$

Intercepts:

Corner Points:

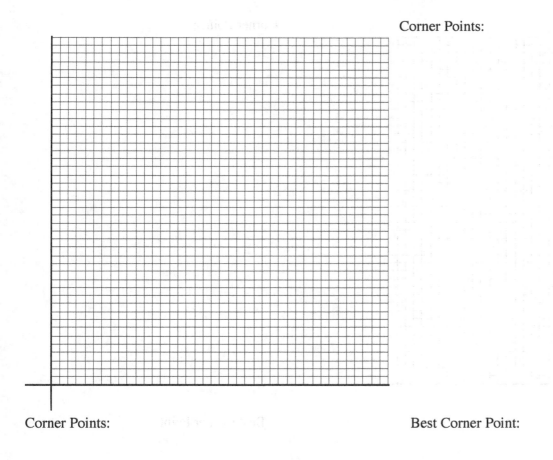

Corner Points:

Best Corner Point:

Solution: Make _____ bottles of orange-pineapple and _____ bottles of orange-grapefruit.

This will earn a profit of _____. There will be _____ quarts of orange juice,

_____quarts of pineapple juice, and _____quarts of grapefruit juice left unused.

Graph the feasible region, identify each corner point of the feasible region and find its coordinates, and use the Corner Point Principle to solve the problem. Complete the sentence below.

35. Problem 15 of Section 3.1.

Let x = # boxes of Rick Pitino mix to make, y = # boxes of Bobby Petrino mix to make.

Maximize $P = \$8.55x + \$6.15y$

subject to   (1) $0.4x + 0.2y \leq 44$ pounds chocolate

(2) $0.2x + 0.2y \leq 26$ pounds nuts

(3) $0.4x + 0.6y \leq 72$ pounds fruit

$x \geq 0, y \geq 0$

Intercepts:

Corner Points:

Corner Points:

Best Corner Point:

<u>Solution</u>: Make _____ boxes of Rick Pitino mix and _____ boxes of Bobby Petrino mix. This

will earn a profit of _____. There will be _____ pounds of chocolate,

_____ pounds of nuts, and _____ pounds of fruit left unused.

Graph the feasible region, identify each corner point of the feasible region and find its coordinates, and use the Corner Point Principle to solve the problem. Complete the sentence below.

36. Problem 16 of Section 3.1.

Let x = number of acres oats to plant, y = number of acres soybeans to plant

Maximize $P = \$150x + \$200y$

Subject to: (1) $x + y \leq 200$ acres of land

(2) $4x + 5y \leq 920$ pounds seed

(3) $3x + 2y \leq 570$ work-days of labor

$x \geq 0, y \geq 0$

Intercepts:

Corner Points:

Corner Points:

Best Corner Point:

<u>Solution:</u> Plant _____ acres of oats and _____ acres of soybeans. This will earn a profit of

_____. There will be _____ acres of land, _____ pounds of seed,

and _____ work-days of labor left unused.

Graph Paper:

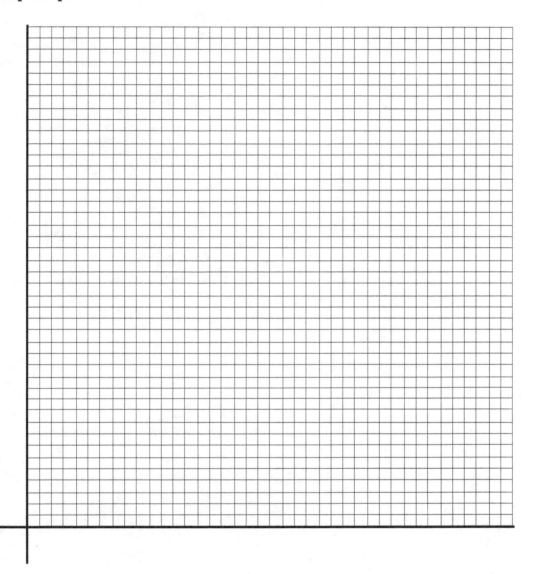

Graph Paper:

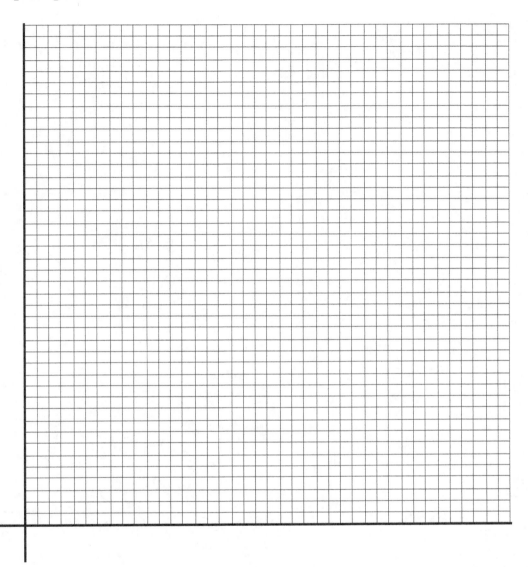

Section 3.3   Linear Programming on a Computer: The Simplex Method
(Optional)

The simplex method is an iterative process for solving a linear programming problem. It works by moving around the feasible region from corner point to corner point until the corner point which yields the largest profit is found. We will discuss just enough of the method to enable you to use a computer program based on the simplex method and to interpret the results of that program in the original problem.

We will deal only with maximization problems in which each problem constraint (other than the minimum constraints $x_i \geq 0$ stating that each variable must be non-negative) can be written in the form

$$a_1x_1 + a_2x_2 + \ldots + a_nx_n \leq b$$

with nonnegative numbers $a_1, a_2, \ldots, a_n$ and b. This means the production variables x_i are multiplied by non-negative numbers, these products are added, and the result is $\leq b$.

As an example, consider the Cardinal Furniture problem discussed in the previous sections:

Let x = the number of chairs made on Monday,
$\qquad y$ = number of tables made on Monday.

Maximize	Profit: $P = \$60x + \$50y$
Given these constraints:	$3x \qquad \leq 1500$ yards of fabric
	$2x + 4y \leq 3000$ board-feet of lumber
	$30x + 15y \leq 18{,}000$ minutes workers' time
	$x \geq 0, y \geq 0$

In Section 3.1 we introduced the idea of the slack in a given resource constraint. We now call this quantity a **slack variable. Thus a slack variable stands for the amount of a resource unused by the current production policy** (x, y). Rather than use different letters for the slack variables, we will use s_i to stand for the slack in the ith constraint. So in the Cardinal Furniture problem above we let

s_1 = the number of yards of fabric unused in our production policy (x, y)

s_2 = the number of board-feet of lumber unused in our production policy (x, y)

s_3 = the number of minutes of workers' time unused in our production policy (x, y)

Each slack variable converts its resource constraint into an equation. In order for our production policy to be feasible, *all the slack variables must be non-negative.*

For example, $3x \leq 1500$ is equivalent to $2x + s_1 = 1500$ with $s_1 \geq 0$.

This allows us to rewrite our system of resource constraints as a system of equations, with **all** the variables, both product variables and slack variables, non-negative:

$$3x \qquad + s_1 \qquad\qquad = 1500$$
$$2x + 4y \qquad + s_2 \qquad = 3000$$
$$30x + 15y \qquad\quad + s_3 = 18{,}000$$
$$s_1 \geq 0, \ s_2 \geq 0, \ s_3 \geq 0, \ x \geq 0, \ y \geq 0$$

To better understand the role of slack variables, the graph of the feasible region is shown at right.

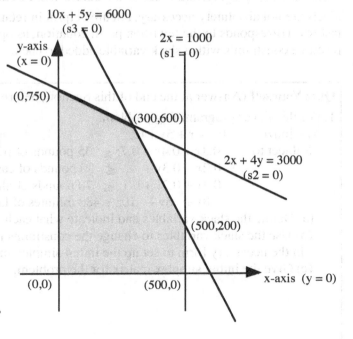

Figure 3.10

Each constraint line that forms part of the boundary of the feasible region in Figure 3.10, such as $2x + 4y = 3000$, is made up of the production policies (x, y) in which all the associated resource that is available is actually used. This means the points on this line are where $s_2 = 0$ where the slack is 0. Also, the coordinate axes are the lines where the production variables x and y are 0. From this we conclude:

In this problem each corner point of the feasible region is determined by setting *two* variables (production or slack) equal zero. (The number of variable set equal to zero is not always 2, as we will see below.) **Once this is done the values of the other variables can be determined.**

To continue preparing for the simplex method, we also rewrite the profit function in the form $-60x - 50y + P = 0$. Appending this to the equations at the bottom of the previous page gives the **initial equations** for the problem (**these equations assume that *all* the variables are nonnegative**):

(1)
$$
\begin{aligned}
3x \quad\;\; + s_1 \qquad\qquad\qquad &= 1500 \\
2x + 4y \qquad + s_2 \qquad\quad\;\; &= 3000 \\
30x + 15y \qquad\qquad + s_3 \quad\; &= 18000. \\
-60x - 50y \qquad\qquad\quad + P &= 0.
\end{aligned}
$$

We will enter the information contained in the initial equations into the computer by entering the **initial simplex matrix** associated with (1):

(2)

x	y	s_1	s_2	s_3	P	
3	0	1	0	0	0	1500
2	4	0	1	0	0	3000
30	15	0	0	1	0	18000
−60	−50	0	0	0	1	0

This initial matrix consists of the coefficients of the variables that appear in the initial equations, as well as the constants to the right of the = sign. **If a variable does not appear in an equation, we enter 0 as its coefficient in that equation.** Each row of the matrix gives the coefficients of an equation. The variables x, y, s_1, s_2, s_3, and P above the matrix will be called <u>labels</u> for the columns of the matrix. These labels are not absolutely necessary, but are helpful in retaining the meaning of the numbers. Note that the last row corresponds to the rewritten profit equation, as opposed to the other rows that came from the resource constraints with a slack variable added to each.

Quiz Yourself (Answer at the end of this Section, before the Problems.)

1. For this linear programming problem:

    Maximize $P = 4x + 5y + 6z$

    Subject to $0.3x + 0.4y + 0.7z \le$ 35 pounds of peanuts

                 $0.2x + 0.3y + \quad\;\; \le$ 80 pounds of cashews

                 $0.3x + 0.2y + 0.1z \le$ 70 pounds of almonds

                   $8x + \;\; 6y + \;\; 10z \le 480$ minutes of labor $x \ge 0, y \ge 0, z \ge 0$

   (a) Define the slack variables and indicate what each represents.

   (b) Use the slack variables to change the constraints into equations, and rewrite the profit function in the necessary form to set up the initial simplex matrix.

   (c) Give the initial simplex matrix for the problem.

Solution of Cardinal Furniture Problem by using Simplex Method Software (continued)
When the Simplex software (http://www.math.louisville.edu/~williams/Simplex.html) is run, you will be asked to enter the number of rows and columns in your initial matrix (4 and 7 in the Cardinal Furniture example; the labels do not count as a row). After you do so a new screen will appear that includes:

Column labels:

Entries:

Type the numerical entries in your initial matrix into the boxes in the array (matrix) labeled Entries. (**Do not enter commas in numbers.**) Use the TAB (or arrow) key to move across the rows and the RETURN (or arrow) key to move down the columns. It is recommended that you also type in the column labels for future reference. When you do this for the Cardinal Furniture problem, you should have the matrix (3) shown next.

Column labels:

(3)   Entries:

x	y	$s1$	$s2$	$s3$	P	
3	0	1	0	0	0	1500
2	4	0	1	0	0	3000
30	15	0	0	1	0	18000
−60	−50	0	0	0	1	0

Make sure the entries in the <u>last row</u> under the product variables, here x and y, are negative.

The simplex method is an iterative method for moving from one corner of the feasible region to another, always increasing the value of P, until the corner that gives the maximum value of P is reached. It starts at the origin ($x = 0$, $y = 0$), where $P = 0$. The computer produces the **final simplex matrix** that contains the values of all the variables, production variables *and* slack variables, that produce the maximum value of P. But to interpret the computer output you must learn about **basic and nonbasic variables**. We will use the final simplex matrix for the Cardinal Furniture problem to illustrate how this is done.

Matrix (4) below is the final simplex matrix from the software for the Cardinal Furniture problem:

(4)

x	y	$s1$	$s2$	$s3$	P	
1	0	0	−0.1667	0.0444	0	300
0	0	1	0.5	−.1333	0	600
0	1	0	0.3333	−.0222	0	600
0	0	0	6.6667	1.5556	1	48000

Each row in this matrix gives the coefficients of an equation using the variables that label the columns. So the matrix corresponds to this system of equations:

(5)

$$
\begin{aligned}
x \quad & - 0.1667s_2 + 0.0444s_3 & = \ 300 \\
s_1 \ + \ & 0.5s_2 - 0.1333s_3 & = \ 600 \\
y \quad & + 0.3333s_2 - 0.0222s_3 & = \ 600 \\
& 6.6667s_2 + 1.5556s_3 \ + P & = 48000.
\end{aligned}
$$

Solution of Cardinal Furniture Problem by using Simplex Method Software (continued)

Equations (5) appear to be messy, and they have more variables that equations, so there isn't just one solution. This is where the idea of basic and nonbasic variables becomes important. **The basic variables associated with a simplex matrix are those variables whose columns have a single "1" and all other entries "0."** For matrix (4) above these are columns 1, 2, 3 and 6; they are labeled by variables x, y, s_1 and P. **All other variables** (here s_2 and s_3) **are called nonbasic variables**. The simplex program will ensure that **there are always as many basic variables as there are rows in the matrix. This means there are as many non-basic variables as there are production variables** (2 in this example).

Once the basic and nonbasic variables have been identified, **set the value of each *nonbasic* variable equal to zero**; in this case we set $s_2 = 0$, $s_3 = 0$. **Substitute these values into the equations (5).** This causes each term that contains one of the basic variables to become 0:

$$
\begin{array}{rrrrrl}
(6) & x & +0 & +0 & & = 300 \\
& s_1 & +0 & +0 & & = 600 \\
& y & +0 & +0 & & = 600 \\
& & +0 & +0 & +P & = 48000.
\end{array}
$$

The resulting equations (6) are very simple, and give us the values of the basic variables:

$$x = 300, \ \ s_1 = 600, \ \ y = 600, \ \text{and } P = 48000.$$

This corresponds to the corner point $(x, y) = (300, 600)$ on the graph of the feasible region where the lines $s_2 = 0$ and $s_3 = 0$ meet.

Interpreting and Checking the Values of the Slack Variables

What does it mean that $s_2 = s_3 = 0$ in the solution? Because s_2 represents the amount of unused board-feet of lumber, and s_3 represents the number of unused minutes of workers' time, the fact that these equal zero means that all of these resources are used up by our optimal solution.

What does it mean that $s_1 = 600$ in the optimal solution? Since s_1 is the slack in the first (fabric) constraints, $s_1 = 600$ means that there will be 600 yards of fabric unused by our optimal production policy.

We can check the values of the slack variables by determining whether the slack in each constraint, found by substituting $x = 300, y = 600$ into the constraint as we did in Section 3.1, agrees with the values of $s_1, s_2,$ and s_3 we determined from the computer output.

(1) Substituting $x = 300, y = 600$ into the fabric constraint $3x \leq 1500$ we obtain $3(300) \leq 1500$. This means that $3(300) = 900$ yards of fabric is actually used out of the 1500 yards available, leaving 600 yards unused, which agrees with the value of the slack variable $s_1 = 600$.

(2) Substituting $x = 300, y = 600$ into the lumber constraint $2x + 4y \leq 3000$ we obtain $2(300) + 4(600) = 3000 \leq 3000$. Thus all of the 3000 board-feet of lumber are used and none are unused, which agrees with the value of the slack variable $s_2 = 0$.

(3) Substituting $x = 300, y = 600$ into the workers' time constraint $10x + 5y \leq 6000$ we obtain $10(300) + 5(600) = 6000$. Thus all of the 6000 minutes of workers' time are used and none are unused, which agrees with the value of the slack variable $s_3 = 0$.

Quiz Yourself (Answer at the end of this Section, before the Problems.)
2. For the simplex matrix below, identify the basic and nonbasic variables, set the nonbasic variables equal to zero, and give the values of all the variables (basic and nonbasic). (Answer at end of this section.)

x	y	$s1$	$s2$	$s3$	P	
1	0	0.5	0	0	0	500
0	0	3	1	−0.8	0	1200
0	1	−1	0	0.2	0	200
0	0	2	0	1	1	4000

Problems with More Than Two Products

If the word problem involves three products then three dimensions are needed to graph the feasible region. In three dimensions the graph of an equation like $x = 0$ or $s_2 = 0$ is a *plane*. Thus the feasible region is a solid bounded by planes. A corner point is where three of these planes come together. In 3 (and even higher) dimensions the method of using basic and nonbasic variables in the final simplex matrix still enables you to find the values of all the variables at the best solution point.

Solution to Problem 17 from Section 3.1: A company makes three types of tables. The first type takes 1 hour of assembly, 2 hours of painting, and 1 hour of finishing, and earns a profit of $40. The second type takes 2 hours of assembly, 1 hour of painting, and 3 hours of finishing, and earns a profit of $50. The third type takes 3 hours of assembly, 2 hours of painting, and 1 hour of finishing, and earns a profit of $90. This week there are 500 hours of assembly time, 400 hours of painting time, and 600 hours of finishing time available. How many of each type table should the company make this week to maximize profit?

Solution: Let $x = $ Number of first type of table to be made
  $y = $ Number of second type of table to be made
  $z = $ Number of third type of table to be made
Then the constraints are: $1x + 2y + 3z \le 500$ hours Assembly
  $2x + 1y + 2z \le 400$ hours Painting
  $1x + 3y + 1z \le 600$ hours Finishing
  $x \ge 0, y \ge 0, z \ge 0.$
The profit function is $P = 40x + 50y + 90z$ dollars

We introduce slack variables, one for each of the three constraints. Let
  $s_1 = $ number of Assembly hours unused $s_2 = $ number of Painting hours unused
  $s_3 = $ number of Finishing hours unused
These allow us to convert the constraints into equalities. We also rewrite the profit function to prepare for the initial simplex matrix:

$$1x + 2y + 3z + s_1 \qquad\qquad = 500$$
$$2x + 1y + 2z + \qquad s_2 \qquad = 400$$
$$1x + 3y + 1z + \qquad\qquad s_3 = 600$$
$$-40x \quad -50y \quad -90z \qquad\qquad + P = 0$$

The initial simplex matrix to be entered into the computer is:

x	y	z	$s1$	$s2$	$s3$	P	
1	2	3	1	0	0	0	500
2	1	2	0	1	0	0	400
1	3	1	0	0	1	0	600
-40	-50	-90	0	0	0	1	0

Solution to Problem 17 from Section 3.1: (Continued)

When we press the **Final** button we obtain:

x	y	z	s1	s2	s3	P	
0	0.75	1	0.5	-0.25	0	0	150
1	-0.25	0	-0.50	0.75	0	0	50
0	2.5	0	0	-0.5	1	0	400
0	7.5	0	25	7.5	0	1	15500

We read off the solution associated with this final matrix:

The basic variables are x, z, s_3, and P. The non-basic variables are thus y, s_1, and s_2.

Set the non-basic variables equal to zero and solve for the basic variables:

$y = 0, s_1 = 0, s_2 = 0.$ $x = 50, z = 150, s_3 = 400, \ P = 15500.$

Now interpret this in the original problem. The company should make 50 of the first table, none of the second table, and 150 of the third table. There will be no hours of assembly or painting (resources 1 and 2) unused, but 400 hours of finishing (resource 3) will be unused. This production policy will result in a profit of $15,500.

Quiz Yourself (Answer at the end of this Section, before the Problems.)

3. A bottler makes three types of drinks, Amazing, Blast, and Cool, by mixing orange juice, pineapple juice, strawberry juice, and water. The company analyst lets A, B, and C be the number of quart bottles of Amazing, Blast, and Cool, respectively, that the company should make. She uses the recipes for the three types of drinks, and profit on a quart of each type drink, to obtain a mathematical formulation of this problem:

Maximize $P = \$2.00A + \$2.50B + \$3.00C$

Subject to: $0.4A + 0.6B + 0.5C \leq 3000$ quarts of orange juice available

$0.3A + 0.2B + 0.3C \leq 1200$ quarts of pineapple juice available

$0.3A + 0.2B + 0.2C \leq 1000$ quarts of strawberry juice available

$A \geq 0, B \geq 0, C \geq 0$

To determine the initial matrix the analyst lets s1 = # quarts of unused orange juice, s2 = # quarts of unused pineapple juice, and s3 = # quarts of unused strawberry juice. Applying our simplex method computer program to the initial simplex matrix, the analyst obtains the following **final simplex matrix**:

A	B	C	s1	s2	s3	P	
-0.5	0	0	1	1	-4	0	200
0	0	1	0	10	-10	0	2,000
1.5	1	0	0	-10	15	0	3,000
1.75	0	0	0	5	7.5	1	13500

Help the analyst determine the best production policy for the company by answering:

(a) What are the basic variables for this matrix?   (b) What are the non-basic variables for this matrix?

(c) What are the values of all seven of the variables in the final solution to the problem?

(d) How many quart bottles of each type drink should the company make to maximize their profit? What will that maximum profit be?

(e) How many quarts of orange juice, pineapple juice, and strawberry juice will be left over if they implement the production policy in (d)?

Summary of Steps for Using the Simplex Method Software
to Solve a Linear Programming Problem

After obtaining the mathematical formulation of the problem (as in Section 3.1):

1. Form the *initial* simplex matrix:
   (a) Add a (different) *slack* variable to each resource constraint, thereby converting the constraint into an equation. **Each slack variable measures the amount of its resource unused by the current production policy**.
   (b) Rewrite the profit function in the form $-ax - by \ldots\ldots + P = 0$
   (c) Extract the matrix of coefficients and constants from the equations formed in (a) and (b).

2. Enter the initial simplex matrix into the computer, and obtain the final simplex matrix.

3. Determine the values of *all* the variables at the corner point identified by the final matrix:
   (a) Identify the basic and nonbasic variables of the matrix. A *basic variable of a simplex matrix* is a **variable whose column has entries consisting of a single one and the rest zeros.** (There should be as many basic variables as there are rows of the matrix.) All other variables are *nonbasic*. (There should be as many nonbasic variables as there are production variables.)
   (b) Set the value of each nonbasic variable to 0. Inserting these values in the equations associated with the matrix effectively wipes out the columns containing the non-basic variables, leaving only the columns of the basic variables (and the last column). You should now be able to immediately read off the values of the other (basic) variables at the corner point. This process gives the values of *all* the variables, production and slack, at the corner point.

4. For the *final* simplex matrix, the values of the production variables found in step 3. give the best production policy, as measured by the profit function, for the original word problem, and the values of the slack variables give the amounts of unused resources associated with that policy. **All the values found in 3. (b) should be interpreted in the context of the original problem.**

Answers to Quiz Yourself:

1. Let $s1$ = number of pounds of peanuts unused, $s2$ = number of pounds of cashews unused,
    $s3$ = number of pounds of almonds unused, $s4$ = number of minutes of labor unused.
Using these in the constraints, and rewriting the profit function:

$$0.3x + 0.4y + 0.7z + s1 \qquad\qquad\qquad = 35 \text{ pounds of peanuts}$$
$$0.2x + 0.3y \qquad\quad + s2 \qquad\qquad\quad = 80 \text{ pounds of cashews}$$
$$0.3x + 0.2y + 0.1z \qquad\quad +s3 \qquad\qquad = 70 \text{ pounds of almonds}$$
$$8x + 6y + 10z \qquad\qquad\qquad + s4 \qquad = 480 \text{ minutes of labor}$$
$$-4x - 5y - 6z \qquad\qquad\qquad\qquad +P \quad = 0$$

The initial simplex matrix is:

x	y	z	$s1$	$s2$	$s3$	$s4$	P	
0.3	0.4	0.7	1	0	0	0	0	35
0.2	0.3	0	0	1	0	0	0	80
0.3	0.2	0.1	0	0	1	0	0	70
8	6	10	0	0	0	1	0	480
-4	-5	-6	0	0	0	0	1	0

2. The basic variables are $x, y, s2$, and P, The nonbasic variables are $s1$ and $s3$.
    Set $s1 = 0$ and $s3 = 0$. The resulting equations are:

$$x \qquad\qquad = 500$$
$$s2 \qquad = 1200$$
$$y \qquad\quad = 200$$
$$P \qquad = 4000$$

3. (a) Basic variables (whose columns contain a single 1 and the rest 0s): $B, C, s1$
   (b) Nonbasic variables: $A, s2, s3$.
   (c) Values of variables: Set nonbasic $= 0$: $A = 0, s2 = 0,$ $s3 = 0$. This gives these equations which give
       the values of the basic variables:

$$s1 \qquad\qquad = 200$$
$$C \qquad\qquad\quad = 2000$$
$$B \qquad\qquad\qquad = 3000$$
$$P \quad = 13500$$

   (d) from (c) and the meanings of the variables, the company should make 0 quarts of Amazing, 3000
       quarts of Blast, and 2000 quarts of Cool, for a profit of $13,500.
   (e) From the meanings of the slack variables there will be $s1 = 200$ quarts of orange juice (in first
       constraint) left over, $s2 = 0$ quarts of pineapple juice (in second constraint) left over, and $s3 = 0$ quarts
       of strawberry juice (in third constraint) left over.

Problems for Section 3.3

Sharpen Your Skills: (Answers in back of text.)

In Problems 1 and 2:

 (a) Define the slack variables and indicate what each represents.

 (b) Use the slack variables to change the constraints into equations, and rewrite the profit function in the necessary form to set up the initial simplex matrix:

 (c) Give the initial simplex matrix for the problem.

1. Maximize $P = 4x + 3y + 2z$

   Subject to $3x + 2y + 5z \leq 23$ pounds of cashews

   $2x + y + z \leq 80$ pounds of almonds

   $x + y + 2z \leq 70$ pounds of peanuts

   $5x + 2y + 8z \leq 250$ minutes of labor

   $x \geq 0, y \geq 0, z \geq 0$

2. Maximize $P = x + 2y + 3z + 4w$

   Subject to $2x + y + 2z + 2w \leq 300$ yards of fabric

   $x + y + 3w \leq 200$ board-feet of lumber

   $3x + 4y + 5z + 4w \leq 600$ pounds of padding

   $x \geq 0, y \geq 0, z \geq 0, w \geq 0$

Sharpen Your Skills: (Answers in back of text.)

In Problems 3 and 4 below the matrix shown is the final simplex matrix obtained from applying the Simplex Method to a linear programming problem. In each answer these questions:

 (a) What are the basic variables and the nonbasic variables for this matrix?

 (b) What are the values of all the variables (basic and nonbasic) in the solution to the problem?

3.

x	y	z	$s1$	$s2$	$s3$	P	
0	1	−2	−1	2	0	0	20
0	0	5	0	-1	1	0	30
1	0	1	1	1	0	0	15
0	0	2	3	4	0	1	820

4.

x	y	z	$s1$	$s2$	$s3$	$s4$	P	
5	0	0	−1	0	1	6	0	180
6	1	0	0	0	0	2	0	210
0.8	0	0	1	1	0	1.5	0	240
1	0	1	2	0	0	8	0	300
2	0	0	1	0	0	1,4	1	15250

5. The Happy Fruit Company makes three types of fruit mixtures labeled X, Y, and Z, from peaches, pears, and cherries. The company analyst lets x, y, and z be the number of cans of mixtures X, Y, and Z, respectively, that the company should make. She formulates the problem as:

$$3x + 2y \quad\quad \leq 30{,}000 \text{ pounds of peaches}$$
$$3x + 2y + 3z \leq 33{,}000 \text{ pounds of pears}$$
$$2y + 3z \leq 27{,}000 \text{ pounds of cherries}$$
$$x \geq 0, y \geq 0, z \geq 0$$
$$P = 2x + 4y + 3z \text{ dollars}$$

After formulating the initial matrix and applying our simplex method computer program to it, she obtains the following final simplex matrix:

x	y	z	$s1$	$s2$	$s3$	P	
1	0	−1	.33	0	−0.33	0	1000
0	0	3	−1	1	0	0	3000
0	1	1.5	0	0	0.5	0	13500
0	0	1	.67	0	1.33	1	56000

(a) What are the basic variables for this matrix?   (b) What are the nonbasic variables?

(c) What are the values of all the variables in the solution to this problem?

(d) How many cans of each kind of mixture should the company make to have the maximum profit?

(e) What will this maximum profit be?

(f) How many pounds of peaches, pears, and cherries will be unused if they do this?

6. Joyous Gifts sells three types of gift boxes, A, B, and C. Each is made up of a mixture of apples, candy bars, and flowers. The company wants to maximize its profit on the gift boxes it sells subject to the availability of the items in the boxes. Using the variables A, B, and C for the number of each type box to make, the company analyst determines that the resource constraints are:

$$3A + 4B + 2C \leq 350 \text{ apples}$$
$$2A + 1B + 3C \leq 200 \text{ candy bars}$$
$$1A + 0.5B + 1.5C \leq 150 \text{ dozen flowers.}$$

and the profit function is $P = 3A + 2B + 3.5C$ dollars.

After setting up the initial simplex matrix and applying our computer software to it, he obtains the following final simplex matrix:

A	B	C	$s1$	$s2$	$s3$	P	
0	1	−1	−0.6	0.4	0	0	20
1	0	2	0.8	−0.2	0	0	90
0	0	0	−0.5	0	1	0	50
0	0	0.5	1.2	0.2	0	1	310

(a) What are the basic variables for this matrix?   (b) What are the nonbasic variables?

(c) What are the values of all the variables in the solution to this problem?

(d) How many of each type of gift box should the company make to have the maximum profit?

(e) What will this maximum profit be?

(f) How much of each resource (apples, candy bars, and flowers) will be unused if they do this?

7. A nut company sells three mixes, *regular*, *deluxe*, and *supreme* out of peanuts, cashews, and hazelnuts. The company analyst decides to let R, D, and S, respectively, be the number of pounds of each type of mix that the company will make today. Using the formulas for each type of mix and the company's profit structure, the company analyst formulates this problem as:

Maximize $P = \$4.00R + 4.00D + 6.00S$

Subject to: $0.5R + 0.3D + 0.2S \le 800$ pounds of peanuts

$0.3R + 0.4D + 0.4S \le 400$ pounds of cashews

$0.2R + 0.3D + 0.4S \le 295$ pounds of hazelnuts. $R \ge 0, D \ge 0, S \ge 0$

After determining the initial matrix and applying our simplex method computer program to it, the analyst obtains the following final simplex matrix:

R	D	S	s1	s2	s3	P	
0	-0.25	0	1	-4	3.5	0	232.5
1	1	0	0	10	-10	0	1050
0	0.25	1	0	-5	7.5	0	212.5
0	1.5	0	0	10	5	1	5475

(a) What are the basic variables for this matrix? (b) What are the nonbasic variables?

(c) What are the values of all the variables in the solution to this problem?

(d) How much of each type of mix should the company make to maximize their profit?

(e) What will that maximum profit be?

(f) How many pounds of peanuts, cashews, and hazelnuts will be unused if they implement this production policy?

8. A fertilizer company makes *lawn*, *garden*, and *general purpose* fertilizer out of phosphate, nitrate, and potash. The company analyst decides to let x, y, and z respectively, be the number of 100 pound sacks of lawn, garden, and general purpose fertilizer, respectively, that the company will make. The analyst formulates this problem as: Maximize $P = \$16.00x + 9.00y + 3.00z$

Subject to: $8x + 8y + 4z \le 8,000$ pounds of phosphate

$20x + 4y + 4z \le 9,000$ pounds of nitrate

$8x + 4y + 2z \le 5,000$ pounds of potash. $x \ge 0, y \ge 0, z \ge 0$

After determining the initial matrix and applying our simplex method computer program to it, the analyst obtains the following final simplex matrix:

x	y	z	s1	s2	s3	P	
0	0	2	1.5	1	-4	0	1000
1	0	0	-0.12	0	0.25	0	250
0	1	0.5	0.25	0	-0.25	0	750
0	0	1.5	0.25	0	1.75	1	10750

(a) What are the basic variables for this matrix?   (b) What are the nonbasic variables?

(c) What are the values of all the variables in the solution to this problem?

(d) How much of each type of fertilizer should the company make to maximize their profit?

(e) What will that maximum profit be?

(f) How many pounds of phosphate, nitrate, and potash will be unused with this production policy?

Communicate Your Knowledge: (Answers in back of text.)
9. Explain what a slack variable is.

10. Explain how to use slack variables to convert a system of constraints into a system of equations.

11. Explain how to rewrite the profit function in preparation for creating an initial simplex matrix.

12. Explain the meaning of a basic variable for a simplex matrix.

13. Explain how to use basic variables to obtain the optimal solution to a linear programming problem from the final simplex matrix for the problem.

14. What is the meaning of the values of the slack variables in the optimal solution to a linear programming problem?

***Apply Your* Knowledge** (Answers to odd-numbered problems in the back of text.)
In *Problems 15 - 24, start from the mathematical formulations obtained in Section 3.1. Then:*
  (i) Introduce slack variables and rewrite the profit function to obtain the initial simplex matrix.
  (ii)Enter the initial matrix into the Simplex Method software over the internet at this web page:
        http://www.math.louisville.edu/~williams/Simplex.html
  (iii) Determine the basic and nonbasic variables in the final matrix obtain in Step (ii), and use them to give the best production policy and the amount of each resource unused if that production policy is followed.
  (iv) If the problem was solved graphically in Section 3.2, compare that solution to the one obtained by the computer software.

15. Problem 11 from Section 3.1. (This was solved graphically in 3.2 #31.)
            Let x = number of shawls to make,
      y = number of afghans to make.
    Maximize $P = \$25\,x + \$40y$ Subject to:
    (1) $x + 2y \leq 14$ hours spinning
    (2) $x + \ y \leq 11$ hours dying
    (3) $x + 6y \leq 30$ hours weaving
          $x \geq 0, y \geq 0$

16. Problem 12 from Section 3.1. (This was solved graphically in 3.2 #32)
Let x = number of pairs of downhill skis to be made
    y = number of pairs of cross-country skis to be made
    Maximize: $P = \$10x + \$8y$
    Subject to: (1) $2x + 2y \leq 140$ man-hours of cutting time
                (2) $x + 2y \leq 120$ man-hours of shaping time
                (3) $3x + \ y \leq 150$ man-hours of finishing time
                    $x \geq 0, y \geq 0$

17. Problem 13 from Section 3.1. (This was solved graphically in 3.2 #33)
   Let S = number of Standard tents,
   D = number of Deluxe tents to be made.
   Maximize $P = \$30S + \$50D$
   Subject to   (1) $2S + 1D \leq 420$ hours of cutting and assembly time
                   (2) $2S + 2D \leq 500$ yards of fabric
                   (3) $2S + 3D \leq 660$ hours of finishing time
                               $S \geq 0, D \geq 0$

18. Problem 14 from Section 3.1. (This was solved graphically in 3.2 #34.)
   Let x = number of **1** qt bottles of orange-pineapple,
       y = number of **1** qt bottles of orange-grapefruit.
   Maximize Profit $P = \$0.50x + \$0.40y$
   Subject to: (1) $0.5x + 0.5y \leq 1000$ quarts orange juice
                (2) $0.5x \qquad\quad \leq 700$ quarts pineapple juice
                (3) $\qquad\quad 0.5y \leq 400$ quarts grapefruit juice
                        $x \geq 0, y \geq 0$

19. Problem 15 from Section 3.1 (This was solved graphically in 3.2 #35)
   Let x = # boxes of Rick Pitino mix to make, y = # boxes of Bobby Petrino mix to make.
   Maximize $P = \$8.55x + \$6.15y$
   subject to   (1) $0.4x + 0.2y \leq 44$ pounds chocolate
                  (2) $0.2x + 0.2y \leq 26$ pounds nuts
                  (3) $0.4x + 0.6y \leq 72$ pounds fruit
       $x \geq 0, y \geq 0$

20. Cardinal Candy in the previous problem is considering offering a Charlie Strong box of mix. It will contain 0.35 pounds of chocolate, 0.15 pounds of nuts, and 0.5 pounds of fruit, and will earn a profit of $7.30 on each box. How many boxes of each of the 3 types of mix should Cardinal Candy make to maximize their profit?
   The problem is now: Let x = # boxes of Rick Pitino mix to make,
       y = # boxes of Bobby Petrino mix to make
       z = # boxes of Charlie Strong mix to make.
   Maximize $P = \$8.55x + \$6.15y + \$7.30z$
       subject to   (1) $0.4x + 0.2y + 0.35z \leq 44$ pounds chocolate
                     (2) $0.2x + 0.2y + 0.15z \leq 26$ pounds nuts
                     (3) $0.4x + 0.6y + 0.50z \leq 72$ pounds fruit
                         $x \geq 0, y \geq 0, z \geq 0$
   Solve this problem. Will Cardinal Candy make a greater profit if they offer the Charlie Strong mix?

21. Solve Example 4 (Arts and Craft Shop) from Section 3.1:

Let x = number of arrangements to make,

y = number of baskets to make

z = number of centerpieces to make.

Maximize $P = \$10x + \$25y + \$35z$

subject to:

$2x + \ 6y + 10z \le \ \ 4{,}800$ minutes of Joan's time

$6x + 10y + \ \ 8z \le 12{,}000$ minutes of Beth's time

$4x + \ \ 8y + 16z \le 12{,}000$ minutes of Carol's time

$x \ge 0, y \ge 0, z \ge 0$

22. Problem 18 from Section 3.1:

Let R = number of pounds of Regular mix,

D = number of pounds of Deluxe mix,

S = number of pounds of Supreme mix

Maximize Profit = $\$4R + \$4D + \$6S$

subject to:

$0.5R + 0.3D + 0.2S \le 800$ pounds peanuts

$0.3R + 0.4D + 0.4S \le 400$ pounds cashews

$0.2R + 0.3D + 0.4S \le 295$ pounds hazelnuts

$R \ge 0, D \ge 0, S \ge 0$

23. Problem 19 from Section 3.1.

Let C = number of cotton-filled jackets to make,

W = number of wool-filled jackets to make,

D = number of down-filled jackets to make.

Maximize $P = \$24C + \$32W + \$36D$

Subject to: $50C + 50W + 50D \le 40000$ minutes of sewing time

$8C + \ \ 9W + \ \ 6D \le 4804$ minutes of stuffing time

$12W \qquad\ \ \ \ \le 3600$ ounces of wool

$12D \le 2160$ ounces of down.

$C \ge 0, \ W \ge 0, \ D \ge 0$

24. Problem 16 from Section 3.1. (This was solved graphically in 3.2 #36)

Let x = number of acres of oats to plant,

y = number of acres of soybeans to plant

Maximize $P = \$150x + \$200y$

(1) $x + \ \ y \le \ 200$ acres of land

(2) $4x + 5y \le \ 920$ pounds seed

(3) $3x + 2y \le \ 570$ work-days of labor

$x \ge 0, y \ge 0$

25. The Kentucky Brewery makes four products called light, dark, ale, and premium. These products are made using water, malt, hops and yeast. The brewery has a free supply of water, but the availability of the other resources restricts the production. The table below gives the lbs (pounds) of each available resource needed to produce one barrel of each product, the pounds of each resource available each week, and the profit received from each barrel of each product.

	light	dark	ale	premium	Available per week
Malt per barrel	1 lb	1 lb	0 lb	3 lb	50 lb.
Hops per barrel	2 lb	1 lb	2 lb	1 lb	150 lb.
Yeast per barrel	1 lb	1 lb	1 lb	4 lb	80 lb.
Profit per barrel	$6	$5	$3	$7	

(a) How many barrels of each of the four products should they make each week to obtain the maximum profit? If the company pursues this production policy, what will their profit be?

(b) How much of each of its resources will be unused if the company pursues this production policy?

(c) Suppose there were only 100 pounds of hops available. How will the production policy change?

(d) By running the software with various profits on the premium (and using the mixture chart of resources above), determine how large must the profit on premium be so that the best production policy includes making at least one barrel of premium.

26. A fruit company makes 3 assortments of fruit, A, B, and C. Assortment A contains 4 apples, 4 grapefruit, and 12 oranges, and sells for $9.40. Assortment B contains 12 apples, 4 grapefruit, and 4 oranges, and sells for $7.40. Assortment C contains 8 apples, 8 grapefruit, and 8 oranges, and sells for $11.00. Each apple costs the company $0.20, each grapefruit costs it $0.25, and each orange costs it $0.30. The company has available 4800 apples, 4000 grapefruit, and 5600 oranges.

(a) How much profit (By definition, profit = selling price - total cost of ingredients) does the company make on each type of assortment?

(b) How many of each assortment should the company make in order to maximize its profit? What will that profit be? How many apples, grapefruit, and oranges will be unused by this production policy?

(c) Suppose the number of grapefruit available is increased to 5000 and all other data remains the same. Describe how your answer to (b) changes.

27. A Girl Scout troop will sell apple muffins, apple pies, and apple cookies to raise money. Each box of four apple muffins uses 3 apples, 1 cup of sugar, and 2 cups of flour, and sells for $1.95. Each apple pie uses 10 apples, 2 cups of sugar, and 3 cups of flour, and sells for $3.75. Each dozen apple cookies uses 1 apple, 3 cups of sugar, and 1 cup of flour, and sells for $1.20. Each apple costs $0.25, each cup of sugar costs $0.10, and each cup of flour costs $0.15. They have 840 apples, 630 cups of sugar, and 450 cups of flour available.

    (a) What is their profit on each box of apple muffins?

    (b) What is their profit on each apple pie?

    (c) What is their profit on each dozen apple cookies?

    (d) How many boxes of apple muffins, how many pies, and how many dozen cookies should the troop make from its resources to maximize their profit? What will that profit be? How much of each resource will be unused by this production policy?

28. A coffee distributor sells four blends of coffee, Excellent, Supreme, Deluxe, and Special. One pound of Excellent contains 16 ounces of Colombian coffee and sells for a profit of $1.80. One pound of Supreme consists of 12 ounces of Hawaiian and 4 ounces of Colombian coffee and sells for a profit of $1.40. One pound of Deluxe contains 6 ounces of African coffee, 8 ounces of Hawaiian coffee, and 2 ounces of Colombian coffee, and sells for a profit of $1.20. One pound of Special consists of 10 ounces of African coffee and 6 ounces of Hawaiian coffee, and sells for a profit of $1.00. At present the distributor has on hand 1100 pounds of African coffee, 1320 pounds of Hawaiian coffee, and 770 pounds of Colombian coffee.

    (a) Assuming they can sell all the pounds of their product blends that they make, how many pounds of each of their blends should the make to maximize their profit? What will be that maximum profit?

    (b) If they make the amounts of their blends found in (a), how much of Colombian, Hawaiian, and African coffee will be unused?

Section 3.4 Overview and Review Problems for Chapter 3

3.1: In this section we learned how to formulate a linear programming word problem mathematically:

(a) Identify the **"products"** to be made and the **"resources"** from which they are to be made. (Be careful about the **units** involved.) Define the **production variables**, which are the number of units of each product to be made.

(b) Write down the **objective function**, which gives the thing to be maximized, usually profit P, in terms of the variables.

(c) Write down a chart with one column for each "product" and one row for each "resource". In it list the amounts of each resource needed for 1 unit of each product. Add an extra column at the right containing the amount of each resource available.

(d) Use the chart to list the **constraints** in terms of the production variables. (Some constraints may not be easily expressed in the chart!) These often are of the form "the amount of this resource used to produce our unknown amounts of the products is $\leq$ the amount of the resource available". Remember to include the non-negativity constraints!

We also learned how to test whether a production policy was **feasible**: it must satisfy *all* the constraints. If a policy was feasible, we learned how to determine the **slack** in each resource constraint.

3.2: In this section we learned how to solve graphically a linear programming problem with only two products.

(a) The graph of a linear *inequality* (<u>constraint</u>) consists of the graph of the associated linear *equality* (<u>constraint line</u>) as well as all the points on one side of the constraint line. To graph such a line:

   1. If there is no x term in the equation, the line is horizontal; if there is no y term the line is vertical.

   2. Otherwise, determine the two intercepts by setting one variable equal to 0 and solving for the other variable, then setting the other variable to 0 and solving for the first.

   2. Plot the two intercepts, and draw the constraint line connecting them.

   3. Once the constraint line is drawn, test a point (usually the origin $(0, 0)$) in the inequality (constraint) to see which side of the constraint line should be included in the graph.

(b) The feasible region is the region in the first quadrant that is common to the graphs of all the constraints, i. e., that is on the proper side of each constraint line. Shade this region.

(c) Visually identify the corner points of the feasible region, and label them A, B, C, ... Find the coordinates of each corner point, using algebra where necessary.

(d) Substitute each corner point into the profit function. The corner that produces the best value of the profit function gives the best choice for x and y.

We learned the **Corner Point Principle**: In a linear programming problem, the maximum value of the profit function is always attained at one (or more) of the corner points of the feasible region.

We also learned two insights into this method of solving a linear programming problem:

The Feasible Region is determined by the system of constraints in the problem. Any problem with the same system of constraints will have the same feasible production policies, regardless of the profit function.

The role of the profit function is to choose the "best" corner point of the feasible region as the best production policy..

3.3: In this section we learned how to take a problem that has been formulated mathematically (regardless of the number of products) as a system of linear inequalities and a profit function and form the Initial Simplex Matrix for the Simplex Method software:

(a) For each constraint define a *slack* variable, which stands for the amount of that resource unused by the production policy, thereby converting the constraint into an equation.

(b) Rewrite the profit function in the form $-ax - by \ldots\ldots + P = 0$

(c) Extract the matrix of coefficients and constants from the equations formed in (a) and (b).

We also learned how to interpret the output of the Simplex Method software so as to find the optimal solution of the original problem:

   (a) <u>Identify the basic and nonbasic variables of the matrix.</u> A *basic variable of a simplex matrix* is a variable whose column has entries consisting of a single one and the rest zeros. (There should be as many basic variables as there are rows of the matrix.) All other variables are *nonbasic*.

   (b) <u>Set the value of each nonbasic variable to 0.</u> Inserting these values in the equations associated with the matrix effectively wipes out the terms containing the non-basic variables, leaving only the terms involving the basic variables and constants. You should now be able to immediately <u>read off the values of the other (basic) variables.</u> This process gives the values of *all* the variables, production and slack, associated with the optimal solution. The values of the production variables tell how much of each product to make, and the values of the slack variables give the amounts of the resources left over. The value of P gives the maximum profit that can be achieved.

Review Problems for Chapter 3 (Answers in back of text)

1. Formulate the following problem mathematically by (a) defining the production variables (including units), (b) writing the constraints (including nonnegativity constraints) as linear inequalities (use a chart if necessary), and (c) giving the profit formula in terms of the variables. (Note: for (c), profit on each product = selling price – total cost of product.) **DO NOT ATTEMPT TO SOLVE THE PROBLEM FURTHER.**

A Girl Scout troop will sell apple muffins, apple pies, and apple cookies to raise money. Each box of four apple muffins uses 3 apples, 1 cup of sugar, and 2 cups of flour, and sells for $1.95. Each apple pie uses 10 apples, 2 cups of sugar, and 3 cups of flour, and sells for $3.75. Each dozen apple cookies uses 1 apple, 3 cups of sugar, and 1 cup of flour, and sells for $1.20. Each apple costs $0.25, each cup of sugar costs $0.10, and each cup of flour costs $0.15. They have 840 apples, 630 cups of sugar, and 450 cups of flour available.

2. Graph this system of linear inequalities. <u>Label</u> the lines associated with inequalities (1), (2), (3), and (4). <u>Label all</u> the corner points A, B, C, . . ., and <u>find their coordinates.</u>   <u>Shade</u> the feasible region.

   (1) $3x + 2y \leq 174$
   (2) $x + y \leq 70$
   (3) $2x + 4y \leq 240$
   (4) $x \leq 50$
   $x \geq 0, y \geq 0$

Intercepts

$x \quad y \qquad x \quad y \qquad x \quad y$

3. The graphs of the constraint lines for the system of constraints listed below are shown below.

$$x + y \le 120$$
$$2x + y \le 200$$
$$2y \le 140$$
$$x \ge 0, y \ge 0$$

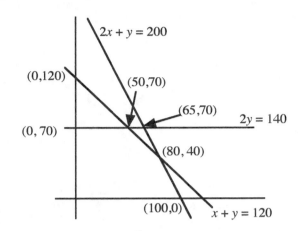

(a) Is the point $(60, 60)$ feasible? If so, what is the slack in each constraint?
(b) Is the point $(90, 22)$ feasible? If so, what is the slack in each constraint?
(c) Shade the feasible region of the system of constraints.
(d) Find the maximum value of $P = 2x + 3y$ on the feasible region and give the coordinates of the point at which it is attained.

4. For the linear programming problem below,
(a) For each constraint define a slack variable and use it to convert the constraint into an equation,
(b) Rewrite the profit function,
(c) Extract the initial simplex matrix for the problem.

Maximize $P = 2x + 3y + 5z + 5w$
Subject to: $3x + 5y + z + 2w \le 300$ skeins of yarn #1
                   $5x + 3y + 7z + 6w \le 400$ skeins of yarn #2
                   $2x + 3y + 4z + 5w \le 500$ hours of weaving
                   $x \ge 0, y \ge 0, z \ge 0, w \ge 0.$

5. The Girl Scout troop in Problem 1 above obtains the following final matrix from of the computer software:

x (boxes muffins)	y (pies)	z (dozen cookies)	s1	s2	s3	P	
0	-3.4	0	1	0.2	-1.6	0	246 (apples)
0	.2	1	0	0.4	-0.2	0	162 (cups sugar)
1	1.4	0	0	-0.2	0.6	0	144 (cups flour)
0	0.62	0	0	0.04	0.38	1	196.2

(a) What are the basic variables?
(b) What are the nonbasic variables?
(c) What are the values of all the variables in the optimal solution?
(d) How many boxes of apple muffins, how many pies, and how many dozen cookies should the troop make from its resources to maximize their profit? What will that profit be? How much of each resource will be unused by this production policy?

3. The graphs of the constraint lines for the system of constraints listed below are shown below.

$x + y \geq 120$
$2x + y \geq 200$
$3x + y \geq 140$
$x \geq 0, y \geq 0$

(a) Is the point $(60, 40)$ feasible? If so, what is the slack in each constraint?
(b) Is the point $(90, 22)$ feasible? If so, what is the slack in each constraint?
(c) Shade the feasible region of the system of constraints.
(d) Find the maximum value of $P = 2x + 3y$ on the feasible region and give the coordinates of the point at which it is attained.

4. For the linear programming problem below:
(a) For each constraint define a slack variable and use it to convert the constraint into an equation.
(b) Rewrite the profit function.
(c) List the initial simplex matrix for the point η.

Maximize: $P = 2x + 3y + 5z + 4w$
Subject to: $3x + 5y + 2z + 2w = 260$ (hours of plant A)
$5x + 3y + 7z + 6w = 370$ (hours of plant A5)
$2x + 3y + 4z + 5w = 340$ (hours of weaving)
$x \geq 0, y \geq 0, z \geq 0, w \geq 0$.

5. The Girl Scout troop in Problem 1 above obtains the following final matrix from it the computer software.

		x_1	x_2	s_1	s_2	p (dozen cookies)	t_1 (pies)	t_2 (boxes by machine)
x_1 (apples)	0	14	0	1.4	0.2	0		
x_2 (cups sugar)	0	2	1	0	3.4	0.2	0	
(cups flour)	1	14	0	0	0.2	0.0	0	
	0.65	0	0.4	0.08	0.28	1	19.2	

(a) What are the slack variables?
(b) What are the nonbasic variables?
(c) What are the values of all the variables in the optimal solution?
(d) How many boxes of apple muffins, how many pies, and how many dozen cookies should the troop make from its resources to maximize their profit? What will that profit be? How much of each resource will be unused by this production policy?

Part 1: Theory of Voting Methods

Voting is a basic right and responsibility of citizens in a democratic society. Often we think of voting as choosing between two candidates, but in this chapter we want to think of it in broader terms. **By a *voting method* we mean a procedure by which a collection of individuals may decide a "winner" from among a list of possibilities.** With this broader interpretation, voting methods also arise in deciding where to build a bridge, which team should be ranked first, which movie wins the Oscar, or who is selected to run a company. The voting method turns *individual* preferences among the possibilities into a single choice for the whole group. Our objective in this first part of Chapter 4 is to investigate various such voting methods and their positive and negative characteristics.

Some situations that involve voting are actually very strategic encounters, ones in which knowing what to do when can be important. For example, getting a bill approved by Congress involves many strategic moves other than votes! In our discussion we will only consider democratic voting methods in which the outcome is decided by a ballot of the electorate. By this we mean that all voters' votes are treated equally; there is no "dictatorship" or predetermined winner; neither are there other hurdles that must be overcome before the vote occurs.

When there are only two alternatives, a mathematical theorem proved in 1952 by Kenneth May assures us that there is only one democratic voting method, known as *majority rule*. In this case a voter just chooses his or her most preferred candidate of the two. But if there are more than two choices, such as in the 2000 presidential race when Florida voters chose from among George W. Bush, Al Gore, Ralph Nader, Patrick Buchanan, and others, the situation becomes much more complicated! In the first part of Chapter 4 we begin by exploring some of the many possible voting methods for choosing among more than two options. As we do so we will describe some of the historical occurrences of the methods, and use mathematical reasoning to measure these voting methods against some "fairness criteria" to try to find a best, or even "perfect", voting method. This will lead to the amazing result that there is no "perfect" voting method!

When there are more than two candidates, we want each ballot to not only list the most preferred, or first place choice, of the voter, but also rank all the other candidates as well. Such a ballot is called a **preference ballot**.

Example 1 A small class of nine students is trying to decide what kind of restaurant they want to go to for lunch. Table 4.1 below shows their preference ballots ranking Mexican (M), Chinese (C), and Italian (I). Each column is the preference ballot of the student named at the top of the column.

	Anne	Brad	Carla	Dave	Ed	Fran	Greg	Harry	Ian
First:	C	C	M	M	M	I	I	M	C
Second:	M	I	C	I	C	C	C	C	I
Third:	I	M	I	C	I	M	M	I	M

Table 4.1 Preference <u>Ballots</u> for lunch restaurant.

Some of the students have the same ballots. For example, Carla, Ed, and Harry list the choices in the same order. To simplify the display of all these preference ballots, we group together ballots that rank the candidates in the same order. This is done by forming a **preference schedule** in which we list in columns all the ranking orders that appear on submitted ballots. At the top of each column we show the number of voters that submitted that ranking order. Table 4.2 shows the preference schedule for our nine-member class.

Number of Voters:	1	2	3	1	2
First Choice:	C	C	M	M	I
Second Choice:	M	I	C	I	C
Third Choice:	I	M	I	C	M

Table 4.2   Preference <u>Schedule</u> for lunch restaurant

<u>Note</u>: Table 4.2 does not include all the possible preference ballots in this situation, because there is one possible ranking order that was not listed by any of the voters. Can you find it? In general, when there are 3 choices there are $3 \times 2 \times 1 = 6$ possible rankings (ballots), because there are 3 possible first place choices, and once that choice is listed there are two remaining possibilities for second. After first and second place choices are listed, the remaining candidate must be ranked third. In general, if there are n candidates then there are $n! = n \times (n-1) \times (n-2) \times \ldots \times 3 \times 2 \times 1$ possible preference ballots.

Basic Assumptions of Preference Ballots

There are two basic assumptions we should remember when working with preference ballots. First, each individual's preferences are assumed to be *transitive*. This means that if any voter prefers A to B, and also prefers B to C, then that voter is assumed to prefer A to C. Thus in Example 1 we assume that since Anne prefers Chinese to Mexican and Mexican to Italian, she must prefer Chinese to Italian. This may seem to be obvious, but we will see later that it is possible for a *group* of voters to prefer A to B, B to C, and C to A!

The second assumption is that the relative rankings of the other candidates by a voter are not affected by the removal of a given candidate. For example, if a voter ranks four candidates in this order: A first, B second, C third, D fourth, and if candidate B drops out, then the voter will rank the remaining candidates in this order: A first, C second, D third. Thus the candidates that were ranked below the candidate that drops out all "move up" one ranking.

Section 4.1   First Voting Methods

The Plurality Method

The simplest method for choosing a winner is to declare that the candidate with the most first place votes is the winner.

The Plurality Voting Method
The winner by the Plurality Method is the candidate with the most first place votes.

Many elections use the Plurality Method, because, since the method ignores the rankings below first place, it actually only requires each voter to pick a favorite candidate. If the class in Example 1 were to use the Plurality Method, the first place votes would be tallied, with this result:

Candidate	First Place Votes
Chinese	3
Mexican	4
Italian	2

Table 4.3   Plurality Method applied to Example 1

Mexican has the most first place votes and so would be chosen as the winner by the Plurality Method.

Advantages and Disadvantages of the Plurality Method

The major advantage of the Plurality Method is that it is easy to implement. In fact, voters only need to choose their most preferred candidate, rather than list all the candidates in an order. This also leads to one of its disadvantages: it does not reflect the preferences of those who did not rank the Plurality winner first. For this reason it can be *manipulable*. For example, in the 2000 presidential election in Florida, some people chose George W. Bush rather than Patrick Buchanan, or Al Gore rather than Ralph Nader, because they felt that to vote for Buchanan or Nader would be "wasting" their vote. So the actual votes probably did not reflect the true feelings of all the voters.

In a criminal trial the jury must decide which of a list of charges to convict the defendant of, if any. Sometimes a jury will decide to convict on a lesser charge even though a large majority do not have it as their first choice. The reason may be that in our system juries are required to reach a unanimous verdict, and a few jurors are adamant about the lesser charge. In A.D. 105 Pliny the Younger described a situation where a jury had to decide whether to execute, banish, or release a group of slaves who were accused of murdering their master. The jury was fairly evenly split among the three choices, but a plurality (not a majority) wanted to release them. However, those who wanted execution decided to support banishment as being much better than releasing the slaves. This resulted in banishment being the decision. Pliny argued that using the Plurality Method, without allowing people to change their votes and manipulate the system, would have been a better method.

Plurality versus Majority

A **majority candidate** is, by definition, one that receives **more than half the first place votes.** With only two candidates there is always a majority candidate. (*We will assume here and in the future that no ties occur.*) But if there are more than two candidates there may not be a majority candidate. In Example 1 the Plurality winner, Mexican, only had 4 out of 9 possible first place votes, and 4 is not more than half of nine. A majority candidate would need at least 5 of the possible 9 first place votes. There is still, however, a candidate that receives the *most* first place votes (again assuming no ties), and hence a Plurality winner.

Quiz Yourself: (Answers at the end of this section, before the problems.)
1. The candidates for president of a small club are Mary (M), Ned (N), and Paul (P). Here are the preference ballots of the voters in the election:

First:	M	P	P	M	M	N	P	M
Second:	N	M	N	P	P	P	N	P
Third:	P	N	M	N	N	M	M	N

   (a) Construct a preference schedule for this election
   (b) Determine the winner when the Plurality Method is used.
   (c) Is there a majority candidate? Why or why not?

The Borda Count Voting Method

The students in Example 1 that rank Chinese first might point out that almost every student ranks Chinese either first or second, while a significant number of voters (4 out of 9) rank Mexican last! One way to take the rankings below first place into account is to award points based on the relative rankings. The method we now investigate, called **Borda Count**, is similar to how sports teams are ranked in some polls.

> ### The Borda Count Voting Method
> Each voter submits a preference ballot ranking all the candidates. If there are n candidates, then each first place ranking is worth n points, each second place ranking is worth n-1 points, and so on down to each last place ranking being worth 1 point. The points awarded to the candidates in this fashion are totalled, and the candidate with the most total points is declared the winner.

Example 2 Find the lunch restaurant that would be chosen if the Borda Count Voting Method is applied to the preference schedule in Example 1.

Solution: For each candidate, we multiply the number of votes in each column of the preference schedule by the assigned point value for that vote for the candidate in that column, and adding these products together. To make this easier to follow we display the preference schedule again:

Number of Voters:	1	2	3	1	2
First Choice: (3 points)	C	C	M	M	I
Second Choice: (2 points)	M	I	C	I	C
Third Choice: (1 point)	I	M	I	C	M

Table 4.2   Preference Schedule for lunch restaurant

C gets 1 first place vote worth 3 points, 2 first place votes worth 3 points, 3 second place votes worth 2 points, 1 third place vote worth 1 point, and 2 second place votes worth 2 points, so:

C gets $1 \times 3 + 2 \times 3 + 3 \times 2 + 1 \times 1 + 2 \times 2$ points = $3 + 6 + 6 + 1 + 4$ points = 20 points

M gets $1 \times 2 + 2 \times 1 + 3 \times 3 + 1 \times 3 + 2 \times 1$ points = $2 + 2 + 9 + 3 + 2$ points = 18 points

I gets $1 \times 1 + 2 \times 2 + 3 \times 1 + 1 \times 2 + 2 \times 3$ points = $1 + 4 + 3 + 2 + 6$ points = 16 points

An alternative calculation method would be reason as follows:

C gets $1 + 2 = 3$ first place votes worth 3 points each = 9 points, and $(3 + 2) = 5$ second place votes worth 2 points each = 10 points, and 1 third place vote worth 1 point. $9 + 10 + 1 = 20$ points.

M gets $(3 + 1) \times 3$ points + 1×2 points + $(2 + 2) \times 1$ point = $12 + 2 + 4$ points = 18 points

I gets 2×3 points + $(2 + 1) \times 2$ points + $(1 + 3) \times 1$ point = $6 + 6 + 4$ points = 16 points

Chinese is declared the winner if the Borda Count Voting Method.

Checking Your Work: One way to check your work is to note that each of the voters awards the same *total* number of points to the candidates. In Example 2, each voter awards 6 points: 3 points for first place, 2 for second, and 1 for third. In general, the total number of points awarded by all voters equals the product of the number of voters times the number of votes each awards. In Example 2, the 9 voters each award 6 points, for a total of $9 \times 6 = 54$ points. This should equal the total of the points awarded to C, M, and I, namely $20 + 18 + 16 = 54$. So our work checks.

You may have decided that the Borda Count Voting Method looks pretty good. Variations of it are often used when there are a large number of candidates, as in sports polls. But it too has a flaw. In Example 2 we saw that the candidate with the most first place votes can be different from the winner by the Borda Count Method. The next example shows that it is even possible for there to be a candidate with a *majority* (more than half) of the first place votes that doesn't win when Borda Count is used.

Example 3 Reviewers rank Morton's (M), Nappa River Grill (N), the Oakroom (O), and Porcini's (P) as shown in the preference schedule in Table 4.4. Show that Morton's has a majority of the first place votes, but that the Oakroom is ranked first if the Borda Count Method is used.

Number of Reviewers:	6	2	3
First Choice: (4 points)	M	N	O
Second Choice: (3 points)	N	O	P
Third Choice: (2 points)	O	P	N
Fourth Choice (1 point)	P	M	M

Table 4.4   Preference Schedule of restaurant reviewers.

Solution: Since Morton's is ranked first by 6 of the 11 reviewers, it has a majority of the first place votes. To find the Borda Count winner we compute the points awarded. Note that a first place vote is now worth 4 points since there are 4 candidates, a second place votes 3 points, etc.

$$M \text{ gets } 6 \times 4 + 2 \times 1 + 3 \times 1 = 24 + 2 + 3 = 29 \text{ points}$$
$$N \text{ gets } 6 \times 3 + 2 \times 4 + 3 \times 2 = 18 + 8 + 6 = 32 \text{ points}$$
$$O \text{ gets } 6 \times 2 + 2 \times 3 + 3 \times 4 = 12 + 6 + 12 = 30 \text{ points}$$
$$P \text{ gets } 6 \times 1 + 2 \times 2 + 3 \times 3 = 6 + 4 + 9 = 19 \text{ points}$$

Check: There are 11 voters who award $4 + 3 + 2 + 1 = 10$ points each, so there should be a total of $11 \times 10 = 110$ points. And $29 + 32 + 30 + 19 = 110$ as required.

So the Nappa River Grill (N) is chosen as the winner when Borda Count is used, even though Morton's had more than half (i. e. a *majority* of) the first place votes. But Morton's also had a significant number of last place votes, causing it to get a smaller number of total points.

The previous example shows that, when there are more than two candidates, a candidate that has a majority of the first place votes may not be chosen as the winner when the Borda Count Method is used. If you have watched sports polls, you may know that, occasionally, a college football team will get a majority of first place votes in a sports poll, but some other team will actually be ranked first using a method like Borda Count. What causes this? Since the point totals are cumulative, a candidate with a large number of second or third place votes (and a respectable number of first place votes) might get a point total that is larger than the point total of a majority candidate that had few (or even no) second and third place votes. In fact, this is exactly what happened in Example 3.

> **Quiz Yourself:** (Answer at the end of this section, before the problems.)
> 2. Which candidate in Quiz Yourself Problem 1 wins if the Borda Count Method is used?

Most people would agree that whenever there is a majority candidate that candidate "should" be chosen as the winner by a good voting method. This condition is made explicit in our first fairness criterion.

> **The Majority Fairness Criterion**
> A voting method satisfies the Majority Fairness Criterion provided that, *whenever there is a majority candidate*, the voting method chooses that majority candidate as the winner of the election.

The Meaning of an Implication

The statement of the Majority Fairness Criterion is what logicians call an **implication**. An implication asserts that whenever a *hypothesis* is true, a *conclusion* must also be true. The hypothesis of the Majority Fairness Criterion is that there is a majority candidate. The conclusion is that the majority candidate is chosen as the winner by the voting method. For a voting method to satisfy the Majority Fairness Criterion we must offer a *logical reason* why, whenever there is a majority candidate, the voting method will **always** choose that candidate as the winner. And to show that a voting method does not satisfy the Majority Fairness Criterion, we only need one example (called a *counterexample*) consisting of a preference schedule in which there is a majority candidate but that candidate is not chosen as the winner by the voting method. This is called a **violation** of the Majority Fairness Criterion by the voting method.

Notice that the Majority Fairness Criterion *only* says what must happen when there is a majority candidate, and says *nothing* about which candidate the voting method will choose as the winner if there is no majority candidate.

> **Quiz Yourself:** (Answer at the end of this section, before the problems.)
> 3. Does the preference schedule in Quiz Yourself problem 1 show a violation of the Majority Fairness Criterion by the Plurality Method?

Example 4 Does the Plurality Method satisfy the Majority Fairness Criterion?

Solution This is really the question, "If there is a majority candidate, *must* the Plurality Method choose that candidate as the winner?" Suppose a candidate has more than half of the first place votes. How many first place votes can another candidate have? Any other candidate *must* have less than half the first place votes. So the majority candidate *must* have more first place votes than any other candidate.

Example 5 Does the Borda Count Method satisfy the Majority Fairness Criterion?

Solution This is asking, if there is a majority candidate, **must** that candidate win if the Borda Count Method is used? Example 3 shows that this does not *always* happen, so *the Borda Count Method does not satisfy the Majority Fairness Criterion*. So Example 3 shows a violation of the Majority Fairness Criterion by the Borda Count Method.

Notes: (1) In Example 5 we saw that the Borda Count Method does not satisfy the Majority Fairness Criterion. However, if there is a majority candidate, it is still possible for the Borda Count Method to choose that candidate as the winner.

(2) In Example 2 there was no violation of the Majority Fairness Criterion by the Borda Count Method. In that example Chinese won using Borda Count even though Mexican had more first place votes than Chinese. But Mexican did not have a *majority* of the first place votes, so no violation of the Majority Fairness Criterion occurred. In general, **if there is no majority candidate, then the preference schedule cannot show a violation of the Majority Fairness Criterion.**

Some History

The Borda Count Method is named for Jean-Charles Borda (1733-1799). During the time of the French Revolution in the late 1700s, when elections were beginning to occur more frequently as monarchs were overthrown, Borda wrote an "Essay on Ballot Elections". In it he describes an election with three candidates in which the Plurality winner would lose if matched against either one of the other two candidates. (In the next section we will call this an example of the "Condorcet Paradox".) Borda called his proposed method "Elections by Ranking of Merit". Actually, this method (under a different name) had been proposed by a German cardinal, Nikolaus Cusanus, in the middle 1400s. Cusanus was concerned with how a Pope should be elected, having observed the controversial election methods in the early 1400s that resulted in 3 different cardinals declaring themselves to be Pope! Cusanus' method was essentially the same as Borda's, but Cusanus described in great detail how the election should occur so as to insure the secrecy of individual ballots.

Many variations of the point assignment scheme used by Borda are possible. For example, in Europe there is a yearly Eurovision Song Contest (their version of American Idol) in which a jury judges songs from a variety of countries. After a process of weeding out the worst songs, each juror votes among 11 songs. Ranking a song 11th earns it 1 point, 10th earns 2 points, etc up to ranking 2nd earns 9 points, but ranking a song first earns it 11 points. In effect, a first place ranking is worth 1 additional "bonus" point.

Quiz Yourself: (Answers at the end of this section, before the problems.)
4. Does the preference schedule in Quiz Yourself Problem 1 show a violation of the Majority Fairness Criterion by the Borda Count Method? Why or why not? Justify your answer.
5. Explain why the Plurality Method satisfies the Majority Fairness Criterion.

Example 6 A small class gets to vote on the date of their final exam. There are 3 possibilities, which we will call A, B, and C. The vote is 10 for A, 5 for B, and 4 for C. This means that A wins if the Plurality Method is used, and that A is a majority candidate. Construct a preference schedule, consistent with these first place votes, in which a different candidate wins when the Borda Count Method is used.

Solution: Since B has the second-most first place votes, we will set up the preference schedule so that B has as many second-place votes as it can get, and A has as few second-place votes as it can get. So we make the 10 who ranked A first also rank B second, and the 4 who ranked C first also rank B second. To make A get as few second place votes as possible, we will have all those who voted for B or C as first also rank A third. This results in this preference schedule:

Number of Votes:	10	5	4
First Choice: (3 points)	A	B	C
Second Choice: (2 points)	B	C	B
Third Choice: (1 point)	C	A	A

Now we calculate the Borda Count points:

A gets $10 \times 3 + 5 \times 1 + 4 \times 1 = 30 + 5 + 4 = 39$ points

B gets $10 \times 2 + 5 \times 3 + 4 \times 2 = 20 + 15 + 8 = 43$ points

C gets $10 \times 1 + 5 \times 2 + 4 \times 3 = 10 + 10 + 12 = 32$ points

Since B has the most points it wins using the Borda Count Method.

This is only one of many possible correct preference schedules for this problem.

Quiz Yourself: (Answer on the next page.)
6. Construct a different preference schedule from the one constructed above, consistent with the first place votes in Example 6, in which B also wins.

Answers to Quiz Yourself Problems:

1. (a) The preference schedule is:

Number of Voters:	1	1	2	3	1
First Choice:	M	P	P	M	N
Second Choice:	N	M	N	P	P
Third Choice:	P	N	M	N	M

(b) The first place votes are: P – 3, M – 4, N – 1. Since M has the most first place votes it is the winner if the Plurality Method is used.

(c) There are 8 voters. Half of this is 4. To have *more than* half, a candidate would need 5 first place votes. No candidate here has that many first place votes, so there is no majority candidate.

2. In order to have a violation of the Majority Fairness criterion there must be a majority candidate that is not chosen as the winner. But there is no majority candidate in the preference schedule above, so there cannot be a violation of that criterion here.

3. Here are the calculation of the Borda Count points:

P: 1×1 point $+ 1 \times 3$ points $+ 2 \times 3$ points $+ 3 \times 2$ points $+ 1 \times 2$ points $= 1 + 3 + 6 + 6 + 2 = 18$ points
M: 1×3 points $+ 1 \times 2$ points $+ 2 \times 1$ point $+ 3 \times 3$ points $+ 1 \times 1$ point $= 3 + 2 + 2 + 9 + 1 = 17$ points
N: 1×2 points $+ 1 \times 1$ point $+ 2 \times 2$ points $+ 3 \times 1$ point $+ 1 \times 3$ points $= 2 + 1 + 4 + 3 + 3 = 13$ points

Check: 8 voters; each award $3 + 2 + 1 = 6$ points; total of 8×6 points $= 48$ points.

$18 + 17 + 13 = 48$ points. They agree.

4. With the above preference schedule there is no violation of the Majority Fairness Criterion by the Borda Count method, because there is no majority candidate (as noted in 1 (c) above). Without a majority candidate there can be no violation of the Majority Fairness Criterion regardless of the Voting Method used. The fact that the candidate that had the most first place votes (M) did not win by the Borda Count Method does not violate the Majority Fairness Criterion unless that candidate has a *majority* of first place votes.

5. This was answered in Example 4. A majority candidate must have more than half the first place votes. So any other candidate must have *less* than half the first place votes. This means that the majority candidate has more first place votes than any other candidate.

6. Consider the preference schedule in the solution to Example 6. B has 4 more points in the Borda Count computation than A does. So we could have a few of the votes in the second column rank A above C and then we should still have B getting more points than A. For example:

Number of Votes:	10	3	2	4
First Choice: (3 points)	A	B	B	C
Second Choice: (2 points)	B	C	A	B
Third Choice: (1 point)	C	A	C	A

This still has 10 first place votes for A, 5 for B, and 4 for C. Here are the Borda Count points:

A gets $10 \times 3 + 3 \times 1 + 2 \times 2 + 4 \times 1 = 30 + 3 + 4 + 4 = 41$ points
B gets $10 \times 2 + 5 \times 3 + 4 \times 2 = 20 + 15 + 8 = 43$ points
C gets $10 \times 1 + 3 \times 2 + 2 \times 1 + 4 \times 3 = 10 + 6 + 2 + 12 = 30$ points

B wins if Borda Count is used. (There are other correct preference schedules.)

Problems for Section 4.1

Sharpen Your Skills: (Answers in back of text.)

1. The Math Club is electing its president by choosing among three candidates, Ruth, Sue, and Tom (denoted R, S, and T below). The other 9 members of the club turn in these preference ballots.

	Anne	Brad	Carla	Dave	Ed	Fran	Greg	Harry	Ian
First:	R	T	T	S	R	T	S	R	T
Second:	S	R	S	R	T	R	R	S	S
Third:	T	S	R	T	S	S	T	T	R

(a) Give the preference schedule for this election.

(b) Find the winner of the election using:
   (i) The Plurality Method.
   (ii) The Borda Count Method.

2. Twelve students rank Coke, Sprite, Pepsi, and Mountain Dew (denoted C, S, P, and M below) on their preference ballots as shown.

	Alice	Ben	Cal	Don	Ed	Fred	Gil	Hap	Ian	Jan	Ken	Lon
First	S	C	P	C	C	C	S	C	S	S	C	S
Second	P	P	M	P	P	P	P	P	P	P	P	P
Third	C	M	C	S	S	M	C	S	C	C	M	C
Fourth	M	S	S	M	M	S	M	M	M	M	S	M

(a) Give the preference schedule for this election.

(b) Find the winner of the election using:
   (i) The Plurality Method.
   (ii) The Borda Count Method.

3. A committee of 35 faculty is used to rank candidates W, X, Y, and Z for the position of Dean. They rank the candidates according to the following table:

Number of faculty:	8	7	9	4	7
First	Z	X	Y	Z	Z
Second	X	Y	X	Y	Y
Third	Y	W	W	X	W
Fourth	W	Z	Z	W	X

(a) Find the winner of the election using the Plurality Method.

(b) Find the winner of the election using the Borda Count Method.

4. A poll of judges is used to choose a winner from among three pieces of artwork (labelled A, B, and C) submitted for a competition. The following table shows the ranking of the judges.

Number of judges:	8	6	4	4	3
First	B	A	C	C	A
Second	C	B	B	A	C
Third	A	C	A	B	B

(a) Find the winner of the election using the Plurality Method.

(b) Find the winner of the election using the Borda Count Method.

5. An election among four candidates W, X, Y, and Z has the following preference schedule:

Number of voters:	5	8	9	1	4
First	Z	W	Y	X	W
Second	Y	X	Z	W	Y
Third	X	Z	W	Z	X
Fourth	W	Y	X	Y	Z

    (a) Find the winner of the election using the Plurality Method.
    (b) Find the winner of the election using the Borda Count Method.

6. An election among five candidates A, B, C, D, and E has the following preference schedule:

Number of voters:	8	7	6	2	1
First	A	D	D	C	E
Second	B	B	B	A	A
Third	C	A	E	B	D
Fourth	D	C	C	D	B
Fifth	E	E	A	E	C

    (a) Find the winner of the election using the Plurality Method.
    (b) Find the winner of the election using the Borda Count Method.

Apply Your Knowledge (Answers to odd-numbered problems in back of text.)

7. An election is held with six candidates and 40 voters. If it is decided using the Borda Count Method:
    (a) What is the maximum number of points any candidate can get?
    (b) What is the minimum number of points any candidate can get?
    (c) What is the total number of points awarded to all the candidates using the Borda Count Method?

8. An election is held with five candidates and 30 voters.
    (a) How many possible preference ballots are there?
    (b) If the Borda Count Method is used, what is the total number of points awarded to all the candidates?

9. Suppose 25 voters rank four candidates A, B, C, and D. Suppose also that when the Borda Count Method is used A receives 63 points, B receives 52 points, and C receives 45 points. How many points did D receive? Who won the election using the Borda Count Method? Explain how you determine this.

10. Suppose 40 voters rank 5 candidates A, B, C, D, and E. Suppose also that when the Borda Count Method is used A receives 111 points, B receives 149 points, C receives 90 points, and D gets 103 points. How many points did E receive? Who won the election using the Borda Count Method?

11. Use your work on Problem 1 of this section (below) to decide whether there is a violation of the Majority Fairness Criterion by the Borda Count Method. Explain why or why not.

Number of Voters	2	2	2	2	1
First:	R	T	T	S	R
Second:	S	R	S	R	T
Third:	T	S	R	T	S

12. Use your work on Problem 2 of this section (shown below) to decide whether there is a violation of the Majority Fairness Criterion by the Borda Count Method. Explain why or why not.

Number of Voters:	5	3	1	3
First:	S	C	P	C
Second:	P	P	M	P
Third:	C	S	C	M
Fourth:	M	M	S	S

13. Use your work on Problem 3 of this section (shown below) to decide whether there is a violation of the Majority Fairness Criterion by the Borda Count Method. Explain why or why not.

Number of faculty:	8	7	9	4	7
First:	Z	X	Y	Z	Z
Second:	X	Y	X	Y	Y
Third:	Y	W	W	X	W
Fourth:	W	Z	Z	W	X

14. Use your work on Problem 4 of this section (shown below) to decide whether there is a violation of the Majority Fairness Criterion by the Borda Count Method. Explain why or why not.

Number of judges:	8	6	4	4	3
First	B	A	C	C	A
Second	C	B	B	A	C
Third	A	C	A	B	B

15. Use your work on Problem 5 of this section (shown below) to decide whether there is a violation of the Majority Fairness Criterion by the Borda Count Method. Explain why or why not.

Number of voters:	5	8	9	1	4
First	Z	W	Y	X	W
Second	Y	X	Z	W	Y
Third	X	Z	W	Z	X
Fourth	W	Y	X	Y	Z

16. Use your work on Problem 6 of this section (shown below) to decide whether there is a violation of the Majority Fairness Criterion by the Borda Count Method. Explain why or why not.

Number of voters:	8	7	6	2	1
First	A	D	D	C	E
Second	B	B	B	A	A
Third	C	A	E	B	D
Fourth	D	C	C	D	B
Fifth	E	E	A	E	C

17. Club members rank Alicia (A), Bert(B) and Carlos(C) when they vote for their president. Here is their preference schedule:

Number of Voters	3	1	2	1	3	2
First:	A	A	B	B	C	C
Second:	B	C	A	C	A	B
Third:	C	B	C	A	B	A

(a) Who wins using the Plurality Method?   (b) Who wins using the Borda Count Method?
(c) Is there a violation of the Majority Fairness Criterion by either method?

18. In a congressional election Republican Chapman received 38% of the vote, Democrat Forsythe received 35%, and Independent Kilpatrick received 27%. Of course, Chapman won since the Plurality Method was used. An exit poll asked voters to rank the three candidates. The results are shown below.

Percentage of Voters	26	12	29	6	20	7
First:	C	C	F	F	K	K
Second:	F	K	K	C	F	C
Third:	K	F	C	K	C	F

Show that based on this poll, the Borda Count Method ranks each of the other candidates higher than Chapman.

19. An election by 21 voters has three candidates, A, B, and C. Create a preference schedule for this election in which A wins by the Plurality Method but B wins by the Borda Count Method.

20. Reconsider Example 6. Construct a preference schedule consistent with the given first place votes, in which C wins.

Communicate the Concepts: (Answers to odd-numbered problems in back of text.)

21. Explain why the Plurality Method satisfies the Majority Fairness Criterion.

22. Describe a benefit of the Borda Count Method as opposed to the Plurality Method.

23. Describe a benefit of the Plurality Method over the Borda Count Method.

24. Suppose an election only has two candidates. Give an argument why the winner by the Plurality Method must also win using the Borda Count Method.

Section 4.2   More Involved Voting Methods

Another way to take into account rankings other than first place votes is to have one or more runoffs. There are many ways to decide which candidates should be in the runoffs. One method is to have a runoff between the two candidates who received the most first place votes. This method is used in many party primaries, because even though there may be many candidates, only one runoff vote will be needed. But if voters were to turn in preference ballots such as the ones we are using there would be no need for another vote (and no opportunity for more campaigning!) and we could quickly conduct whatever runoffs might be necessary using the original ballots.

In the **Plurality With Elimination Method** at each stage the candidate with the fewest first place votes is eliminated, and the preference schedule is redrawn with the other candidates "moved up" in each voter's rankings. This continues until some candidate has a majority of the first place votes. (If there is a tie for which candidate has the fewest first place votes at some stage, all such candidates are eliminated.)

The Plurality With Elimination Voting Method
(1) If a candidate now has a majority of the first place votes they win. Otherwise, eliminate the candidate (or candidates if there is a tie) that has the fewest first place votes. Redraw the preference schedule, moving up candidates that were ranked below the eliminated candidate(s).
(2) Repeat the process in (1) until a candidate has a majority of first place votes.

This voting method was developed by Thomas Hare in 1861, and is sometimes referred to as "instant runoff", since it performs a runoff without requiring another voting to occur. It is used in Australia and Ireland, as well as mayoral elections in San Francisco and Oakland. In the 2010 mayoral election in Oakland its use led to a different winner than the Plurality Method would have chosen.

Example 1 Determine the winner of the class restaurant choice in Example 1 of the previous section by the Plurality With Elimination Method

Solution Here again is the preference schedule of the class:

Number of Voters:	1	2	3	1	2
First Choice:	C	C	M	M	I
Second Choice:	M	I	C	I	C
Third Choice:	I	M	I	C	M

Table 4.2   Preference Schedule for lunch restaurant

Since there is no candidate that has a majority of the first place votes, we eliminate the candidate with the fewest first place votes. In this case that is I, since M has 4 and C has 3 first place votes. After removing I from each column and moving the candidate(s) ranked below I in each column up, we obtain this schedule:

Number of Voters:	1	2	3	1	2
First Choice:	C	C	M	M	C
Second Choice:	M	M	C	C	M

Table 4.5   Preference Schedule for lunch restaurant after removing I

We add up the first place votes again: M has 3 + 1 = 4, but C has 1 + 2 + 2 = 5, a majority, so C wins if Plurality With Elimination is used. (Recall that M won when Plurality was used.)

When Plurality With Elimination is used and there are n candidates it may take up to n-1 repetitions of the process before a winner is determined. The next example shows a situation in which there are four candidates, and three repetitions of the process are needed.

Example 2 A 24-member committee ranks four cites that are vying to host the 2022 Olympics, Berlin (B), Houston (H), Paris (P), and Tokyo (T), according to the following preference schedule:

Number of Members:	8	6	2	3	3	2
First	T	H	T	B	P	P
Second	H	B	P	P	T	T
Third	B	P	H	T	B	H
Fourth	P	T	B	H	H	B

Table 4.6   Preference Schedule for Olympic Host Cities

Solution   There are a total of 24 voters, so 13 first place votes are need for a majority. With these ballots the first place votes are: T: 8 + 2 = 10, H: 6, B: 3, P: 3 + 2 = 5. Since no city has a majority, a runoff is needed. B is eliminated since it has the fewest first place votes. This yields a new preference schedule:

Number of Members:	8	6	2	3	3	2
First	T	H	T	P	P	P
Second	H	P	P	T	T	T
Third	P	T	H	H	H	H

Table 4.7   Revised Preference Schedule after Berlin is eliminated.

Now the first place votes are: T: 8 + 2 = 10, H: 6, P: 3 + 3 + 2 = 8. No city has a majority yet, so H, with the fewest first place votes, is eliminated. This yields a new preference schedule:

Number of Members:	8	6	2	3	3	2
First	T	P	T	P	P	P
Second	P	T	P	T	T	T

Table 4.8   Revised Preference Schedule after Houston is also eliminated.

Now Tokyo has 8 + 2 = 10 first place votes, and Paris has 6 + 3 + 3 + 2 = 14, first place votes, a majority. Paris is declared the winner using Plurality With Elimination.

Notice that if we had conducted a runoff between the two candidates with the most first place votes in the original election (a voting method used in Kentucky and some other states), that runoff would have been between Tokyo and Houston and would have resulted in a different winner that what was chosen using Plurality With Elimination.

> **Quiz Yourself:** (Answer at the end of this section, before the problems.)
> 1. Use the Plurality With Elimination Method to determine the winner of an election in which the preference schedule is the one shown in the table below.
>
> | Number of Voters: | 9 | 12 | 4 | 5 | 4 | 1 |
> |---|---|---|---|---|---|---|
> | First | C | D | C | A | A | B |
> | Second | A | A | B | D | B | C |
> | Third | B | B | D | B | C | A |
> | Fourth | D | C | A | C | D | D |

The Method of Pairwise Comparisons

It would seem natural that the "winner" in an election should be able to beat any one of the other candidates in a two-person contest. While this is not always true, trying to achieve it is the basis for our fourth voting method.

The Voting Method of Pairwise Comparisons (MPC)

1. Perform a two-person contest ("pairwise comparison") between each pair of candidates, counting how many voters prefer the first candidate to the second and how many prefer the second to the first in each pairing.
2. For each such pairing award 1 point to the winner, or award 1/2 point to each if there is a tie.
3. The winner by the Pairwise Comparison Method is the candidate that receives the most points.

Example 3 Determine the winner of Example 1 if the Method of Pairwise Comparisons is used.

Solution Here is that preference schedule again:

Number of Voters:	1	2	3	1	2
First Choice:	C	C	M	M	I
Second Choice:	M	I	C	I	C
Third Choice:	I	M	I	C	M

Table 4.2   Preference Schedule for lunch restaurant

There are 3 possible pairings:

(i) <u>C vs. M</u>. Since I has been momentarily eliminated, voters in the last column rank C first, and C gets a total of 5 first place votes to 4 for M. C gets 1 point for winning this match.

(ii) <u>C vs. I</u>. When M is eliminated from the original schedule. C gets the first place votes of the voters in the first three columns, a total of 6 votes, while I gets the other 3 votes. C gets 1 point for winning this match.

(iii) <u>M vs. I</u>. When C is eliminated from the original schedule. M gets the first place votes of the voters in first, third, and fourth columns, a total of 5. I gets the other 4. M gets 1 point for winning this match.

Using the Method of Pairwise Comparisons, C gets two points, M gets 1 point, and I gets no points. C is declared the winner by the Method of Pairwise Comparisons.

Llull and Condorcet

A voting method like the Method of Pairwise Comparisons was first proposed by a Spanish theologian and philosopher named Ramon Llull. In 1283 he proposed a method to choose an abbess from a list of candidates. Llull felt that using such pairwise comparisons would "reveal God's will." Llull's goal was that there be a candidate that was preferred to all the others in pairwise comparisons. Unfortunately, Llull's work was not widely known outside Spain, or outside monasteries, so the method was momentarily forgotten. The Marquis de Condorcet (1743 - 1794), shown at right, was a famous mediator between the two main factions in the French Revolutions. He wrote a pamphlet investigating the use of pairwise comparisons to decide elections. Both Llull and Condorcet felt that if there were a candidate that won all their pairwise comparisons, that candidate would have greater claim to be the winner, as great as a majority candidate. **A candidate that wins all its pairwise comparisons will be called a Condorcet candidate**. In Example 3 above, C is a Condorcet candidate, but C is not a majority candidate. The next result clarifies the relationship between a majority candidate and a Condorcet candidate.

Result 1 **Show that any majority candidate is a Condorcet candidate, but that a Condorcet candidate does not have to be a majority candidate.**

Solution: Suppose an election has a majority candidate X. Then X has more than half of the first place votes available. When X is paired against any other candidate, X will still have at least as many first place votes as it did originally, and thus win the comparison. So X will win all its pairwise comparisons and be a Condorcet candidate. However, as we noted above, in Example 3, C is a Condorcet candidate that is not a majority candidate.

Example 4 Using MPC can occasionally lead to strange outcomes. Condorcet gave an example like the schedule below, and pointed out that it shows a paradox. What is **Condorcet's paradox**?

Number of voters:	3	5	4
First	C	S	P
Second	S	P	C
Third	P	C	S

Table 4.9

Solution You can check that each candidate wins one of the three pairwise comparisons: C defeats S 7 to 5, S defeats P 8 to 4, and P defeats C 9 to 3. Thus each candidate receives one point using the Method of Pairwise Comparisons, and there is no winner. Paradoxically, the group seems to have a "circular" preference ranking: they prefer C to S, S to P, and P to C! We would not allow this as the preference ranking of an individual; it violates the first basic assumption of preference ballots discussed in Section 4.1. But *groups* can exhibit such circular preferences.

Example 5 Suppose the preference schedule in Table 4.10 below shows the preference ballots of 22 voters among 4 candidates. Determine the winner by the Method of Pairwise Comparisons.

Number of Voters:	2	6	4	1	5	4
1st Choice	A	B	B	C	D	C
2nd Choice	D	A	A	B	A	D
3rd Choice	C	C	D	A	C	B
4th Choice	B	D	C	D	B	A

Table 4.10

Solution There are now 6 possible pairings of two candidates. We first list all the pairings of A with another candidate, then B with another candidate, etc. (Of course, A vs. B is the same pairing as B vs. A.) In each pairing we add up the number of voters who prefer each candidate. Notice that with each pairing there are a total of 22 votes for the two candidates.

A vs. B: 2 + 5 = 7 prefer A to B;   6 + 4 + 1 + 4 = 15 prefer B to A   B wins   1 point to B
A vs. C: 2 + 6 + 4 + 5 = 17 prefer A to C; 1 + 4 = 5 prefer C to A   A wins   1 point to A
A vs. D: 2 + 6 + 4 + 1 = 13 prefer A to D; 5 + 4 = 9 prefer D to A   A wins   1 point to A
B vs. C: 6 + 4 = 10 prefer B to C;   5 + 1 + 5 + 4 = 15 prefer C to B   C wins   1 point to C
B vs. D: 6 + 4 + 1 = 11 prefer B to D;   2 + 5 + 4 = 11 prefer D to B   Tie   1/2 point to B & D
C vs. D: 6 + 1 + 4 = 11 prefer C to D;   2 + 4 + 5 = 11 prefer D to C   Tie   1/2 point to C & D

Total Points: A: 1 + 1 = 2 points   B: 1 + 1/2 = 1 1/2 points   C: 1 + 1/2 = 1 1/2 points
D: 1/2 + 1/2 = 1 point

Since A won the most points, A is declared the winner using the Method of Pairwise Comparisons. Notice that in this example there is no Condorcet Candidate.

Quiz Yourself: (Answer at the end of this section, before the problems.)
2. Referring to the preference schedule in Quiz Yourself Problem 1, who wins if the Method of Pairwise Comparisons is used?

Our Second Fairness Criterion

It would seem reasonable that if a voting method is to be "fair", then a Condorcet candidate, like a majority candidate, "should" be chosen as the winner if such a candidate exists. This leads to:

The Condorcet Fairness Criterion

A voting method satisfies the Condorcet Fairness Criterion if, whenever there is a candidate that beats every other candidate in pairwise comparison (a **Condorcet candidate**), the voting method always chooses that candidate as the winner.

Note that the Condorcet Fairness Criterion, like the Majority Fairness Criterion, is an implication. It begins with an "if" clause, and *only* addresses situations in which that clause is true. A voting method that satisfies this criterion will always choose a Condorcet candidate as the winner *when there is such a candidate*. **If there is no Condorcet candidate, the criterion does not apply.**

Note also that the Condorcet Fairness Criterion refers to pairwise comparisons, but is <u>not</u> the same as the Voting Method of Pairwise Comparisons. The Method of Pairwise Comparisons is a voting method for choosing a winner from a preference schedule, and the Condorcet Fairness Criterion is a fairness criterion that says who the winner should be only in certain situations.

Example 6 Show that the following preference schedule in Table 4.11 is an example of a violation of the Condorcet Fairness Criterion by the Plurality Method.

Number of Voters:	5	4	2
First	A	B	C
Second	B	C	B
Third	C	A	A

Table 4.11

Solution: Candidate A, who has the most first place votes, wins by the Plurality Method. However, Candidate B wins both its pairwise comparison:

A vs. B: 5 people prefer A to B, the other 6 prefer B to A. B wins this comparison.

B vs. C: 5 + 4 = 9 people prefer B to C, the other 2 prefer C to B. B wins this comparison.

So B is a Condorcet Candidate that does not win using the Plurality Method. We conclude that:

Result 2 The Plurality Method does not satisfy the Condorcet Fairness Criterion.

Quiz Yourself: (Answer at the end of this section, before the problems.)
3. Referring to the preference schedule in Quiz Yourself Problem 1, does this schedule show a violation of the Condorcet Fairness Criterion by the Plurality with Elimination Method? Explain.
4. Referring to the preference schedule in Quiz Yourself Problem 1, does this schedule show a violation of the Condorcet Fairness Criterion by the Borda Count Method? Explain.

We have now seen four different voting methods for choosing a winner when there are more than two candidates. We will see in the next section that they all have good and bad points. But if they all result in the same winner chosen, why worry? Because, as the next example shows, it is even possible to have a preference schedule in which *each* candidate wins *by some voting method*! For this reason it is important to make clear how the winner of an election is to be chosen before the election is done, since the method of choosing the winner may actually determine who the winner is.

Example 7 Suppose a social club of 37 people is trying to choose among a Chinese (C), Mexican (M), Italian (I), or Fish (F) restaurant for their banquet, and that the preference schedule of the members is:

Number of Voters:	13	10	8	5	1
First	C	M	F	I	M
Second	I	I	M	F	F
Third	M	F	I	M	I
Fourth	F	C	C	C	C

Table 4.12

For each of our four voting methods decide which restaurant would be chosen by that method.

Solution (1) Totalling first place votes, we see C has 13, M has $10 + 1 = 11$, F has 8, and I has 5. So **Chinese wins if the Plurality Method is used**.

(2) Here are the Borda Count computations:

C: $13 \times 4 + 10 \times 1 + 8 \times 1 + 5 \times 1 + 1 \times 1 = 52 + 10 + 8 + 5 + 1 = 76$

I: $13 \times 3 + 10 \times 3 + 8 \times 2 + 5 \times 4 + 1 \times 2 = 39 + 30 + 16 + 20 + 2 = 107$

M: $13 \times 2 + 10 \times 4 + 8 \times 3 + 5 \times 2 + 1 \times 4 = 26 + 40 + 24 + 10 + 4 = 104$

F: $13 \times 1 + 10 \times 2 + 8 \times 4 + 5 \times 3 + 1 \times 3 = 13 + 20 + 32 + 15 + 3 = 83$.

Italian wins if the Borda Count Method is used.

(3) If Plurality With Elimination is used, since no one has a majority of first place votes we eliminate the choice with the fewest first place votes, I. The redrawn preference schedule is:

Number of Voters:	13	10	8	5	1
First	C	M	F	F	M
Second	M	F	M	M	F
Third	F	C	C	C	C

Table 4.13

Now C has 13 first place votes, M has 11, and F has 13. No one has a majority of first place votes, so M is eliminated. According to Table 4.13 all the people who ranked M first now vote for F, giving F 24 first place votes, a majority. So **Fish wins using Plurality With Elimination**.

(4) Finally we determine the winner using the Method of Pairwise Comparisons. The 6 possible pairings and the result of those comparisons are shown below.

C vs. M: C gets 13, M the other 24, so M wins   1 point to M

C vs. F: C gets 13, F gets the other 24, so F wins   1 point to F

C vs. I: C gets 13, I gets the other 24, so I wins   1 point to I

M vs. F: M gets $13 + 10 + 1 = 24$, F gets $8 + 5 = 13$ 1 point to M

M vs. I: M gets $10 + 8 + 1 = 19$, I gets $13 + 5 = 18$ 1 point to M

F vs. I: F gets $8 + 1 = 9$, I gets $13 + 10 + 5 = 28$ 1 point to I

Totalling the points, we see that M has 3 points, I has 2 points, F has 1 point, and C has 0 points. So **Mexican wins if the Method of Pairwise Comparisons is used.**

Example 7 above shows that each of the four types of restaurant wins using one of our four voting methods, emphasizing that **the winner of an election may depend on the method used to pick a winner.** It also shows that **of our four voting methods, only the Method of Pairwise Comparisons satisfies the Condorcet Fairness Criterion.** That is because in this example Mexican is a Condorcet candidate, but each of the other voting methods chooses a winner other than Mexican.

Example 8 In the 2014 primary for the Indiana District 5 seat in the U. S. House, the results were Denney 42%, Ford 33%, Davidson 25%.
   (a) Construct a preference schedule, consistent with these first place votes, in which Ford wins if the Method of Pairwise Comparisons is used.
   (b) Does your example show a violation of the Condorcet Fairness Criterion by the Plurality Method? Explain why or why not.

   Solution: As in Example 7 of Section 4.1, we need preference schedule in which Ford is ranked high on each ballot and Denney as low as possible, but consistent with these first place votes. Here is one (there are other possible correct schedules):

Number of Voters:	42%	33%	25%
First	Denney	Ford	Davidson
Second	Ford	Davidson	Ford
Third	Davidson	Denney	Denney

   The pairwise comparisons are:

       Denney vs Ford: Denney 42%, Ford 58%
       Denney vs Davidson: Denney 42%, Davidson 58%
       Ford vs Davidson: Ford 75%, Davidson 25%

   So Ford wins all his (or her) pairwise comparisons, wins by the Method of Pairwise Comparisons, and is a Condorcet Candidate.

   (b) Since Ford is a Condorcet Candidate, but Denney wins by the Plurality Method, this is a violation of the Condorcet Fairness Criterion by the Plurality Method.

Quiz Yourself: (Answer on the next page.)
5. Construct a preference schedule, consistent with these first place votes in the example above, in which Davidson wins if the Method of Pairwise Comparisons is used. Does your example show a violation of the Condorcet Fairness Criterion by the Plurality with Elimination Method? Explain why or why not.

Answers to Quiz Yourself Problems:
1. The first place votes are: A: 5 + 4 = 9, B: 1; C: 9 + 4 = 13; D: 12.
   There are a total of 35 voters, so 18 votes are needed for a majority. No candidate has that many, so B, with 1 first place vote, is eliminated:

Number of Voters:	9	12	4	5	4	1
First	C	D	C	A	A	C
Second	A	A	D	D	C	A
Third	D	C	A	C	D	D

Now the first place votes are: A: 5 + 4 = 9; C: 9 + 4 + 1 = 14; D: 12. Still no candidate has the 18 votes needed for a majority, so A is eliminated since it has the fewest first place votes:

Number of Voters:	9	12	4	5	4	1
First	C	D	C	D	C	C
Second	D	C	D	C	D	D

Now the first place votes are: C: 9 + 4 + 4 + 1 = 18, D: 12 + 5 = 17. C is declared the winner using Plurality with Elimination.

Answers to Quiz Yourself Problems: (continued)

2. Using the Method of Pairwise Comparisons on the same schedule, here are the results:

A vs B: 9 + 12 + 5 + 4 = 30 prefer A to B   4 + 1 = 5 prefer B to A   A wins and gets 1 point
A vs C: 12 + 5 + 4 = 21 prefer A to C   9 + 4 + 1 = 14 prefer C to A   A wins and gets 1 point
A vs D: 9 + 5 + 4 + 1 = 19 prefer A to D   12 + 4 = 16 prefer D to A   A wins and gets 1 point
B vs C: 12 + 5 + 4 + 1 = 22 prefer B to C   9 + 4 = 13 prefer C to B   B wins and gets 1 point
B vs D: 9 + 4 + 4 + 1 = 18 prefer B to D   12 + 5 = 17 prefer D to B   B wins and gets 1 point
C vs D: 9 + 4 + 4 + 1 = 18 prefer C to D   12 + 5 = 17 prefer D to C   C wins and gets 1 point

Final result: A has 3 points, B has 2 points, C has 1 point, and D has 0 points.
   A wins using the Method of Pairwise Comparisons.

3. Referring to the preference schedule above, does this schedule show a violation of the Condorcet Fairness Criterion by the Plurality with Elimination Method? The results of problem 1 above show that C wins using Plurality with Elimination. The work in problem 2 above show that A wins all its pairwise comparisons and so is a Condorcet candidate. So in this schedule there is a Condorcet candidate, but the Plurality with Elimination Method does not choose that candidate as the winner. This is a violation of the Condorcet Fairness Criterion by the Plurality with Elimination Method.

4. We know from the work in problem 2 above that A is a Condorcet candidate. We must determine the winner by the Borda Count Method.
Points for A: $(5 + 4) \times 4 + (9 + 12) \times 3 + 1 \times 2 + 4 \times 1 = 36 + 63 + 2 + 4 = 105$
Points for B: $1 \times 4 + (4 + 4) \times 3 + (9 + 12 + 5) \times 2 = 4 + 24 + 52 = 80$
Points for C: $(9 + 4) \times 4 + 1 \times 3 + 4 \times 2 + (12 + 5) \times 1 = 52 + 3 + 8 + 17 = 80$
Points for D: $12 \times 4 + 5 \times 3 + 4 \times 2 + (9 + 4 + 1) \times 1 = 48 + 15 + 8 + 14 = 85$
(Check: 35 voters award 10 points each for 350 total points. 105 + 80 + 80 + 85 = 350.)
A wins using the Borda Count Method. So the Condorcet candidate wins by the Borda Count Method, and there is no violation here of the Condorcet Fairness Criterion by the Borda Count Method.

5. We need preference schedule in which Davidson is ranked high on each ballot, but consistent with these first place votes. Here is one (there are other possible correct schedules):

Number of Voters:	42%	33%	25%
First	Denney	Ford	Davidson
Second	Davidson	Davidson	Ford
Third	Ford	Denney	Denney

The pairwise comparisons are:

Denney vs Ford: Denney 42%, Ford 58%
Denney vs Davidson: Denney 42%, Davidson 58%
Ford vs Davidson: Ford 33%, Davidson 67%

So Davidson wins all his (or her) pairwise comparisons, wins by the Method of Pairwise Comparisons, and is a Condorcet Candidate. Since Davidson is a Condorcet Candidate, but is eliminated first by the Plurality with Elimination Method, this is a violation of the Condorcet Fairness Criterion by the Plurality Method.

Problems for Section 4.2

Sharpen your Skills: (Answers in back of text.)

1. Answer the following questions for the Math Club election in Problems 1 and 11 from Section 4.1.

Number of Voters	2	2	2	2	1
First:	R	T	T	S	R
Second:	S	R	S	R	T
Third:	T	S	R	T	S

(a) Who wins if the Plurality With Elimination Method is used?
(b) Who wins if the Method of Pairwise Comparisons is used?

2. Fourteen voters rank Coke, Pepsi, Sprite, and Mountain Dew as shown at right.

Number of Voters	5	3	1	3	2
First:	S	C	P	C	M
Second:	P	P	M	P	P
Third:	C	S	C	M	C
Fourth:	M	M	S	S	S

(a) Who wins if the Plurality With Elimination Method is used?
(b) Who wins if the Method of Pairwise Comparisons is used?

3. The preference schedule of the election in Problems 5 and 15 of Section 4.1 is shown below.

Number of voters:	5	8	9	1	4
First	Z	W	Y	X	W
Second	Y	X	Z	W	Y
Third	X	Z	W	Z	X
Fourth	W	Y	X	Y	Z

(a) Who wins if the Plurality With Elimination Method is used?
(b) Who wins if the Method of Pairwise Comparisons is used?

4. The preference schedule of the election in Problems 6 and 16 of Section 4.1 is shown below.

Number of voters:	8	7	6	2	1
First	A	D	D	C	E
Second	B	B	B	A	A
Third	C	A	E	B	D
Fourth	D	C	C	D	B
Fifth	E	E	A	E	C

(a) Who wins if the Plurality With Elimination Method is used?
(b) Who wins if the Method of Pairwise Comparisons is used?

5. A small class is polled regarding their rankings of Coke (C), Pepsi (P), and Sprite (S).

Number of students:	1	5	3	4	7
First	C	S	C	S	P
Second	S	C	P	P	C
Third	P	P	S	C	S

(a) Explain why the Plurality with Elimination Method results in a tie for first place.
(b) Which network wins if the Method of Pairwise Comparisons is used?

6. An informal poll of TV viewers must rank major networks from among ABC, CBS, Fox, and NBC. The results are shown in the preference schedule below. (Consider each % of viewers as a vote.)

% of viewers:	35	15	30	10	10
First	CBS	ABC	NBC	Fox	ABC
Second	ABC	Fox	ABC	CBS	Fox
Third	Fox	CBS	CBS	NBC	NBC
Fourth	NBC	NBC	Fox	ABC	CBS

(a) Who wins if the Plurality with Elimination Method is used?

(b) Which network wins if the Method of Pairwise Comparisons is used?

7. The Super Bowl Selection Committee must choose a site for the next super Bowl from among Atlanta (A), Houston (H), Los Angeles (L), or Miami (M). Their preference schedule is shown below.

Number of Voters:	10	6	5	4	2
First	A	H	H	L	M
Second	L	M	L	A	L
Third	H	L	A	M	H
Fourth	M	A	M	H	A

(a) Which city wins if the Plurality With Elimination Method is used?

(b) Which city wins if the Method of Pairwise Comparisons is used?

8. For the preference schedule shown below, determine the winner if:

Number of Voters:	15	7	13	5	2
First	C	E	G	D	E
Second	D	D	F	G	F
Third	E	G	E	F	G
Fourth	F	F	D	E	D
Fifth	G	C	C	C	C

(a) The Plurality With Elimination Method is used.

(b) The Method of Pairwise Comparisons is used.

Apply Your Knowledge: (Answers to odd-numbered problems in back of text.)

9. Use your results from Problem 1 (preference schedule shown below) to answer these questions:

Number of Voters	2	2	2	2	1
First:	R	T	T	S	R
Second:	S	R	S	R	T
Third:	T	S	R	T	S

(a) Does this example show a violation of the Condorcet Fairness Criterion by the Plurality with Elimination Method? Explain why or why not.

(b) Does this example show a violation of the Condorcet Fairness Criterion by the Plurality Method? Explain why or why not.

(c) In Section 4.1 you showed that R won if the Borda Count Method is used. Is this a violation of the Condorcet Fairness Criterion by the Borda Count Method? Explain why or why not.

10. Use your results from Problem 2 (preference schedule shown below) to answer these questions:

Number of Voters	5	3	1	3	2
First:	S	C	P	C	M
Second:	P	P	M	P	P
Third:	C	S	C	M	C
Fourth:	M	M	S	S	S

(a) Does this example show a violation of the Condorcet Fairness Criterion by the Plurality with Elimination Method? Explain why or why not.

(b) Does this example show a violation of the Condorcet Fairness Criterion by the Plurality Method?

(c) In Section 4.1 you showed that P won if the Borda Count Method is used. Is this a violation of the Condorcet Fairness Criterion by the Borda Count Method? Explain why or why not.

11. Use your results from Problem 3 (preference schedule shown below) to answer these questions:

Number of voters:	5	8	9	1	4
First	Z	W	Y	X	W
Second	Y	X	Z	W	Y
Third	X	Z	W	Z	X
Fourth	W	Y	X	Y	Z

(a) Does this example show a violation of the Condorcet Fairness Criterion by the Plurality with Elimination Method? Explain why or why not.

(b) Does this example show a violation of the Condorcet Fairness Criterion by the Plurality Method?

(c) In Section 4.1 you showed that W won if the Borda Count Method is used. Is this a violation of the Condorcet Fairness Criterion by the Borda Count Method? Explain why or why not.

12. Use your results from Problem 4 (preference schedule shown below) to answer these questions:

Number of voters:	8	7	6	2	1
First	A	D	D	C	E
Second	B	B	B	A	A
Third	C	A	E	B	D
Fourth	D	C	C	D	B
Fifth	E	E	A	E	C

(a) Does this example show a violation of the Condorcet Fairness Criterion by the Plurality with Elimination Method? Explain why or why not.

(b) Does this example show a violation of the Condorcet Fairness Criterion by the Plurality Method?

(c) In Section 4.1 you showed that B won if the Borda Count Method is used. Is this a violation of the Condorcet Fairness Criterion by the Borda Count Method? Explain why or why not.

13. Use your results from Problem 5 (preference schedule shown below) to answer these questions:

Number of students:	1	5	3	4	7
First	C	S	C	S	P
Second	S	C	P	P	C
Third	P	P	S	C	S

(a) Does this example show a violation of the Condorcet Fairness Criterion by the Plurality with Elimination Method? Explain.

(b) Does this example show a violation of the Condorcet Fairness Criterion by the Plurality Method? Explain.

14. Use your results from Problem 6 (preference schedule shown below) to answer these questions:

% of viewers:	35	15	30	10	10
First	CBS	ABC	NBC	Fox	ABC
Second	ABC	Fox	ABC	CBS	Fox
Third	Fox	CBS	CBS	NBC	NBC
Fourth	NBC	NBC	Fox	ABC	CBS

   (a) Does this example show a violation of the Condorcet Fairness Criterion by the Plurality with Elimination Method? Explain why or why not.
   (b) Does this example show a violation of the Condorcet Fairness Criterion by the Plurality Method?
   (c) Determine the winner if Borda Count is used. Then decide whether this example shows a violation of the Condorcet Fairness Criterion by the Borda Count Method, and explain your conclusion.

15. Use your results from Problem 7 (preference schedule shown below) to answer these questions:

Number of Voters:	10	6	5	4	2
First	A	H	H	L	M
Second	L	M	L	A	L
Third	H	L	A	M	H
Fourth	M	A	M	H	A

   (a) Does this example show a violation of the Condorcet Fairness Criterion by the Plurality with Elimination Method? Explain why or why not.
   (b) Does this example show a violation of the Condorcet Fairness Criterion by the Plurality Method?
   (c) Determine the winner if Borda Count is used. Then decide whether this example shows a violation of the Condorcet Fairness Criterion by the Borda Count Method, and explain your conclusion.

16. Use your results from Problem 8 (preference schedule shown below) to answer these questions:

Number of Voters:	15	7	13	5	2
First	C	E	G	D	E
Second	D	D	F	G	F
Third	E	G	E	F	G
Fourth	F	F	D	E	D
Fifth	G	C	C	C	C

   (a) Does this example show a violation of the Condorcet Fairness Criterion by the Plurality with Elimination Method? Explain why or why not.
   (b) Does this example show a violation of the Condorcet Fairness Criterion by the Plurality Method?
   (c) Determine the winner if Borda Count is used. Then decide whether this example shows a violation of the Condorcet Fairness Criterion by the Borda Count Method, and explain why your answer is correct.

17. Consider the preference schedule below that has two columns and three candidate, but unknown numbers a and b of voters who submit the two preference ballots.

Number of Voters	a	b
First:	B	A
Second:	A	C
Third:	C	B

   (i) Find an example of values of a and b that will cause there to be a Condorcet candidate who does not win when the Borda Count Method is used.
   (ii) Find a condition on the values of a and b that will insure there is a Condorcet candidate who does not win when the Borda Count Method is used.

18. Suppose an election in which 21 voters choose among 3 candidates K, L, and M. Create a possible preference schedule for this election so that M has the fewest first place votes, but M is also a Condorcet candidate. Justify your answer.

19. Suppose an election in which 21 voters choose among 3 candidates K, L, and M. Create a preference schedule with candidates K, L, and M which shows an example of Condorcet's Paradox when the Plurality Method is used. Explain why your schedule is such an example.

Communicate the Concepts: (Answers to odd-numbered problems in back of text.)
20. Explain why the Plurality with Elimination Method satisfies the Majority Fairness Criterion.

21. Explain why the Method of Pairwise Comparisons satisfies the Majority Fairness Criterion.

22. Suppose an election only has two candidates. Give an argument why the winner by the Plurality also wins using Plurality With Elimination and the Method of Pairwise comparisons.

23. Explain why any voting method that violates the Majority Fairness Criterion must also violate the Condorcet Fairness Criterion.

Section 4.3 Is There an Ideal Voting Method?

So far we have considered four voting methods, and judged them by two fairness criteria. Ever since the study of voting methods began social scientists, theologians, and mathematicians have sought an "ideal" voting method, one that would adhere to as many fairness criteria as possible. We now consider two other fairness criteria by which to judge voting methods.

The Monotonicity Fairness Criterion

Suppose candidate X wins an election using a voting method. If a second election is done with the only change in the preference schedule being that some voters rank X higher in the second election than the first, then X must win the second election if the same method is used.

Result 3 All our voting methods except Plurality With Elimination satisfy the Monotonicity Fairness Criterion.

Solution: The argument for the Plurality Method is as follows: If candidate X has the most first place votes in the first election, and then some voters move X up in their rankings, then X must then have at least as many first place votes as they had in the first election, and no other candidate can gain first place votes. So X still has the most first place votes and will win using the Plurality Method. (Similar arguments are possible for the Borda Count Method and the Method of Pairwise Comparisons; see the problems for this Section.)

To see that Plurality With Elimination does not satisfy the Monotonicity Fairness Criterion, we must create an example in which moving the original winner up changes the order of elimination and causes the original eventual winner to be eliminated early.

Example 1 A class of 33 students ranks its preferences for Coke (C), Pepsi (P), and Sprite (S) as shown in the preference schedule below. Who wins if Plurality With Elimination is used? Can the voters in the last column change their votes to show a violation of the Monotonicity Fairness Criterion?

Number of Voters:	12	10	8	3
First	C	S	P	P
Second	P	C	S	C
Third	S	P	C	S

Table 4.14

Solution If Plurality With Elimination is used on this schedule, then Sprite has the fewest first place votes, and so is eliminated in the first round. The 10 people who ranked Sprite first now all rank Coke first, so Coke has a total of 12 + 10 = 22, a majority. So Coke wins.

But suppose the 3 voters in the last column decide to move Coke up, so that they rank Coke first, Pepsi second, and Sprite third, as shown in Table 4.15.

Number of Voters:	12	10	8	3
First	C	S	P	C
Second	P	C	S	P
Third	S	P	C	S

Table 4.15

Now Pepsi has the fewest first place votes, and so is eliminated in the first round. The 8 people who ranked Pepsi first now all rank Sprite first, giving Sprite 10 + 8 = 18 first place votes, a majority. Now Sprite is declared the winner! This is a violation of the Monotonicity Fairness Criterion. *This example shows that moving a candidate up in an early round of Plurality With Elimination may actually cause that candidate to fare worse in a later round.*

Quiz Yourself (Answers at the end of this section, before the Problems.)
1. Explain how the two preference schedules below may be used to show that the Plurality with Elimination Method does not satisfy the Monotonicity Fairness Criterion.

	5	4	3	1
First	A	C	B	B
Second	B	B	C	A
Third	C	A	A	C

	5	4	3	1
First	A	C	B	A
Second	B	B	C	B
Third	C	A	A	C

Our final fairness criterion says that a voting *method* should *guarantee* that the original winner will still win if the original ballots are used but a losing candidate withdraws. We often see discussion in the newspapers before an election of the political effects of a candidate dropping out. Is it too much to ask that a truly deserving candidate still win if one of his or her opponents drops out? *That's not the question here!* We are concerned with the fairness of the *voting method*.

The Independence of Irrelevant Alternatives Fairness Criterion

Suppose candidate X wins an election using a voting method. If one of the losing candidates drops out and then the original ballots are used for a second election, X must still win if that same voting method is used. Otherwise the method fails to satisfy the Independence of Irrelevant Alternatives Criterion.

Example 2 Use the preference schedule below to give an example of a violation of the Independence of Irrelevant Alternatives Fairness Criterion by the Plurality Method.

Number of Voters:	5	4	2
First	A	B	C
Second	B	C	B
Third	C	A	A

Table 4.16

Solution: A has the most first place votes and wins if the Plurality Method is used. However, if C withdraws, the 2 voters in the last column now vote for B, giving B 6 first place votes to 5 for A and making B the winner!

In Problems 7 and 10 of this section you are asked to show a violation of the Independence of Irrelevant Alternatives Fairness Criterion by the Plurality with Elimination Method.

Example 3 Use the preference schedule below to give an example of a violation of the Independence of Irrelevant Alternatives Fairness Criterion by the Method of Pairwise Comparisons.

Number of Voters:	2	6	4	1	5	4
1st Choice	A	B	B	C	D	C
2nd Choice	D	A	A	B	A	D
3rd Choice	C	C	D	A	C	B
4th Choice	B	D	C	D	B	A

Table 4.10

Solution: In Example 5 of Section 4.2 it was shown that the 6 pairwise comparisons resulted in the awarding of these points: A: 2 points, B: 1 1/2 points, C: 1 1/2 points, D: 1 point. Thus A won.

Now suppose C drops out. This causes the candidates below C in each column to move up, as shown in Table 4.17.

Number of Voters:	2	6	4	1	5	4
1st Choice	A	B	B	B	D	D
2nd Choice	D	A	A	A	A	B
3rd Choice	B	D	D	D	B	A

Table 4.17

Here are the results of the pairwise comparisons from Table 4.17:

A vs. B: A gets $2 + 5 = 7$ votes; B gets $6 + 4 + 1 + 4 = 15$ votes   B gets 1 point

A vs. D: A gets $2 + 6 + 4 + 1 = 13$ votes; D gets $5 + 4 = 9$ votes   A gets 1 point

B vs. D: B gets $6 + 4 + 1 = 11$ votes; D gets $2 + 5 + 4 = 11$ votes   B and D get 1/2 point

So B gets a total of 1 1/2 points, A gets 1 point, and D gets 1/2 point. Now B wins, rather than the original winner A. This is a violation of the Independence of Irrelevant Alternatives Criterion.

Quiz Yourself (Answer on the next page.)

2. Consider the preference schedule shown below.
    (a) Who wins if the Borda Count Method is used?
    (b) Suppose C drops out. Who wins if the Borda Count Method is used?
    (c) Is this a violation of the Independence of Irrelevant Alternatives Fairness Criterion? Explain why or why not.

	8	4	5	1
First	A	D	C	D
Second	C	A	D	A
Third	D	C	A	C

Summary of Which Voting Methods Satisfy Which Fairness Criteria

The chart below summarizes which of our four voting methods satisfy which fairness criteria. Many of these have been shown or argued in previous examples and problems; some will be investigated in the problems of this section.

	Majority Criterion	Condorcet Criterion	Monotonicity Criterion	Independence of Irrelevant Alternatives
Plurality	Y (Example 4 Section 4.1)	N (Example 6 Section 4.2)	Y (Result 3)	N (Example 3)
Borda Count	N (Example 3 Section 4.1)	N (Example 7 Section 4.2)	Y (Problem 15)	N (Problems 8, 13)
Plurality With Elimination	Y (Problem 20, Section 4.2)	N (Example 7 Section 4.2)	N (Example 1)	N (Problems 7, 10, 11)
Pairwise Comparisons	Y (Problem 21, Section 4.2)	Y (Definition of that method.)	Y (Problem 16)	N (Example 3)

Notice that none of our four voting methods satisfied all four of the fairness criteria. In the two centuries since the French and American revolutions there has been a great deal of work by social scientists and mathematicians with the goal of creating a "perfect" voting method, one that would satisfy all the fairness criteria. For example, Charles Dodgson, a mathematician who was a Don at Oxford in the late nineteenth century, and who wrote children's books under the name Lewis Carroll, became interested in voting methods after a faculty vote did not turn out as he had hoped. After a number of attempts, he came up with this method:

1) First check for a Condorcet candidate. If one existed, that candidate won.
2) Otherwise, look at the cycles in the pairwise matches, such a A beats B, B beats C, and C beats A. For each cycle determine the smallest number of vote changes necessary to break the cycle. Make that smallest number of vote changes and look again for a Condorcet candidate. If there is one, that candidate is declared the winner.
3) Otherwise, reconsider the remaining cycles as before. Keep changing small numbers of votes in this way until a Condorcet candidate is obtained.

Can you imagine trying to implement this method with a large number of voters or candidates?

In 1952 economist Kenneth Arrow (shown at right) proved mathematically that it is *impossible* to find a democratic voting method that satisfies all our four fairness criteria. This result is known as **Arrow's Impossibility Theorem**, and he won a Nobel Prize in Economics for this mathematical result. It began a wave of "mathematization" of the social sciences that has continued into the twenty-first century.

Ed Souza/Stanford News Service

Answers to Quiz Yourself Problems:

1. With the first schedule, shown at right, when Plurality with Elimination is used B and C tie for fewest first place votes, so they are both eliminated and A is declared the winner.

	5	4	3	1
First	A	C	B	B
Second	B	B	C	A
Third	C	A	A	C

With the second schedule, shown at right, B has the fewest first place votes and so is eliminated. The 3 voters in the next-to-last column then vote for their second choice, C. This gives C 7 first place votes to 6 for A, so C wins.

	5	4	3	1
First	A	C	B	A
Second	B	B	C	B
Third	C	A	A	C

This is a violation of the Monotonicity Fairness Criterion by the Plurality with Elimination Method because the difference between the two schedules is that the winner of the first schedule, A, was moved up in the last column of the second schedule. Having a voter rank A higher than in the first schedule should not cause A to lose.

2. (a) Using Borda Count the points are:

   A: $8 \times 3 + (4 + 1) \times 2 + 5 \times 1 = 39$;

   C: $5 \times 3 + 8 \times 2 + (4 + 1) \times 1 = 36$;

   D: $(4 + 1) \times 3 + 5 \times 2 + 8 \times 1 = 33$.   A wins.

(b) If C drops out the result is the schedule at right. With this schedule the Borda Count points are: A: 26; D: 28. Now D wins.

	8	4	5	1
First	A	D	D	D
Second	D	A	A	A

(c) Yes this is a violation of the Independence of Irrelevant Alternatives Fairness Criterion by the Borda Count Method. Originally A wins, but when losing C drops out, D wins.

Problems for Section 4.3

Sharpen Your Skills: (Answers in back of text.)

1. State the Monotonicity Fairness Criterion.

2. Which of our four voting methods satisfy the Monotonicity Fairness Criterion?

3. State the Independence of Irrelevant Alternatives Fairness Criterion.

4. Which of our voting methods satisfy the Independence of Irrelevant Alternatives Fairness Criterion?

5. One of our voting methods satisfies all but one of our four fairness criteria. Which voting method is it?

6. State Arrow's Impossibility Theorem.

Apply Your Knowledge: (Answers to odd-numbered problems in back of text.)

7. A 24-member committee ranks four cites that are vying to host the 2012 Olympics, Berlin (B), Houston (H), Paris (P), and Tokyo (T), according to the following preference schedule:

Number of Members:	8	6	2	3	3	2
First	T	H	T	B	P	P
Second	H	B	P	P	T	T
Third	B	P	H	T	B	H
Fourth	P	T	B	H	H	B

In Example 2 of Section 4.2 it was shown that P wins if Plurality With Elimination is used. Suppose, before the actual voting begins, H drops out. Show that a different candidate now wins if Plurality With Elimination is used. Is this a violation of one of our fairness criteria? If so, which one?

8. Explain how the preference schedule below shows an example of a violation of the Independence of Irrelevant Alternatives Fairness Criterion by the Borda Count Method.

Number of voters:	6	3	4
First	A	B	B
Second	C	A	C
Third	B	C	A

9. A class ranks four alternatives for its school field trip: Atlanta (A), Boston (B), Cincinnati (C), or Denver (D), according to the following preference schedule:

Number of students:	7	8	10	4	1
First	B	C	D	B	A
Second	C	D	B	D	C
Third	A	A	C	A	B
Fourth	D	B	A	C	D

(a) Decide the winner using Plurality With Elimination.

(b) Suppose the 4 students in the next-to-last column figure out the winner, and decide to change their rankings to move D up to first in their rankings, giving:

Number of students:	7	8	10	4	1
First	B	C	D	D	A
Second	C	D	B	B	C
Third	A	A	C	A	B
Fourth	D	B	A	C	D

Determine the winner now, still using Plurality With Elimination.

(c) Do parts (a) and (b) illustrate a violation of one of our Fairness criteria? *Explain*.

10. Use the preference schedule in Example 1 of this Section to show a violation of the Independence of Irrelevant Alternatives Fairness Criterion by the Plurality With Elimination Method.

11. The election for this preference schedule is to be decided by the Plurality With Elimination Method:

Number of voters:	10	6	5	4	2
First	W	X	Y	Z	Z
Second	Y	Z	X	Y	W
Third	Z	Y	Z	X	X
Fourth	X	W	W	W	Y

(a) Is there a Majority Candidate?

(b) Is there a Condorcet Candidate?

(c) Find the winner using Plurality With Elimination Method.

(d) Suppose Z drops out of the race. Who wins the election then, still using the Plurality With Elimination Method?

(e) Based on the results of parts (a) - (d), of which of our four fairness criteria does this preference schedule show a violation by the Plurality With Elimination Method? *Explain*.

12. Four candidates, E, F, G, and H, are running for president of the metro council. The preference schedule of the council members is:

Number of members:	16	10	8	2
First	E	G	H	H
Second	F	F	E	E
Third	G	H	G	F
Fourth	H	E	F	G

(a) Who wins the election if the Method of Pairwise Comparisons is used?

(b) Suppose candidates F and G drop out prior to the announcement of the election results. Which candidate would then be declared the winner between E and H using the same voting method?

(c) Do the results of (a) and (b) show a violation of one of our fairness criteria? If so, tell which one and explain why this is a violation.

13. The election for this preference schedule is to be decided by the Borda Count Method:

Number of Voters:	5	3	5	3	2	3
First	A	A	C	D	D	B
Second	B	D	E	C	C	E
Third	C	B	D	B	B	A
Fourth	D	C	A	E	A	C
Fifth	E	E	B	A	E	D

(a) Is there a Majority Candidate?

(b) Is there a Condorcet Candidate?

(c) Find the winner using the Borda Count Method.

(d) Suppose E drops out of the race. Who wins the election then, still using the Borda Count Method?

(e) Based on the results of parts (a) - (d), of which of our four fairness criteria does this preference schedule show a violation by the Borda Count Method? *Explain*.

14. Four candidates, A, B, C, and D, are running for president of the metro council. The preference schedule of the council members is:

Number of members:	15	9	9	3
First	A	D	C	D
Second	B	A	B	A
Third	C	C	D	B
Fourth	D	B	A	C

(a) Who wins the election if the Method of Pairwise Comparisons is used?

(b) Suppose candidates B and C drop out prior to the announcement of the election results. Which candidate would then be declared the winner between A and D using the same voting method?

(c) Do the results of (a) and (b) show a violation of one of our fairness criteria? If so, tell which one and explain why this is a violation.

15. The 100 members of a club vote for a new president among four candidates, A, B, C, and D. Their preference schedule is:

Number of Votes	27	23	22	13	11	4
First:	B	D	A	C	C	B
Second:	C	A	C	B	D	A
Third:	D	B	D	A	A	C
Fourth:	A	C	B	D	B	D

(a) Who wins if Plurality with Elimination is used?

(b) Suppose the voters in column 4 had ranked B first and C second, resulting in this schedule:

Number of Votes	27	23	22	13	11	4
First:	B	D	A	B	C	B
Second:	C	A	C	C	D	A
Third:	D	B	D	A	A	C
Fourth:	A	C	B	D	B	D

Who wins now, if Plurality With Elimination is still used?

(c) Do the results of (a) and (b) show a violation of one of our fairness criteria? If so, tell which one and explain why this is a violation.

16. (a) Use Plurality with Elimination to determine the winner of this election:

% of ballots:	30	28	27	15
First	X	Y	Z	Z
Second	Y	X	Y	X
Third	Z	Z	X	Y

(b) Interchange the order of two candidates in one column in such a way that a violation of the Monotonicity Fairness Criterion occurs.

17. Twenty-one voters choose among 3 candidates K, L, and M. The first place votes are 8 for K, 7 for L, and 6 for M. Create a preference schedule, consistent with the first place votes, which shows an example of a violation of the Independence of Irrelevant Alternatives Fairness condition by the Plurality Method. Explain why your schedule is such an example.

18. Suppose 21 voters choose among 3 candidates K, L, and M. The first place votes are 8 for K, 7 for L, and 6 for M. Create a preference schedule, consistent with the first place votes, which shows an example of a violation of the Monotonicity Fairness condition by the Plurality with Elimination Method. Explain why your schedule is such an example. (Hint: Look at Example 1 again, and adapt it to fit this problem.)

Communicate the Concepts: (Answers to odd-numbered problems in back of text.)
19. Explain why the Borda Count Method satisfies the Monotonicity Fairness Criterion.

20. Explain why the Method of Pairwise Comparisons satisfies the Monotonicity Fairness Criterion.

21. Suppose an election is held among three candidates, and that the preference schedule shows a violation of the Condorcet Fairness Criterion by the Plurality Method. Give an argument why this schedule must also show a violation of the Independence of Irrelevant Alternative Criterion by the Plurality Method.

Part 2: Apportionment

The U. S. Constitution requires that a census be conducted every ten years and the House of Representatives be apportioned based on that census. The number of representatives to which each state is entitled must be proportional to the state's population. This is in contrast to the U. S. Senate, where each state always has two senators regardless of its population. Our system, in which these two governing bodies have very different structure, is a result of *The Great Compromise* in the Constitutional Convention of 1787. The apportionment of the House of Representatives is described in Article 1, Sections 2 and 3, of our Constitution:

> [Seats in the House of Representatives] ... *shall be apportioned among the several states which may be included within this Union, according to their respective Numbers. ... The actual enumeration shall be made ... every ... ten Years in such manner as they [the House of Representatives] shall by Law direct. The number of Representatives shall not exceed one for every thirty thousand, but each state shall have at least one representative.*

The Constitution does not make clear how this apportionment is to actually be done. Neither does it state a specific size of the House, only that there be at least 30,000 people per representative, and each state has at least one representative. Each state is entitled to a number of seats that is proportional to its population. So if the state has *p%* of the country's population it is entitled to *p%* of the seats in the legislature. While this seems easy to calculate, the problem is that it usually results in a state being entitled to a *fractional* number of seats, whereas a state must receive a *whole* number of seats. In order to give each state a whole number of seats some states must get a little more than they are entitled to, and some must get a little less. To make this clearer let's look at a simple example.

Example 1 Suppose a country has four states whose populations are listed in Table 4.18 and has a representative body with 15 seats. How many seats should be apportioned to each state if the apportionments are to be proportional to the state populations?

State	Population
A	105,200
B	79,800
C	67,200
D	47,800
Total	300,000

Table 4.18

Solution: First we find what per cent of the total population is in each state, and then calculate that per cent of the 15 seats available:

State A is entitled to $\left(\frac{105,200}{300,000}\right) = .35 = 35\%$ of the 15 seats, or $\left(\frac{105,200}{300,000}\right) \times 15 = 5.26$ seats

State B is entitled to $\left(\frac{79,800}{300,000}\right) \times 15 = 3.99$ seats   State C is entitled to $\left(\frac{67,200}{300,000}\right) \times 15 = 3.36$ seats

State D is entitled to $\left(\frac{47,000}{300,000}\right) \times 15 = 2.39$ seats

However, each state must be given a <u>whole</u> number of seats. That is, one or more states get a little more than they are entitled to, others get a little less.

Probably your first thought about how to make these decimals into whole numbers is to simply round each of them in the standard fashion: If the fractional part is less than 0.5, drop it; otherwise round up to the next whole number. But if we do that in this example, State A will get 5 seats, State B will get 4 seats, State C will get 3 seats, and State D will get 2 seats, for a total of 14 seats, whereas the actual number of seats to be apportioned is 15! So **just rounding the decimals may not produce a valid apportionment!**

Apportionment Notation

To make our discussion of apportionment methods easier we need to adopt some standard notation. We will state our notation in terms of apportionment of a legislative body. It can be adapted for other apportionment problems.

The **Standard Quota** of a state is the (perhaps fractional) number of seats to which it is actually entitled. In the previous example we saw that this may be calculated in the following way:

$$\textbf{State Standard Quota} = \frac{\text{State's population}}{\text{total population}} \times (\text{total number of seats}) = \text{number of representatives state deserves.}$$

The **standard divisor** of an apportionment problem is the average number of people per seat being apportioned. That is,

$$\textbf{Standard divisor} = \frac{\text{total population}}{\text{total number of seats to be apportioned}} = \text{average number of people per seat}$$

For each state, its **standard quota** may then be obtained by dividing the state's population by the standard divisor. The box below shows this yields the same answer as before:

$$\text{State Standard Quota} = \frac{\text{state's population}}{\text{standard divisor}} = \frac{\text{state's population}}{\left(\dfrac{\text{total population}}{\text{total seats}}\right)} = \frac{\text{state's population}}{\text{total population}} \times (\text{total seats})$$

Example 1 Again Let's redo the first example using the notation above. The total population is 300,000, and the total number of seats is 15, so the standard divisor is 300,000 / 15 = 20,000. This is the average number of people per seat. Dividing each state's population by this standard divisor gives the standard quotas we found before, as shown in Table 4.19 below.

State	Population	Standard Quota = Population / 20,000
A	105,200	5.26
B	79,800	3.99
C	67,200	3.36
D	47,800	2.39
Total	300,000	15.00

Table 4.19

Note that the standard quotas sum to the total number of seats available; this will always be true.

Quiz Yourself: (Answers at end of Section, before the Problems.)

1. A country has 3 states with populations shown below, and wants to apportion 9 seats in a legislature according to these populations.

State	Population	Standard Quota
A	4,700,000	
B	3,700,000	
C	1,600,000	

(a) Determine the standard divisor. What does it represent in this problem?

(b) Find the Standard Quotas of the states. Fill them in the chart. What do these represent in this problem?

We are still faced with the basic problem of assigning whole numbers of seats to each state so that the whole numbers sum to the total number of seats available and so that the whole numbers are "proportional to population". (As we saw previously, rounding the standard quotas may not produce a collection of whole numbers whose sum is the total number of seats to be apportioned.) Over the history of the U. S. House of Representatives many methods for doing this have been offered. Our goal in this chapter is to discuss the major ones in their historical context, and also to see a number of other problems that are general apportionment problems.

Section 4.4   The Hamilton Method

After the Constitutional Convention of 1787 set up a House of Representatives a census was done in 1790. Based on that data the first Congress faced the task of agreeing on a method for apportioning the House. The first apportionment bill was proposed by Alexander Hamilton (shown at right) , who would soon be Secretary of the Treasury. His apportionment method starts with each state being given the whole number part of its standard quota; this is called the **lower quota** of the state. These whole numbers are then summed, and if this sum is less than the desired total number of seats in the House, then one additional seat (each) is apportioned to the states whose standard quotas have the largest fractional parts, until the desired total number of seats is attained. In summary:

The Hamilton Method of Apportionment:
<u>Step 1:</u> Compute the standard quota and lower quota for each state.
<u>Step 2:</u> Each state starts with its lower quota as its apportionment. These lower quotas are summed to determine how many seats remain to be allocated to reach the desired house size.
<u>Step 3:</u> Seats are allocated to those states whose quotas have the largest fractional parts until the desired house size is reached. (No state is allocated more than one seat in this manner.)

<u>**Example 1 Continued**</u> Use Hamilton's Method to apportion the legislature in Example 1.

<u>Solution:</u> In Example 1 we found the standard quotas of the four states. Dropping the fractional parts of these gives the lower quotas in Table 4.20 below. These add up to 13, so 2 more seats must be apportioned to reach the desired House size of 15. Since states B and D have the largest fractional parts (0.99 and 0.39, respectively) they are awarded an extra seat each. The final column shows the apportionment of the legislative body by the Hamilton Method.

State	Population	Standard Quota	Lower Quota	Extra Seat?	Hamilton Apportionment
A	105,200	5.26	5		5
B	79,800	3.99	3	+ 1	4
C	67,200	3.36	3		3
D	47,800	2.39	2	+ 1	3
Total	300,000	15.00	13		15

Table 4.20

Recall that the Standard Divisor of 20,000 represents the average number of people per seat in the country as a whole. If the Standard Quotas were all whole numbers there would also be 20,000 people per seat in each state. But, as in this example, when the Standard Quotas are not whole numbers, the resulting apportionment will not have 20,000 people per seat in each state. For example, State A has 105,200 / 5 = 21,040 people per state, and state D has 47,800 / 3 = 15,933 people per seat. So we view the Standard divisor as a kind of "ideal" number of people per seat in each state, and would like the apportionment to make the number of people per seat in each state be as close as possible to the ideal, just as we would like the actual apportioned numbers of seats to be as close as possible to the Standard Quotas that represent the "deserved" number of seats.

Quiz Yourself: (Answer at end of Section, before the Problems.)
2. The country in Quiz Yourself Problem 1 had 3 states with populations shown below, and wanted to apportion 9 seats in a legislature according to these populations.

State	Population	Standard Quota			Hamilton Apportionment
A	4,700,000				
B	3,700,000				
C	1,600,000				

Use the Hamilton Method to apportion the 9 seats.

The Hamilton Method has some good properties. **The most important property of the Hamilton Method is that the apportionments it produces always satisfy the Quota Rule**:

The Quota Rule: Each state should be apportioned its standard quota rounded up or down, that is, either its lower quota or 1 more than its lower quota.

Recall that with Hamilton's Method each state starts with its lower quota, and then some states receive one additional seat. So it is clear that Hamilton's Method always produces an apportionment that satisfies the Quota Rule. It would seem that we should expect a good apportionment method to make the actual apportionment for each state as near as possible to its standard quota. In particular, it should make the state's apportionment one of the whole numbers on either side of the standard quota of seats to which the state is entitled. This is precisely what the Quota Rule says should be satisfied. Surprisingly, many of the apportionment methods we will study can violate this rule!

Since Hamilton's Method is simple and satisfies the reasonableness test of the Quota Rule, you may be surprised to learn that, on Thomas Jefferson's advice, in 1792 President George Washington issued the first presidential veto when he vetoed the bill by which Hamilton's Method would have been adopted. One reason was that the process of awarding additional seats angered those from states that did not get an additional seat. We will discuss another reason in Section 4.6.

The Alabama Paradox

The most serious (and politically the fatal) flaw in Hamilton's Method can occur when the number of seats to be apportioned increases. It would seem that if there are more seats to go around, each state should get at least as many as when there were fewer seats, but that is not always the case!

If an increase in the number of seats to be apportioned, *without any change in the populations of the individual states*, causes some state to receive fewer seats, then this situation is said to be an example of the **Alabama Paradox**.

The name Alabama Paradox comes from a situation involving the apportionment for the state of Alabama that occurred in 1880. Throughout the 1800s the size of the House of Representatives kept increasing as the U. S. population grew. After each census Congress had considerable leeway in choosing the exact total number of representatives. In 1850 Congressman Samuel Vinton proposed the Hamilton Method again (newly renamed the "Method of Major Fractions"), and it was used from 1850 through 1900. In 1881 two of the possibilities for the House size were 299 or 300 total seats. With a House size of 299 seats Alabama would have gotten 8 seats, but with a House size of 300 seats Alabama would only get 7 seats. Because, among other reasons, the political party in power in Alabama was not the party in control of Congress, a House size of 300 seats was adopted, and Alabama "lost a seat" from what its apportionment would have been with a House size of 299. Such political maneuvering occurred in other subsequent apportionments of the U. S. House, until the political repercussions caused Hamilton's Method to be abandoned forever.

Example 2 Suppose the country in Example 1 decides to have a legislative body with 16 seats, one more seat than before. Apportion the 16 seats by Hamilton's Method, and discuss how an example of the Alabama Paradox occurs.

Solution With a house size of 16 seats, the standard divisor is 300,000 / 16 = 18,750. Dividing each state's population by 18,750 gives the standard quotas in Table 4.21 below. The lower quotas sum to 14, which is two less than the desired house size of 16. So the two states whose standard quotas have the largest fractional parts, A and C, get additional seats. This gives the Hamilton Apportionment when the house size is 16 (shown in the last column). Comparing this to Table 4.20 in Example 1 we see that when the house size was 15 total seats, state D got 3 seats. But when the house size increased to 16, D only got 2 seats! Since D's apportionment went down when the house size increased, this is an example of the Alabama Paradox.

State	Population	Standard Quota	Lower Quota	Extra Seat?	Hamilton Apportionment With 16 Seats
A	105,200	5.61	5	+ 1	6
B	79,800	4.26	4		4
C	67,200	3.584	3	+ 1	4
D	47,800	2.55	2		2
Total	300,000	16.00	14		16

Table 4.21

Note: The Standard Quota for State D in this example is 2.549333333… We rounded it to a decimal place that will allow us to compare it with the Standard Quota for State C, namely hundredths. If we rounded to the nearest tenth, obtaining 2.6 and 3.6, we would not be able to decide which has the largest fractional part. **So, round Standard Quotas to a decimal place that will allow you to compare their fractional parts.**

Quiz Yourself: (Answers at end of Section, before the Problems.)

3. The country in Quiz Yourself Problems 1 and 2 had 3 state with populations shown below, and wanted to apportion 9 seats in a legislature according to these populations. Suppose instead they wanted to apportion 10 seats in a legislature. Determine the Hamilton Apportionment of that legislature.

State	Population	Standard Quota with 10 seats			Hamilton Apportionment
A	4,700,000				
B	3,700,000				
C	1,600,000				

4. Explain how the results of Quiz Yourself Problems 2 and 3 show an example of the Alabama Paradox.

How can one explain the Alabama Paradox mathematically? Increasing the house size decreases the standard divisor (number of people per seat), and decreasing the standard divisor increases each state's standard quota. However, *these increases are proportional to the original standard quotas*, so that large standard quotas are increased more than small standard quotas. This can cause the ranking of the fractional parts of the standard quotas to change, meaning a state may no longer have a large enough fractional part to get an additional seat.

The Population Paradox

Although the Alabama Paradox was the political downfall of Hamilton's Method, later analysis showed that it suffers from another flaw too. Suppose that the house size stays fixed but we change the populations of some of the states (and perhaps the total population as well). In this case the Population Paradox may occur:

Suppose two apportionments of a legislative body are done *with the same house sizes*. If a state whose population increases loses a seat while a state whose population decreases gains a seat, this is said to be an example of the **Population Paradox.**

Example 3 Suppose the country in Example 1 takes a new census and now obtains the state populations shown in Table 4.22. Use the Hamilton Method to apportion the 16 seats. Then compare your results to those in Example 1 and explain how they show an example of the Population Paradox.

State	Population
A	105,300
B	97,900
C	67,100
D	47,700
Total	318,000

Table 4.22

<u>Solution:</u> The Standard divisor is 318,000 / 16 = 19,875. Dividing the state populations by this gives the Standard Quotas shown in Table 4.23, which also shows the Lower Quotas and Hamilton Apportionment.

State	Population	Standard Quota	Lower Quota	Extra Seat?	Hamilton Apportionment With 16 Seats
A	105,300	5.298	5		5
B	97,900	4.926	4	+1	5
C	67,100	3.376	3		3
D	47,700	2.400	2	+1	3
Total	318,000	16.000	14		16

Table 4.23

Now compare the populations and resulting Hamilton Apportionment in Example 1to the populations and Hamilton Apportionment shown in Table 4.24:

State	Original Population	Hamilton Apportionment	New Population	Hamilton Apportionment
A	105,200	6	105,300	5
B	79,800	4	97,900	5
C	67,200	4	67,100	3
D	47,800	2	47,700	3
Total	300,000	16	318,000	16

Table 4.24

Notice that State A's population increased by 100 people, but its apportionment decreased from 6 to 5, while State D's population decreased by 100 people, but its apportionment increased from 2 to 3. This is why this is an example of the Population Paradox.

By fixing the size of the House of Representatives at 435 in 1912 Congress was able to avoid the Alabama Paradox in the future. But since populations will always change, there was no way to avoid the Population Paradox if Hamilton's Method continued to be used!

Quiz Yourself: (Answers at end of Section, before the Problems.)

5. Suppose the country in Quiz Yourself Problem 3 had its state populations change to the populations shown below. Find the Hamilton Apportionment of the 10-seat legislature using the new populations.

State	New Population	Standard Quota with 10 seats	Hamilton Apportionment
A	4,710,000		
B	4,200,000		
C	1,590,000		

6. Explain how the results of Quiz Yourself Problems 3 & 5 show an example of the Population Paradox.

Applying Apportionment Methods to Other Situations

Any time there are a fixed number of indivisible objects to be allotted to groups based on some data about the groups, apportionment methods apply. The indivisible objects play the role of the seats in a legislature, the groups play the role of the states, and the data plays the role of the populations of the states. Here are some examples:

1. A fixed number of police officers are to be apportioned to districts proportional to the populations of the districts. The police officers play the role of seats and the districts play the role of states. Standard Divisor = (total population) / (total number of police officers) = average number of people per officer; Standard Quota = number of officers a district "deserves".

2. A fixed number of police officers are to be apportioned to districts proportional to the numbers of crimes in the districts. The police officers play the role of seats, the districts play the role of states, and the numbers of crimes play the role of populations. Standard Divisor = (total number of crimes) / (total number of police officers) = average number of crimes per officer; Standard Quota = number of officers a district "deserves".

3. A fixed number of polling places are to be apportioned to voting districts proportional to the numbers of voters in the districts. The polling places play the role of seats, the districts play the role of states, and the numbers of voters play the role of populations. Standard Divisor = (total number of voters) / (total number of polling places) = average number of voters per polling place; Standard Quota = number of polling places a district "deserves".

4. A fixed number of sections are to be apportioned to courses based on the enrollments in those courses. The sections play the role of seats, the courses play the role of states, and the enrollments play the role of populations. Standard Divisor = (total enrollments) / (total number of sections) = average enrollment per section; Standard Quota = number of sections a course "deserves".

Quiz Yourself: (Answer at end of Section, before the Problems.)

7. A fixed number of firemen are to be apportioned to fire districts based on the number of recent fires in the districts. Why is this an apportionment problem? What plays the role of seats? What plays the role of states? what plays the role of populations? How is the Standard Divisor calculated? What does it represent? What does each Standard Quota represent?

Here is an example of apportionment methods applied to such a situation.

Example 4 A town has three districts A, B, and C, and a force of 40 police officers. The populations of the three districts are shown in the second column of Table 4.25. The town uses the Hamilton Method to apportion the 40 police officers to the districts in proportion to the populations of the districts. However, just after this is done, new census figures shown in the third column are obtained, so the apportionment must be redone. When the re-apportionment is done, what, if any, paradox occurs?

District	Population	New Population
A	12,950	12,995
B	8,410	8,730
C	6,640	6,635
Total	28,000	28,360

Table 4.25

Solution The officers play the role of seats in a legislature. The districts play the role of states. The standard divisor for the original populations is (28,000 people) / (40 officers) = 700, and is the *average number of people per officer in the town*. The standard quotas are shown in Table 4.26 on the next page. Since it is officers, not seats, that are being apportioned, *the standard quotas represent the number of police officers each district is entitled to*.

District	Population	Standard Quota with Stan. Divisor = 700	Lower Quota	Hamilton Apportionment
A	12,950	18.50	18	19
B	8,410	12.01	12	12
C	6,640	9.49	9	9
Total	28,000	40.00	39	40

Table 4.26   Hamilton Apportionment of 40 Officers with Original Populations

The lower quotas sum to 39, so one more seat is awarded. It goes to A, since its Standard Quota has the largest fractional part. Table 4.26 above gives the resulting Hamilton apportionment.

When the populations of the districts are changed as shown in Table 4.27, the total population is changed to 28,360, so the standard divisor is 28,360 / 40 = 709. The new standard quotas are shown in Table 4.27. The lower quotas still sum to 39, and the additional seat goes to C whose Standard Quota has the largest fractional part. Table 4.24 also gives the resulting Hamilton apportionment.

District	Population	Standard Quota with Standard Divisor = 709)	Lower Quota	Hamilton Apportionment
A	12,995	18.33	18	18
B	8,730	12.31	12	12
C	6,635	9.36	9	10
Total	28,360	40.00	39	40

Table 4.27   Hamilton Apportionment of 40 Officers with Revised Population

This is an example of the Population Paradox for the following reason. Even though district A's population increased from 12,950 to 12,995, its apportionment decreased from 19 to 18, while C's population decreased from 6,640 to 6,635 and its apportionment increased from 9 to 10.

Quiz Yourself Answers

1. The total population is 10,000,000. The standard divisor is 10,000,000 / 9 = 1,111,111.11 It represents the average number of people per seat. Dividing each state population by this gives the standard quotas shown in the table below. These represent the number of seats that the states "deserve".

State	Population	Standard Quota	Lower Quota	Extra Seats	Hamilton Apportionment
A	4,700,000	4.23	4		4
B	3,700,000	3.33	3		3
C	1,600,000	1.44	1	+1	2
Total	10,000,000	9	8		10

2. The lower quotas are shown in the table above. They total 8, one short of the desired 9 seats. An additional seat is given to the state with the largest fractional part in its standard quota, so C gets a total of 2 seats. The Hamilton Apportionment is given in the last column.

3. With 10 seats the standard divisor is 10,000,000 / 10 = 1,000,000. The resulting standard quotas are shown in the table below. The lower quotas sum to 8, so an extra seat is given to A and B, the states whose standard quotas have the largest fractional parts.

State	Population	Standard Quota with 10 seats	Lower Quota	Extra Seats	Hamilton Apportionment
A	4,700,000	4.7	4	+1	5
B	3,700,000	3.7	3	+1	4
C	1,600,000	1.6	1		1
Total	10,000,000		8		10

4. When there were 9 seats to be awarded, C got 2 seats. When the number of seats increased to 10, C's number of seats decreased to 1. This is an example of the Alabama Paradox.

5. The calculations for the Hamilton Apportionment of 10 seats with the new populations is shown below.

State	New Population	Standard Quota with 10 seats	Lower Quota	Extra Seats	Hamilton Apportionment
A	4,710,000	4.4857	4		4
B	4,200,000	4	4		4
C	1,590,000	1.514	1	+1	2
Total	10,500,000	Divisor = 1,050,000	9		10

6. State A's population increased by 10,000, but its apportionment decreased from 5 to 4. State C's population decreased by 10,000, but its apportionment increased from 1 to 2 seats.

7. This is an apportionment problem because a fixed number of indivisible objects (the firemen) are to be allocated to districts based on data about the districts (number of fires). The firemen play the role of seats, the districts play the role of states, and the numbers of fires play the role of populations. The standard divisor is the total number of fires divided by the number of firemen. It represents the average number of fires per fireman. Each standard quotas represents the number of firemen that district deserves by proportionality.

Problems for Section 4.4

Sharpen Your Skills: (Answers in back of text.)

In the tables in problems 1 and 2, the second column shows the standard quotas of the states listed when apportioning a 20 seat legislature. Find the lower quotas, and determine which state(s) get an extra seat if Hamilton's Method is used.

1.

State	Standard Quota	Lower Quota	Extra Seat?
A	3.4		
B	2.15		
C	5.6		
D	4.05		
E	4.8		
Total:			

2.

State	Standard Quota	Lower Quota	Extra Seat?
A	1.335		
B	5.415		
C	3.5		
D	4.42		
E	5.33		
Total:			

3. The enrollments at Parkview High School for three math classes are shown below. There are a total of 25 sections to be apportioned among the three courses.

	Enrollment	Standard Quota
Pre-Algebra	224	
Geometry	346	
Algebra	425	
Total:		

(a) Find the standard divisor and explain what it means in the context of this problem.

(b) Find the standard quotas and explain what they mean in the context of this problem.

4. A clinic has 225 nurses working four different shifts. The number of nurses working each shift is to be apportioned to the shifts according to the average number of patients in that shift.

Shift	Avg. Number of Patients	Standard Quota
A	869	
B	1025	
C	619	
D	187	
Total:		

(a) Find the standard divisor and explain what it means in the context of this problem.

(b) Find the standard quotas and explain what they mean in the context of this problem.

Communicate the Concepts: (Answers in back of text.)

5. How does the Hamilton Method use fractional parts in determining an apportionment?

6. In apportionment of a legislative body, what does the standard divisor represent? What does each standard quota represent?

7. Suppose a legislative body is apportioned twice. What needs to be true about the two apportionments in order for there to be an example of the Alabama Paradox?

8. Suppose a legislative body is apportioned twice. What needs to be true about the two apportionments in order for there to be an example of the Population Paradox?

9. State the Quota Rule, and explain why Hamilton's Method always produces an apportionment that satisfies this rule.

10. What does the sum of the standard quotas equal in any apportionment problem?

Apply Your Knowledge: (Answers to odd-numbered problems in back of text.)

11. A small country has 3 states and a legislature of 15 seats, as shown in the table below. Apportion the 15 seats using the Hamilton method.

Standard Divisor:

State	Population	Standard Quota			Hamilton Apportionment
Blue	12,600				
Yellow	6,800				
Green	10,600				
Total:					

12. A small country has 3 states and a legislature of 20 seats, as shown in the table below. Apportion the 20 seats using the Hamilton method.

Standard Divisor:

State	Population	Standard Quota			Hamilton Apportionment
Blue	11,750				
Yellow	5,650				
Green	3,600				
Total:					

13. Suppose a town must apportion its 50 polling places among 6 districts according to the number of eligible voters in each district.

District	Eligible Voters	Standard Quota			Hamilton Apportionment
1	7671				
2	9010				
3	5497				
4	8925				
5	3641				
6	6056				
Total:					

(a) Find the standard divisor and explain what it means in the context of this problem.
(b) Find the standard quotas and explain what they mean in the context of this problem.
(c) Apportion the polling places to the districts according to the numbers of eligible voters in the districts using the Hamilton Method.

14. A clinic has 225 nurses working four different shifts. The number of nurses working each shift is to be apportioned to the shifts according to the average number of patients in that shift. Apportion the nurses to the shifts using the Hamilton Method. (Your work on Problem 4 may help.)

Shift	Avg. Number of Patients	Standard Quota			Hamilton Apportionment
A	869				
B	1025				
C	619				
D	187				
Total:					

15. The State of Rhode Island has 5 counties, whose populations are shown in the table below, and a Legislature with 50 seats.

County	Population	Standard Quota			Hamilton Apportionment
Bristol	48,859				
Kent	161,135				
Newport	87,194				
Providence	596,270				
Washington	110,006				
Total:	1,003,464				

(a) Apportion the 50 seats in the Legislature using the Hamilton Method.

(b) Does rounding the standard quotas in the conventional manner produce a valid apportionment of the Legislature? Explain.

16. Delaware has 3 counties, whose populations are shown below, and an Assembly with 41 seats.

County	Population	Standard Quota			Hamilton Apportionment
Kent	110,993				
New Castle	441,946				
Sussex	113,229				
Total:	666,168				

(a) Apportion the 41 seats in the Assembly using the Hamilton Method.

(b) Does rounding the standard quotas in the conventional manner produce a valid apportionment of the Assembly? Explain.

17.(a) In June, the enrollments at Parkview High School for classes in Pre-Algebra, Geometry, and Algebra are 224, 346, and 425 respectively. Apportion 25 sections among these three subject areas using Hamilton's Method. (Your work on Problem 3 may help.)

	Enrollment	Standard Quota			Hamilton Apportionment
Pre-Alg	224				
Geometry	346				
Algebra	425				
Total:					

(b) In August, the enrollments have changed somewhat and are now 223, 379, and 428 respectively. There are still only 25 sections to be offered. Find the Hamilton apportionment based on the new enrollments.

Standard Divisor:

	Enrollment	Standard Quota			Hamilton Apportionment
Pre-Alg	223				
Geometry	379				
Algebra	428				
Total:					

(c) Does anything paradoxical occur? If so, which paradox occurs? Explain.

18. Suppose the legislature in Problem 12 is changed so as to have **21 seats**. Apportion the **21 seats** using the Hamilton method.

New Standard Divisor:

State	Population	Standard Quota			Hamilton Apportionment
Blue	11,750				
Yellow	5,650				
Green	3,600				
Total:					

Explain how Problems 12 and 18 show an example of a paradox we studied.

19.Suppose the legislature in Problem 11 is changed so as to have **16 seats**. Apportion the **16 seats** using the Hamilton method.

New Standard Divisor:

State	Population	Standard Quota			Hamilton Appor.
Blue	12,600				
Yellow	6,800				
Green	10,600				
Total:					

Explain how Problems 11 and 19 show an example of a paradox we studied.

20. A town has three districts A, B, and C, and a force of 35 police officers. The populations of the three districts are shown below.

District	Population	Standard Quota			Hamilton Apportionment
A	9,900				
B	6,615				
C	4,485				
Total:					

(a) Calculate the standard divisor, and the standard quota of police officers for each district. Interpret the meaning of these numbers *in the context of this problem*.

(b) Apportion the 35 officers to the districts using Hamilton's Method.

(c) Suppose the populations of the districts change as shown below. Reapportion the 35 officers to the districts using Hamilton's method.

New Standard Divisor:

District	Population	Standard Quota			Hamilton Apportionment
A	9,955				
B	6,915				
C	4,480				
Total:					

(d) The results of parts (b) and (c) give an example of a paradox we studied. Name the paradox, and <u>explain</u> how this is an example of it.

21. Louisville Fire has 80 firemen it wants to assign to three fire districts based on the number of fire alarms in those districts last year. Those numbers are shown in the table below.

District	Fire Alarms	Standard Quota			Hamilton Apportionment
A	1,843				
B	2,160				
C	3,197				
Totals					

(a) Find the standard divisor, and standard quotas for each district. Interpret the meaning of each of these <u>in the context of this problem</u>.

(b) Find the Hamilton apportionment of the 80 firemen.

(c) Suppose the numbers of fire alarms in the districts is adjusted as shown in the table below. Reapportion the 80 firemen using Hamilton's Method.

New Standard Divisor:

District	Fire Alarms	Standard Quota			Hamilton Apportionment
A	1,842				
B	2,200				
C	3,198				
Totals					

(d) Are the results in (b) and (c) an example of a paradox we studied? If so, name the paradox, and <u>explain</u> how this is an example of it.

22. Suppose the clinic in Problem 14 gets funds to add an extra nurse, making a total of **226** nurses. Reapportion the **226** nurses to the shifts based on the average number of patients per shift..

New Standard Divisor:

Shift	Avg. Number of Patients	Standard Quota			Hamilton Apportionment
A	869				
B	1025				
C	619				
D	187				
Total:					

Explain how Problems 14 and 22 show an example of a paradox we studied.

23. Suppose the town in Problem 13 gets funds to add an extra polling place, making a total of **51** polling places. Reapportion the **51** polling places to the districts based on the numbers of eligible voters.

District	Eligible Voters	Standard Quota		Hamilton Apportionment
1	7671			
2	9010			
3	5497			
4	8925			
5	3641			
6	6056			
Total:				

Explain how Problems 13 and 23 show an example of a paradox we studied.

24. A company has 40 salespeople it wants to assign to districts based on the number of potential customers in those districts. The number of potential customers in each district is shown below.

District	Potential Customers	Standard Quota			Hamilton Apportionment
X	9,184				
Y	9,608				
Z	13,208				

(a) Find the standard divisor, and standard quotas for each district. Interpret the meaning of each of these in the context of this problem.
(b) Find the Hamilton apportionment of the 40 salespeople.
(c) Suppose the numbers of potential customers in the districts change as shown in the table below. Reapportion the 40 salespeople using Hamilton's Method.

District	Potential Customers	Standard Quota			Hamilton Apportionment
X	9,180				
Y	9,890				
Z	13,210				

(d) Are the results in (b) and (c) an example of a paradox we studied? If so, name the paradox, and explain how this is an example of it.

25. A small country consists of four states A, B, C, and D. The total population of this country is 10,000. Suppose the standard quotas for the states are as shown in the table below:

State	A	B	C	D
Standard Quota	0.84	4.14	3.66	1.36

   (a) What was the House size for this problem?

   (b) Find the standard divisor for this apportionment problem.

   (c) Find the population of State C.

26. A country has four states with populations as follows. It has decided to use Hamilton's method to apportion its Supreme Council. However, it has not decided whether to use a council size of 26, 27, or 28. (a) Find the apportionment using each of these council sizes.

   (i) 26 Seats

State	Population				
E	4,130,163				
F	2,632,663				
G	943,935				
H	786,690				

   (ii) 27 Seats

State	Population				
E	4,130,163				
F	2,632,663				
G	943,935				
H	786,690				

   (iii) 28 seats

State	Population				
E	4,130,163				
F	2,632,663				
G	943,935				
H	786,690				

   (b) Does anything paradoxical occur in these apportionments? If so, name the paradox and explain how this is an example of the paradox.

Section 4.5   Early Divisor Methods

After President George Washington vetoed Alexander Hamilton's Method of
Apportionment, Congress adopted a plan proposed by Thomas Jefferson,
Washington's Secretary of State (shown at right). The Jefferson Method is an
example of a class of apportionment methods called **divisor methods** that are
fundamentally different from the Hamilton Method. With the Hamilton
Method the fractional parts of the standard quotas are dropped, and then
enough extra seats are awarded based on those fractional parts to reach the
desired house size. (In the future, **we will refer to dropping the fractional
part as "rounding down."**) With the Jefferson Method, "extra seats" are not
awarded based on the fractional parts of the standard quotas. Rather, a new
divisor is used, and this divisor is chosen so that when the whole number parts
of the quotients it generates are summed, this sum equals the desired house
size.

©Everett Historical/Shutterstock.com

Jefferson Method of Apportionment

Select a **divisor D** (try the standard divisor first, but usually this will need to be adjusted) that
creates for each state a $\text{quotient} = \dfrac{\text{State Population}}{D}$ so that, when **rounded down**, these rounded
quotients sum to the house size. Then apportion to each state its rounded down quotient. A divisor
D that causes the rounded quotients to sum to the house size is called a **valid divisor.**

The difficulty with the Jefferson Method (and with any of the divisor methods we will discuss) is finding a
valid divisor. We will discuss two methods for doing this. Both start with calculating the *standard* divisor
and *standard* quotas, and checking whether the rounded down standard quotas sum to the house size. If they
do the standard divisor is a valid divisor for the Jefferson Method, and we apportion to each state its rounded
down standard quota. If they do not sum to the house size, we must "adjust" the divisor and check again.
Our two methods differ in how to find a valid divisor.

Example 1 Reapportion the 15-seat legislature in Example 1 of Section 4.4 using the Jefferson Method.

Solution Table 4.28 below gives the populations of the four states from that example, and their standard
quotas which were found using the standard divisor of $D = 300{,}000 / 15 = 20{,}000$.

State	Population	Standard Quota	Rounded Down
A	105,200	5.26	5
B	79,800	3.99	3
C	67,200	3.36	3
D	47,800	2.39	2
Total	300,000	15.00	13

Table 4.28

The rounded down standard quotas sum to 13, which is less than the desired house size of 15. We need
to adjust the divisor; should we adjust the divisor to be larger or smaller? We want to make the quotients
larger so that when we round them down the sum is larger than the current value of 13. Recall that each
quotient is the result of dividing the state population by the divisor, so to make the quotients larger we
must make the divisor *smaller*. How small is a guess at present. To illustrate the process we will adjust
the divisor down from 20,000 to 18,000, and recalculate the quotients in Table 4.29.

State	Population	Quotient ($D = 18000$)	Rounded Down
A	105,200	5.8444...	5
B	79,800	4.4333...	4
C	67,200	3.7333...	3
D	47,800	2.6555...	2
Total	300,000		14

Table 4.29

Although the rounded down quotients (shown in Table 4.29 above) now have a sum closer to the desired house size of 15, the sum has not reached that size yet. Because the sum is only 14, we need an even smaller divisor. We try 17,000.

State	Population	Quotient ($D = 17000$)	Rounded Down and Jefferson Apportionment
A	105,200	6.188..	6
B	79,800	4.694..	4
C	67,200	3.953..	3
D	47,800	2.812..	2
Total	300,000		15

Table 4.30

Because the rounded down quotients now sum to the desired house size of 15, those rounded down quotients are the Jefferson Apportionment of the 15 seats, as shown in Table 4.30.

Important Notes:

1. If at some point the sum of the rounded quotients is too small, we need to *increase* the divisor.
2. We saw above shows that $D = 17,000$ is a valid divisor for this problem. We will see that any divisor between 16,800 and 17,534 is valid for this problem. That is, any divisor in this range produces rounded down quotients that sum to 15. The goal of the problem is to arrive at the Jefferson Apportionment, and finding a valid divisor is just a means to that end. Any valid divisor suffices.
3. The divisor and quotients we use to obtain the Jefferson Apportionment have no intrinsic meaning as opposed to those for the *standard* divisor and *standard quotas* discussed in Section 4.4.
4. Notice that the apportionment resulting from the Jefferson Method gives 6 seats to State A, the largest state, rather than the 5 it got with the Hamilton Method. We will see that in general the Jefferson Method tends to favor the large states.

Quiz Yourself: (Answer at the end of this Section, before the problems.)
1. A country wanted to apportion 10 seats to the 3 states with populations shown below.

State	Population	Standard Quota			Jefferson Apportionment
A	4,600,000				
B	3,650,000				
C	1,750,000				
Total	10,000,000				

Apportion the seats using the Jefferson Method. Compare your result to the Hamilton apportionment.

After the first Congress adopted the Jefferson Method it remained in use until 1842. During this time the size of the House grew at every census, so that it was unusual for a state to lose a seat from one apportionment to the next. Some of the opponents of Jefferson's method noted that it tended to favor large states like his. In 1822 the size of the House was set at 181, and the Standard Quota for New York was 32.5, but the Jefferson Method gave it 34 seats! Politicians railed at this as obviously unfair. Of course, we recognize it as an example showing that **the Jefferson Method violates the Quota Rule**. In 1840 New York had a Standard Quota of 38.6, but the Jefferson Method gave it 40 seats. Two violations of the Quota Rule in a row were enough to cause Congress to look for alternatives, and a number were proposed. Daniel Webster (shown at right) had proposed the method that was adopted. His method differs from Jefferson's only in the way the quotas are rounded. Instead of always rounding down, Webster proposed to round the quotients in the way we are used to rounding numbers.

Webster Method of Apportionment

Select a **divisor** D (try the standard divisor first, but it may need to be adjusted) that creates for each state a

$\text{quotient} = \dfrac{\text{State Population}}{D}$ so that, when **rounded naturally** (up if the fractional part is greater than or

equal to 0.5, down if the fractional part is less than 0.5), these rounded quotients sum to the house size.
Then apportion to each state its rounded quotient. A divisor D that causes the rounded quotients to sum to
the house size is called a **valid divisor** for the Webster Method

Example 2 Reapportion the 15 seat legislative body in Example 1 using the Webster Method.

Solution: Again we start by calculating the standard divisor and standard quotas, and then round them in
the natural fashion used by Webster's Method. The results are shown in Table 4.31.

State	Population	Standard Quota	Webster Rounded
A	105,200	5.26	5
B	79,800	3.99	4
C	67,200	3.36	3
D	47,800	2.39	2
Total	300,000	15.00	14

Table 4.31

The rounded standard quotas only sum to 14. Since we want a larger sum, we must try a smaller
divisor. Our guess is D = 19,100. The third and fourth columns of Table 4.32 below show the resulting
quotients and rounded quotients for this divisor, which now sum to 17, too many. We note that the
quotients for states A, C, and D have fractional parts that are just large enough to make them round up.
We need a slightly larger divisor so that only one of the 3 resulting quotients rounds up. The last two
columns show the quotients and rounded quotas for D = 19,150, which do sum to 15, the desired house
size. So the last column of Table 4.32 is the Webster Apportionment.

State	Population	Quotients D = 19100	Rounded Quotients	Quotients D = 19150	Rounded Quotients (Webster Apportionment)
A	105,200	5.507..	6	5.493..	5
B	79,800	4.178..	4	4.167..	4
C	67,200	3.518..	4	3.509..	4
D	47,800	2.502..	3	2.496..	2
Total	300,000		17		15

Table 4.32

*Note that some quotients here are very close to the cut off between rounding up or down. Be sure to
give enough decimal places for the quotient to be able to decide how to round it correctly.*

Congress used the Webster Method for the apportionment of 1842. In 1850 Senator Samuel Vinton
proposed a "new" method which was actually the Hamilton Method in disguise, and it was adopted. The
Hamilton Method continued to be the official apportionment method of the House through the rest of the
1800s, although in 1840 - 1870 the size of the House was chosen so that the Hamilton and Webster
Methods agreed. During 1880 - 1900 the Alabama Paradox and Population Paradox and other problems
with the Hamilton Method surfaced. After the census of 1900 Congress went back officially to the Webster
Method, partly due to the efforts of Cornell University statistician Walter Willcox, and some references to
the Webster Method now refer to it as the Webster-Willcox Method.

Quiz Yourself: (Answer at the end of this section, before the Problems.)
2. The country in Quiz Yourself problem 1 wants to consider using the Webster Method.

State	Population	Standard Quota				Webster Apportionment
A	4,600,000					
B	3,650,000					
C	1,750,000					
Total	10,000,000					

Apportion the 10 seats using the Webster Method.

Finding a Valid Divisor

The Jefferson and Webster Methods are examples of a *divisor* method of apportionment.

> A **divisor method** is an apportionment method in which one must find a divisor D so that the quotients of the states found using that divisor, (state population) / D, when rounded in a prescribed fashion, sum to the correct house size.

The only difference among the divisor methods is how the rounding is done. With the Jefferson Method we round down and with the Webster Method we round "naturally". Other divisor methods include the Adams Method, which is explored in the problems for this section, and the Huntington-Hill Method, which is what is presently used to apportion the House and which will be discussed in a Section 4.7. When using a divisor method, how does one find a valid divisor D that produces rounded quotients that sum to the house size?

Method 1 "Guess, Check, and Adjust". This is the method we used in Examples 1 and 2. The steps are:
1) Start with D being the standard divisor.
2) Calculate the quotients using D.
3) Round the quotients in the fashion prescribed by the apportionment method.
4) Test whether the sum of these rounded standard quotas equals the desired house size:
   a. If the sum of the rounded quotients equals the desired house size, those rounded quotients are the apportionments.
   b. If the sum is too small, use a smaller divisor D to get larger quotients, and go back to step 2).
   c. If the sum is too large, use a larger divisor D to get smaller quotients, and go back to step 2).
   Repeat this adjustment process until the sum of the rounded quotients equals the House Size.

Method 2 Using Algebra to Find a Valid Divisor. Table 4.33 below gives the calculations we made for the Standard Quotas in Example 1, with a legislature of 15 seats being apportioned. In this first example we will show how to use algebra with the Jefferson Method.

State	Population	Standard Quota	Rounded Down
A	105,200	5.26	5
B	79,800	3.99	3
C	67,200	3.36	3
D	47,800	2.39	2
Total	300,000	15.00	13

Table 4.33

The numbers in the last column show the result of rounding the standard quotas down, as required by the Jefferson Method. Think of them as giving the current Jefferson allotments of seats to the states using the Standard Divisor $D = 20,000$. We need to find a new divisor D so that <u>two</u> more seats are allotted, that is, exactly two of the quotients for that D round down to the *next larger integer* than they currently do. For example, for state A to get another seat its quotient 105,200 / D would have to reach at least 6. We solve this statement for D, using the rules of inequalities that are reviewed at the end of this section:

Original Statement for A to get additional seat: $\dfrac{105,200}{D} \geq 6$

Multiply by D: $105,200 \geq 6D$

Divide by 6: $\dfrac{105,200}{6} \geq D$ Evaluate quotient: $17,533 \geq D$

Similarly for state B to get another seat would require $\dfrac{79,800}{D} \geq 4$, which we solve for D:

$$79,800 \geq 4D, \qquad \dfrac{79,800}{4} \geq D \quad 19,950 \geq D$$

For state C: $\dfrac{67,200}{D} \geq 4$, $67,200 \geq 4D,$ $\dfrac{67,200}{4} \geq D$, $16,800 \geq D$

For state D: $\dfrac{47,800}{D} \geq 3$, $47,800 \geq 3D,$ $\dfrac{47,800}{3} \geq D$, $15,933 \geq D$

The numbers 17,533, 19,950, 16,800, and 15,933 found above are called the **critical divisors** for states A, B, C, and D, respectively, to add a seat. If D decreases from the standard divisor 20,000 until exactly two of these inequalities are true, then the quotients for 2 states will round up and at least 2 states will get "extra seats". (**But see the caution at the end of this section**.) As D decreases from 20,000, the first critical divisor it passes is 19,950, then it passes 17,533. It may be useful to locate the critical divisors on a number line:

If D passes 16,800 then three of the inequalities are true and three states get "extra seats, making the total too big. So we want D to be in the range $16,800 < D \leq 17,533$. Any D in that range, such as the $D = 17,000$ that we saw worked in Example 1, should give rounded down quotients that have the correct sum of 15. (**See the caution at the end of this section. Be sure to check that 17,000 is indeed a valid divisor**.)

Note that the two original inequalities satisfied by a divisor in this range are the inequalities derived from states A and B, and these are indeed the states awarded "extra seats" in the Jefferson Method.

Quiz Yourself: (Answer at the end of this Section, before the problems.)
3. A different country wants to apportion 10 seats to its 3 states with populations shown below.

State	Population	Standard Quota						Jeff. Apportion.
A	4,250,000							
B	3,300,000							
C	2,450,000							
Total	10,000,000							

Show how to use algebra to find the range of valid divisors that produce the Jefferson Apportionment.

Using Algebra to Help Find a Valid Divisor for the Webster Method.

We will rework Example 2 in which we apportioned the same legislature using the Webster method. Table 4.34 gives the standard quotas again, this time rounded as in the Webster Method:

State	Population	Standard Quota	Webster Rounded
A	105,200	5.26	5
B	79,800	3.99	4
C	67,200	3.36	3
D	47,800	2.39	2
Total	300,000	15.00	14

Table 4.34

The Webster rounded standard quotas add to 14, too small, so we need a *smaller* divisor to get larger quotients. That divisor D must make exactly <u>one</u> of the quotients round to the next whole number *above* the rounded value in the table. This will happen with the Webster Method if the fractional part of the quotient is greater than or equal to the rounded number in the table plus 0.5. For example, in order for A to get 6 seats its quotient 105,200 / D will have to reach at least $5 + 0.5 = 5.5$ in order to be rounded up to 6 by the Webster Method. Thus we seek a D that satisfies exactly one of these:

State A: $\dfrac{105,200}{D} \geq 5 + 0.5$ $105,200 \geq 5.5D$ $\dfrac{105,200}{5.5} \geq D$ $19,127 \geq D$

State B: $\dfrac{79,800}{D} \geq 4 + 0.5$ $79,800 \geq 4.5D$ $\dfrac{79,800}{4.5} \geq D$ $17,733 \geq D$

State C: $\dfrac{67,200}{D} \geq 3 + 0.5$ $67,200 \geq 3.5D$ $\dfrac{67,200}{3.5} \geq D$ $19,200 \geq D$

State D: $\dfrac{47,800}{D} \geq 2 + 0.5$ $47,800 \geq 2.5D$ $\dfrac{47,800}{2.5} \geq D$ $19,120 \geq D$

To have D satisfy exactly one of these it must be less than or equal to the largest of the critical divisors 19,127, 17,733, 19,200, and 19,120, but greater than all the others. So D must be in the range $19,127 < D \leq 19,200$. (See the number line below.) This includes $D = 19,150$ which we used in Example 2.

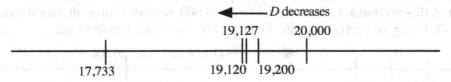

Quiz Yourself: (Answer at the end of this section.)
4. Explain how to use algebra to find the range of valid divisors for the Webster Apportionment of 10 seats to the three states in Quiz Yourself problem 2:

State	Population	Standard Quota			Jeff. Apportion.
A	4,600,000				
B	3,650,000				
C	1,750,000				
Total	10,000,000				

Example 3: A school can offer a total of 35 sections of mathematics courses. Students have registered for the courses as shown in Table 4.35 below. Apportion the 35 sections to the 4 types of courses proportional to the enrollments using (a) the Jefferson Method and (b) the Webster Method.

Course	Enrollment	Standard Quota	Standard Quota Rounded Down (Jefferson)	Standard Quota Rounded Naturally (Webster)
Algebra	339	13.56	13	14
Geometry	230	9.20	9	9
Precalculus	190	7.60	7	8
Calculus	116	4.64	4	5
Total	875		33	36

Table 4.35

<u>Solution</u> The standard divisor is 875 / 35 = 25. This represents the average number of students per section. Dividing the enrollments by 25 gives the standard quotas for the courses, which represent the number of sections each course is entitled to. Table 4.35 also shows the result of rounding each of these by the Jefferson and Webster methods. For neither method does the sum of these rounded standard quotas equal the desired 35 sections, so we must adjust the divisor for each method.

(a) Since the sum of the rounded standard quotas for the Jefferson Method is 33, we need to adjust the divisor *downward* until two more sections are obtained. To decide how far downward, we calculate the critical divisors necessary for each of the courses to add a section.

Algebra:: $\frac{339}{D} = 13 + 1$ yields $D = \frac{339}{14} = 24.21$ Geometry: $\frac{230}{D} = 9 + 1$ yields $D = \frac{230}{10} = 23$

Precalculus: $\frac{190}{D} = 7 + 1$ yields $D = \frac{190}{8} = 23.75$ Calculus: $\frac{116}{D} = 4 + 1$ yields $D = \frac{116}{5} = 23.2$

As D decreases from 25, it crosses 24.21 first, then 23.75, then 23.2. (See the number line below.)

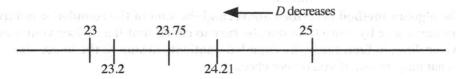

A divisor D between 23.2 and 23.75 should be a valid divisor for the Jefferson Method. The Table 4.36 below shows the quotients for $D = 23.5$. (Be sure to confirm this by making the calculations in Table 4.36! See the Caution below.) The rounded quotients now sum to 35, and give the Jefferson Apportionment.

Course	Enrollment	Quotient $D = 23.5$	Quotient Rounded Down (Jefferson Apportionment)
Algebra	339	14.426	14
Geometry	230	9.787	9
Precalculus	190	8.085	8
Calculus	116	4.936	4
Total	875		35

Table 4.36

(b) Notice that when the standard quotas are rounded naturally (see below) the sum is 36, one too many.

Course	Enrollment	Standard Quota	Standard Quota Webster Rounded
Algebra	339	13.56	14
Geometry	230	9.20	9
Precalculus	190	7.60	8
Calculus	116	4.64	5
Total	875		36

Table 4.35

So we must *increase* the divisor from the current 25 until one course *loses* a section. For each section we calculate the critical divisor necessary for that course to lose a section. This requires the quotient for that section to be 0.5 less than the current Webster rounded quotient.

Algebra: $\frac{339}{D} = 14 - 0.5$ yields $D = \frac{339}{13.5} = 25.11$ Geometry: $\frac{230}{D} = 9 - 0.5$ yields $D = \frac{230}{8.5} = 27.06$

Precalculus: $\frac{190}{D} = 8 - 0.5$ yields $D = \frac{190}{7.5} = 25.33$ Calculus: $\frac{116}{D} = 5 - 0.5$ yields $D = \frac{116}{4.5} = 25.78$

As the divisor increases from the standard divisor $D = 25$, the first critical divisor crossed is the critical divisor for Algebra to gain a section, 25.11, and the second is 25.33. (See the number line below.)

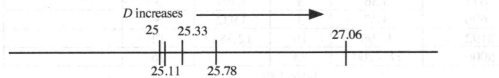

Any divisor between the critical divisors 25.11 and 25.33 produces the Webster Apportionment, and causes Algebra to lose a section. To check this Table 4.37 on the next page gives the quotients for $D = 25.2$. The Webster rounded quotients for this divisor sum to 35, so this is the Webster Apportionment.

Course	Enrollment	Quotient D = 25.2	Quotient Rounded Naturally (Webster Apportionment)
Algebra	339	13.45	13
Geometry	230	9.13	9
Precalculus	190	7.54	8
Calculus	116	4.60	5
Total	875		35

Table 4.37

Caution: **If you use the algebra method described above, and the sum of the rounded standard quotas differs from the house size by more than one, be sure to check that the divisor your work indicates is a valid divisor does, in fact, cause the rounded quotients to sum to the house size.** Here is an example of what may happen if you do not check.

Example 4 A country has 4 states with populations shown in the table 4.38. Apportion the 25 seats in its legislature using the Jefferson Method.

State	Population (in Thousands)	Standard Quota	Round Down				Jefferson Apportionment
Red	1440	7.2	7				
White	672	3.36	3				
Blue	696	3.48	3				
Green	2192	10.96	10				
Total:	5000	D = 200	23				

Table 4.38

Solution: The standard divisor is 5,000/25 = 200. The rounded standard quotas are shown in Table 4.38. The sum is 2 less than the 25 desired. Here are the critical divisors for each section to gain a seat (from the rounded down standard quotas):

Red: $\frac{1440}{D} = 7+1$ yields $D = \frac{1440}{8} = 180$ White: $\frac{672}{D} = 3+1$ yields $D = \frac{670}{4} = 167.5$

Blue: $\frac{696}{D} = 3+1$ yields $D = \frac{696}{4} = 174$ Green: $\frac{2192}{D} = 10+1$ yields $D = \frac{2192}{11} = 199.27$

As D decreases from the standard divisor 200, it first crosses the critical divisor 199.27, then 180, then 174. A divisor in the range $174 < D < 180$ should cause both Red and Green to "gain" a seat. Let's check what happens with $D = 177$:

State	Population (in Thousands)	Standard Quota	Round Down	Quotients D = 177	Round Down	Jefferson Apportionment?
Red	1440	7.2	7	8.136	8	
White	672	3.36	3	3.797	3	
Blue	696	3.48	3	3.932	3	
Green	2192	10.96	10	12.384	12	
Total:	5000	D = 200	23		26	

Table 4.39

Red and Green did indeed get extra seats, but **Green got 2 extra seats, for a total of 12!** What would the critical divisor be to have Green get 12 seats? The calculation is on the next page:

$$\frac{2192}{D} = 12 \text{ yields } D = \frac{2192}{12} = 182.67$$

So as the divisor decreases from 200 it crosses the critical divisor for Green to get 11 seats, 199.27, and then the critical divisor for Green to get 12 seats, 182.67, before it crosses the critical divisor for Red to get 8 seats, 180. (See the number line below.)

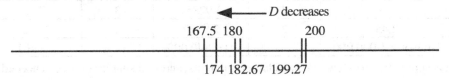

A divisor in the range $180 < D < 182.67$ should be valid. Let's check $D = 181$:

State	Population (in Thousands)	Standard Quota	Round Down	Quotients D = 181	Round Down	Jefferson Apportionment
Red	1440	7.2	7	7.9558	7	7
White	672	3.36	3	3.7127	3	3
Blue	696	3.48	3	3.8453	3	3
Green	2192	10.96	10	12.11	12	12
Total:	5000	D = 200	23		25	25

Table 4.40

In summary, when the sum of the rounded standard quotas differs from the desired house size by more than one, be sure that your divisor does indeed produce the desired apportionment!

In the problems for this section we will also investigate a third divisor method that was proposed by John Adams in 1820 but never used to apportion the U. S. House of Representatives. (Its rounding method is to round any quotient with a fractional part up to the next whole number.) A fourth divisor method, proposed by Joseph Hill and perfected by E. V. Huntington in the early twentieth century, was adopted in 1942 and is the apportionment method in use for the U. S. House of Representatives today. That method will be investigated in Section 4.7.

Quiz Yourself Answers

1.

State	Population	Standard Quota with 10 seats	Round Down	New Quotient	Round Down	Jefferson Apportionment
A	4,600,000	4.6	4	5.111..	5	5
B	3,650,000	3.65	3	4.055..	4	4
C	1,750,000	1.75	1	1.944…	1	1
Total	10,000,000		8	D = 900,000		10

Standard divisor = 1,000,000. The rounded down standard quotas total 8. Need a smaller divisor to give larger quotients; try 900,000 (others are possible). The rounded down quotients now sum to 10, so those rounded down quotients give the Jefferson Apportionment. Hamilton's Method would have given A only 4 seats, B 4 seats, and C 2 seats.

2.   Same standard divisor and standard quotas as in Quiz Yourself 1.

State	Population	Standard Quota	Webster Round	New Quotient	Webster Round	Webster Apportionment
A	4,600,000	4.6	5	4.466	4	4
B	3,650,000	3.65	4	3.544	4	4
C	1,750,000	1.75	2	1.699	2	2
Total	10,000,000	Divisor = 1,000,000	11	D = 1,030,000		10

But the rounded standard quotas sum to 11, too many, so we need smaller quotients and thus a *larger* divisor. One valid divisor is 1,030,000. It gives the New Quotients shown above. When these quotients are rounded using the Webster rounding method they sum to 10, so the rounded new quotients give the Webster Apportionment. (See Quiz Yourself problem 4 for a discussion of finding a valid divisor in this problem.)

Quiz Yourself Answers (continued)

3. A country wanted to apportion 10 seats to the 3 states with populations shown below.

State	Population	Standard Quota	Jeff. Rounded	New Quotient	Jeff. Rounded	Apportionment
A	4,250,000	4.25	4	5.0595	5	5
B	3,300,000	3.3	3	3.92857	3	3
C	2,450,000	2.45	2	2.9167	2	2
Total	10,000,000	Divisor = 1,000,000	9	D = 840,000		10

The rounded standard quotas sum to 9, 1 too few. We need larger quotients, and so a smaller divisor is needed. Here are the critical divisors for each state to gain a seat.

$$\text{A: } \frac{4,250,000}{D} = 4+1 \text{ yields } D = \frac{4,250,000}{5} = 850,000$$

$$\text{B: } \frac{3,300,000}{D} = 3+1 \text{ yields } D = \frac{3,300,000}{4} = 825,000$$

$$\text{C: } \frac{2,450,000}{D} = 2+1 \text{ yields } D = \frac{2,450,000}{3} = 816,667$$

←——— D decreases

816,667   850,000   1,000,000

825,000

As D decreases from 1,000,000 it first crosses the critical divisor of A, 850,000, then the critical divisor of B, 825,000. Any divisor in the range $825,000 < D < 850,000$ is a valid divisor for the Jefferson Apportionment. This is checked for $D = 840,000$ in the table above.

4. The standard quotas are shown in the table below.

State	Population	Standard Quota	Webster Rounded	New Quotient	Webster Rounded	Webster Apportionment
A	4,600,000	4.6	5	4.466	4	4
B	3,650,000	3.65	4	3.544	4	4
C	1,750,000	1.75	2	1.699	2	2
Total	10,000,000	Divisor = 1,000,000	11	D = 1,040,000		10

The Webster rounded standard quotas sum to 11, one too many. We need smaller quotients, and so a larger divisor is needed. Here are the critical divisors for each state to lose a seat.

$$\text{A: } \frac{4,600,000}{D} = 5-0.5 \text{ yields } D = \frac{4,600,000}{4.5} = 1,022,222$$

$$\text{B: } \frac{3,650,000}{D} = 4-0.5 \text{ yields } D = \frac{3,650,000}{3.5} = 1,042,857$$

$$\text{C: } \frac{1,750,000}{D} = 2-0.5 \text{ yields } D = \frac{1,750,000}{1.5} = 1,166,667$$

1,000,000   1,042,857 D increases ——————→

1,022,222   1,166,667

As D increases from the standard divisor 1,000,000, first the critical divisor 1,022,222 for A is crossed, then the critical divisor 1,042,857 of B. Any D satisfying $1,022,222 < D < 1,042,857$ should make A lose a seat but not B or C, and so that divisor will be a valid divisor. The new quotients in the table above show that $D = 1,040,000$ produces quotients which, when rounded, sum to 10. So 1,040,000 is indeed a valid divisor for the Webster Method. Quiz Yourself Problem #2 showed that 1,030,000 is also valid.

Problem for Section 4.5

Sharpen Your Skills: (Answers in back of text.)

1. Round each of the numbers in the chart below using the Jefferson and Webster Methods.

Number	Jefferson Rounded	Webster Rounded
3.499		
5.5		
7.501		
6.99		

In problems 2. – 4. you are given the standard quotas for an apportionment problem in which the house size is 16. For each, decide whether or not a new divisor is needed for the apportionment, and whether that divisor will be larger than or smaller than the standard divisor.

2. House size 16, standard quotas shown.

   (a) Does the Jefferson Method require a new divisor? If so, is a valid divisor larger or smaller than the standard divisor? Explain.

   (b) Does the Webster Method require a new divisor? If so, is a valid divisor larger or smaller than the standard divisor? Explain.

State	Standard Quota		
A	4.4		
B	3.6		
C	2.4		
D	5.6		

3. House size 16, standard quotas shown.

   (a) Does the Jefferson Method require a new divisor? If so, is a valid divisor larger or smaller than the standard divisor? Explain.

   (b) Does the Webster Method require a new divisor? If so, is a valid divisor larger or smaller than the standard divisor? Explain.

State	Standard Quota		
A	4.6		
B	3.6		
C	2.7		
D	5.1		
Total			

4. House size 16, standard quotas shown.

   (a) Does the Jefferson Method require a new divisor? If so, is a valid divisor larger or smaller than the standard divisor? Explain.

   (b) Does the Webster Method require a new divisor? If so, is a valid divisor larger or smaller than the standard divisor? Explain.

State	Standard Quota		
A	4.2		
B	3.15		
C	2.35		
D	6.3		

5. A state with a population of 2,500,000 has a standard quota of 4.6 seats. What is the critical divisor for the state to get:

   (a) 5 seats with the Jefferson Method.

   (b) 4 seats with the Webster Method.

6. A state with a population of 1,500,000 has a standard quota of 5.45 seats. What is the critical divisor for the state to get:

   (a) 6 seats with the Jefferson Method.

   (b) 6 seats with the Webster Method.

Communicate the Concepts: (Answers in back of text.)

7. Explain how a divisor apportionment method differs from the Hamilton Method.

8. What are the rounding methods used by the Jefferson and Webster Methods?

9. When using a divisor apportionment method, if the rounded standard quotas are too small, should the divisor be adjusted to be larger or smaller? Why?

10. What does the term "valid divisor" mean when using a divisor apportionment method?

11. Suppose a state with population P has a standard quota of 10.3 in a legislative apportionment. Explain how to find the critical divisor D so that P/D rounds to 11 using:
    (a) Jefferson Method rounding
    (b) Webster Method rounding

12. Suppose a state with population P has a standard quota of 10.6 in a legislative apportionment. Explain how to find the critical divisor D so that P/D rounds to 10 using Webster Method rounding

Apply Your Knowledge (Answers to odd-numbered problems in back of text.)

13. A country with 4 states has 50 seats in its legislature. Apportion the 50 seats among the 4 states according to the populations of the states, using the methods listed below. For each method give a divisor that yields the apportionment and show the quotients for that divisor.
    (a) The Jefferson Method.

State	Population	Stand. Quota					Appor.
Red	2,390						
White	3,450						
Blue	2,480						
Green	1,680						
Total:							

    (b) The Webster Method.

State	Population	Stand. Quota					Appor.
Red	2,390						
White	3,450						
Blue	2,480						
Green	1,680						
Total:							

14. A state university wants to apportion 250 faculty positions among 4 schools according to the enrollments of the schools that are shown in the table below. Apportion the positions using the two methods below. For each method, give a divisor that yields the apportionment and show the quotients for that divisor.
    (a) The Jefferson Method.

School	Enrollment	Stand. Quota					Appor.
Arts	1,828						
Business	3,146						
Education	2,581						
Sci. & Eng.	4,945						
Total:							

    (b) The Webster Method.

School	Enrollment	Stand. Quota					Appor.
Arts	1,828						
Business	3,146						
Education	2,581						
Sci. & Eng.	4,945						
Total:							

15. Apportion the 50 polling places in problem 13 from Section 4.4 using the methods below. For each, give a divisor that yields the apportionment and show the quotients for that divisor.

(a) The Jefferson Method.

District	Voters	Stand. Quota					Appor.
1	7671						
2	9010						
3	5497						
4	8925						
5	3641						
6	6056						
Total:							

(b) The Webster Method.

District	Voters	Stand. Quota					Appor.
1	7671						
2	9010						
3	5497						
4	8925						
5	3641						
6	6056						
Total:							

16. Apportion the 225 nurses in problem 14 from Section 4.4 using the methods below. For each, give a divisor that yields the apportionment and show the quotients for that divisor.

(a) The Jefferson Method.

Shift	# of Patients	Stand. Quota				Appor.
A	869					
B	1025					
C	619					
D	187					
Total:						

(b) The Webster Method.

Shift	# of Patients	Stand. Quota				Appor.
A	869					
B	1025					
C	619					
D	187					
Total:						

17. A city wants to apportion 42 police cars to its 6 districts based on the number of crimes in each district during the last three years. Apportion the police cars using the methods listed below. For each method, give a divisor that yields the apportionment and show the quotients for that divisor.
(a) The Jefferson Method.

District	# of Crimes	Stand. Quota					Appor.
Inner	7873						
North	7124						
East	5896						
South	5126						
West	5005						
Outer	2324						
Total:							

(b) The Webster Method.

District	# of Crimes	Stand. Quota					Appor.
Inner	7873						
North	7124						
East	5896						
South	5126						
West	5005						
Outer	2324						
Total:							

18. A school can offer a total of 40 sections of mathematics. Apportion the 40 sections among the 4 courses according to these registrations shown in the table below. For each method listed, give a divisor that yields the apportionment for that method and show the quotients for that divisor.
(a) The Jefferson Method

Course	Registration	Stand. Quota					Appor.
Geometry	441						
Algebra	348						
PreCal	273						
Calculus	138						
Total:							

(b) The Webster Method

Course	Registration	Stand. Quota					Appor.
Geometry	441						
Algebra	348						
PreCal	273						
Calculus	138						
Total:							

19. A country with 4 states has 20 seats in its legislature. Apportion the 20 seats among the 4 states according to the populations of the states, using the methods listed below. For each method, show the quotas resulting from a divisor that yields the apportionment. (**Warning**: Be sure to verify that your divisor actually produces the required apportionment.)

(a) The Jefferson Method.

State	Pop (in Thousands)	Std. Quota					Jeff. Appor.
Red	2490						
White	590						
Blue	620						
Green	1300						
Total:							

(b) The Webster Method.

State	Pop (in Thousands)	Std. Quota					Webster Appor.
Red	2490						
White	590						
Blue	620						
Green	1300						
Total:							

(c) Do either of the apportionments in (a) or (b) violate the Quota Rule? Explain

20. The 75 members of a 1996 German Parliament must be apportioned among the five political parties according to the percentage of votes they received as shown in the table below. Use the methods listed below to apportion the 75 members. For each, give a divisor that yields the apportionment.

(a) The Jefferson Method.

Party	Vote %	Std. Quota					Jeff. Appor.
Social Dems.	39.8						
Christian Dems.	37.2						
Green Party	8.1						
Free Dems.	5.7						
Voters Union	2.3						
Total:							

(b) The Webster Method.

Party	Vote %	Std. Quota					Webster Appor.
Social Dems.	39.8						
Christian Dems.	37.2						
Green Party	8.1						
Free Dems.	5.7						
Voters Union	2.3						
Total:							

(c) Do either of the apportionments in (a) or (b) violate the Quota Rule? Explain.

21. **Adams Method**. John Quincy Adams proposed an divisor method in which all quotas are rounded *up to the next whole number* (unless they are already a whole number, in which case no rounding is necessary.) Use the Adams Method to apportion the legislature with 15 seats which was apportioned in Example 1. Toward what size state does this method seem to be biased?

State	Population	Std. Quota				
A	105,200	5.26				
B	79,800	3.99				
C	67,200	3.36				
D	47,800	2.39				
Total	300,000	15.00				

22. Apportion the 50 seats in the legislature in problem 13 of this Section using the Adams Method described in the previous Problem.

State	Population	Std. Quota				
Red	2,390					
White	3,450					
Blue	2,480					
Green	1,680					
Total:						

23. Explain why, in any apportionment problem, a valid divisor for the Jefferson Method cannot be larger than the standard divisor.

Cumulative Review For Sections 4.4 and 4.5 (Answer in back of text.)

24. The table below gives the enrollments in 4 divisions of a college. The administration wants to apportion 180 new computers among the divisions based on their enrollments.

Division	Enrollment	Stand. Quota			
Arts	3455				
Business	5780				
Humanities	1896				
Science	4678				
Total:	15,809				

(a) What is the standard divisor for this apportionment? What does it mean in the context of this problem?

(b) Give the standard quotas for this problem in the chart above. What do they represent in the context of this problem?

(c) Use the chart above to apportion the computers using the Hamilton Method.

(d) Use the chart below to apportion the computers using the Jefferson method.

Division	Enrollment	Std. Quota				
Arts	3455					
Business	5780					
Humanities	1896					
Science	4678					
Total:	15,809					

What is the range of valid divisors for the Jefferson Method in this problem?

(e) Use the chart below to apportion the computers using the Webster Method.

Division	Enrollment	Std. Quota				
Arts	3455					
Business	5780					
Humanities	1896					
Science	4678					
Total:	15,809					

What is the range of valid divisors for the Webster Method in this problem?

Section 4.6 Measuring Unfairness in Apportionments

During the early part of the twentieth century, several members of the scientific and academic community began a more systematic evaluation of apportionment. Their analyses focused on how to measure the inevitable unfairness that occurs in any apportionment due to the fact that, in real life apportionments, a state's standard quota, which is what it deserves, never works out to be a whole number and so cannot be what it is apportioned.

Recall that the Constitution states: "*The number of Representatives shall not exceed one for every thirty Thousand*". The total population of the states at the time of the 1790 census was 3,615,920. Hamilton divided this by 30,000 and obtained 120.53, so he chose a house size of 120. Hamilton's apportionment of the first 15 states based on this house size is then obtained by applying his method. The results are given in Table 4.41 on the next page (you should verify this apportionment). In examining Hamilton's bill, Washington discovered that this apportionment allots *more that one representative for every thirty thousand* in some states, or equivalently, *has less than 30,000 people per representative* in some states. To see this, take each state's population and divide by its number of representatives to get the average number of people per representative for that state. This number is called the **average constituency** of the state.

$$\text{The } \textbf{average constituency} \text{ of a state} = \frac{\text{population of state}}{\text{number of seats awarded to the state}}$$

For example, Connecticut's population in 1790, 236,841, divided by its number of representatives, 8, gives its average constituency of 29,605.125. This means each representative in Connecticut represents, on the average, about 29,605 people. The average constituencies for each state under Hamilton's apportionment are in given in the last column of Table 4.41 on the next page (you should verify these). In a *perfect* apportionment all average constituencies would be exactly the same, and this would equal the standard divisor, that is, the total population of the country divided by the total number of seats in the legislative body. But in practice this perfection is not possible; some states will have average constituencies larger than the standard divisor, some will have average constituencies smaller than the standard divisor. Notice that in Table 4.41 there are 8 states whose average constituency is less than 30,000. Washington considered this a violation of the Constitution's provision that "The number of Representatives shall not exceed one for every thirty Thousand", and so he exercised the first presidential veto! After that, Washington signed into law a bill with a house size of 105 and a divisor of 33,000 using Jefferson's method.

Table 4.41 on the next page shows Hamilton's proposed apportionment of the 15 states at that time. We can see that the states with smaller average constituencies have an advantage. In Delaware, each representative represents 27,770 people, while in Georgia each representative represents 35,418 people. The people in Georgia would think they have "poorer representation" than those in Delaware because there are more people, on average, per representative in Georgia than in Delaware. In general,

> We say that State A is **more poorly represented** than State B
> if the average constituency of State A is greater than the average constituency of State B.

Differences in average constituency between states are one of the measures of the amount of unfairness (or inequity as he called it) studied by E.V. Huntington (shown at right) in the 1920's. Huntington was a Professor of Mechanics and Mathematics at Harvard who had worked at the Census Bureau. At Harvard, he had been a classmate of Joseph Hill, who later became a statistician at the Census Bureau. Hill presented a method which Huntington perfected and began to champion as his own. During this time, Huntington studied 64 different ways to measure the amount of inequity between states. By doing this Huntington converted the apportionment problem into an optimization problem. According to Huntington, the optimum apportionment is the one with the least inequity, that is, one in which the inequity cannot be lessened by transferring a seat (representative) from one state to the other.

State	Population	Quota	Lower Quota	Apportionment	Average Constituency
Connecticut	236,841	7.860	7	8	$236841/8 \approx 29605$
Delaware	55,540	1.843	1	2	$55540/2 \approx 27770$
Georgia	70,835	2.351	2	2	$70835/2 \approx 35418$
Kentucky	68,705	2.280	2	2	$68705/2 \approx 34353$
Maryland	278,514	9.243	9	9	$278514/9 \approx 30946$
Massachusetts	475,327	15.774	15	16	$... \approx 29708$
New Hampshire	141,822	4.707	4	5	$... \approx 28364$
New Jersey	179,570	5.959	5	6	$... \approx 29928$
New York	331,589	11.004	11	11	$... \approx 30144$
North Carolina	353,523	11.732	11	12	$... \approx 29460$
Pennsylvania	432,879	14.366	14	14	$... \approx 30920$
Rhode Island	68,446	2.271	2	2	$... \approx 34223$
South Carolina	206,236	6.844	6	7	$... \approx 29462$
Vermont	85,533	2.839	2	3	$... \approx 28511$
Virginia	630,560	20.926	20	21	$... \approx 30027$
Total	3,615,920	120.000	111	120	

Table 4.41 The First Apportionment Bill Passed by Congress 1792 (Hamilton's)

Note: *All average constituencies are rounded down to an integer*

As we will see in the next section, the Huntington-Hill method was actually developed to minimize this inequity. This was a departure from developing a method by focusing on how to round the fractional parts, as had been the case with the Jefferson and Webster methods.

Quiz Yourself (Answers at the end of this section, before the problems.)

1. Based on the 2010 census, Kentucky had a population of 4,350,606 and was apportioned 6 seats. Florida had a population of 18,900,773 and was apportioned 27 seats. Determine the average constituency of each state. Which one was more poorly represented?

For the rest of this section we will concentrate on the particular measure of inequity that Huntington and Hill used to devise their apportionment method, namely average constituency, and refer to it as "unfairness". This unfairness may be measured in either absolute or relative terms.

The **absolute difference** between two numbers = the larger number minus the smaller.

The **relative difference** between two numbers = $\dfrac{\text{their absolute difference}}{\text{smaller of the two numbers}}$

= the percent change from the smaller to the larger number.

Example 1 Find the absolute and relative difference in these prices, and interpret their significance.

(a) The price of gasoline went from $1.40 per gallon to $2.00 per gallon in 1976.

(b) The price of gasoline went from $2.60 per gallon to $3.20 per gallon in 2010.

Solution (a) The absolute difference is $0.60, which doesn't sound like a large amount of money. But the relative difference is $0.60 / 1.40 \approx 0.42857 = 42.857\%$. This relative difference means that $1.40 must grow by 42.857% to reach $2.00.

(b) The relative difference (percent change) is $0.60 / 2.60 \approx 0.23077 = 23.077\%$, a smaller percent change than in (a). The increase in 2010 was less significant.

We will also measure unfairness in two ways, on an absolute basis and a relative basis:

> The **absolute unfairness** between the apportionments of two states A and B
> **is the absolute difference between their average constituencies**.

The average constituencies of Delaware and Georgia in Table 4.41 are 27,770 and 35,418 respectively.   If we subtract the smaller from the larger, we get

Absolute unfairness between apportionments of Georgia and Delaware = 35,418 − 27,770 = 7,648.

So Georgia had 7,648 more people per representative, on the average, than Delaware. However, is this a significant difference? Consider a person who receives a $10,000 raise. If she earns $25,000 and receives this raise, it is significant! But if she earns $500,000, this is a minuscule raise. Also, winning an election by 100,000 votes may be a landslide if the election is for Governor of Kentucky, but winning by 100,000 in a presidential election is considered a very close election!

To see whether the unfairness, as measured by difference in average constituency, is significant, we need to compute the **relative unfairness**:

> The **relative unfairness** between the apportionments of two states A and B is
>
> $$\text{Relative unfairness} = \frac{\textbf{absolute unfairness of the two states' apportionment}}{\textbf{smaller average constituency of the two states}}$$

Relative unfairness is usually expressed as a percentage rounded to two decimal places. In the above example, we would have

Relative unfairness between apportionments of Georgia and Delaware = $\dfrac{35,418 - 27,770}{27,770} \approx 0.2754 = 27.54\%$

This means that Georgia would have had, on the average, about 27.54% more people per representative than Delaware. A sizable relative difference!

Example 2 In the apportionment described in Table 4.41, find the relative unfairness between the apportionments of Kentucky and Virginia. Which state does the apportionment favor?

Solution: In Hamilton's proposed apportionment the average constituency of Kentucky is 68,705 / 2 ≈ 34,353 and the average constituency of Virginia is 630,560 / 21 ≈ 30,027 rounded to the nearest integer.

The apportion favors the state with the smaller average constituency, Virginia. The absolute unfairness of the apportionment between these two states is 34,353 - 30,027 = 4,326, and the relative unfairness of the apportionment between these two states is 4,326 / 30,027 ≈ 0.144 = 14.4%.

> **Quiz Yourself** (Answer at end of this section, before the problems.)
> 2. Based on the 2010 census, Kentucky had a population of 4,350,606 and was apportioned 6 seats. Florida has a population of 18,900,773 and was apportioned 27 seats. In Quiz Yourself 1 you found the average constituency of each state. What was the absolute unfairness and relative unfairness between these two sates apportionments? Round the latter to the nearest hundredth percent.

Example 3 Table 4.42 shows the number of first and second grade teachers in a school district and the number of students in each of those grades. A new teacher is to be hired. To which grade should the teacher be assigned to minimize the relative unfairness between the grades' apportionments?

	Number of teachers	Number of Students
First Grade	332	8317
Second Grade	307	7678

Table 4.42

<u>Solution</u>: In this example average constituency means the number of students per teacher. We need to calculate these under the scenario that the first grade gets the extra teacher (shown in column 2 of Table 4.43) and in the scenario that the second grade gets the extra teacher (shown in column 3 of Table 4.43).

	Extra to First Grade	**Extra to Second Grade**
First Grade Avg. Constituency	$\dfrac{8317}{332+1} \approx 24.976$	$\dfrac{8317}{332} \approx 25.051$
Second Grade Avg. Constituency	$\dfrac{7678}{307} \approx 25.010$	$\dfrac{7678}{307+1} \approx 24.929$

Table 4.43

So the relative unfairness under each scenario is:

First Grade gets extra teacher: $\dfrac{25.010 - 24.976}{24.976} \approx 0.00136 = 0.136\%$

Second Grade gets extra teacher: $\dfrac{25.051 - 24.929}{24.929} \approx .00325 = 0.325\%$

Based on these calculations, giving the First Grade the new teacher produces the smaller relative unfairness between the grades' apportionment of teachers.

Quiz Yourself (Answer at end of this section, before the problems.)
3. The table below shows the number of policemen in two districts and the number of crimes in each of those district. A new policeman is to be hired. To which district should the policeman be assigned to minimize the relative unfairness between the districts' apportionments of policemen?

	Number of policemen	Number of crimes
District A	23	631
District B	20	550

Average Constituency in the House of Representatives from 1910 to 2010

According to the 2010 census the United States has 309,183,463 people. To apportion the House of Representatives, which still has 435 members, the standard divisor would be 309,183,463 / 435 ≈ 710,766.58; this is the average number of people per congressional seat, which is the average constituency for the entire country. (Compare this to the Constitution's statement that "the number of representatives shall not exceed 1 for every 30,000"!) Any state with an average constituency greater than this is represented more poorly than average, and any state with a smaller average constituency is better represented than average. When Congress fixed the size of the house at 435 in 1910 the population was 92,228,531, so the country's average constituency was 92,228,531 / 435 = 212,019.61, much smaller than today. The chart on the next page shows how the average constituency of house seats has grown over the years.

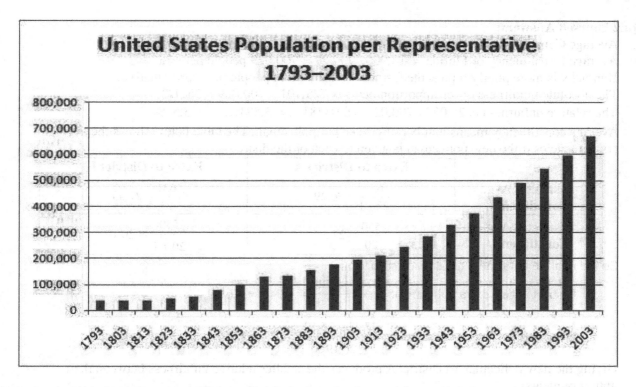

In a January 23, 2011 New York Times article[1], Dalton Conley and Jacqueline Stevens argued for increasing the size of the House to alleviate some problems caused by rising average constituencies:

This disparity [between average constituencies today and in 1910] increases the influence of lobbyists and special interests: the more constituents one has, the easier it is for money to outshine individual voices. And it means that representatives have a harder time connecting with the people back in their districts. What's needed, then, is a significant increase in the size of the House by expanding the number, and shrinking the size, of districts. Doing so would make campaigns cheaper, the political value of donations lower and the importance of local mobilizing much greater. Smaller districts would also end the two-party deadlock. Orange County, Calif., might elect a Libertarian, while Cambridge, Mass., might pick a candidate from the Green Party. More districts would likewise mean more precision in distributing them equitably, especially in low-population states. Today the lone Wyoming representative covers about 500,000 people, while her lone counterpart in Delaware reports to 900,000. Moreover, with additional House members we'd likely see more citizen-legislators and fewer lifers. In places like New York or Chicago, we would cross at least one Congressional district just walking a few blocks to the grocery store. Our representatives would be our neighbors, people who better understood the lives and concerns of average Americans.

The biggest obstacle to this is Congress itself. Such a change would require a noble act - routine in the 19th century as the size of the House rose every ten years, but unheard of since, of representatives voting to diminish their own power. So if such reform is to happen, it will have to be driven by grassroots movements. Luckily, we are living in just such a moment: the one thing Move On and the Tea Party can agree on is that the Washington status quo needs to change. So far this year, that has meant shrinking government. But in this case, the best solution might just be to make government — or at least the House of Representatives — bigger.

Quiz Yourself (Answer on the next page.)
4. Think of at least two good things not mentioned in the quote above that should happen if the size of the House of Representatives were increased. Also think of a bad thing that should happen.

---

[1] http://www.nytimes.com/2011/01/24/opinion/24conley.html

Quiz Yourself Answers:

1. Average Constituency of Kentucky = 4,350,606 / 6 = 725,101 people per seat.
    Average Constituency of Florida = 18,900,773 / 27 = 700,029 people per seat.
    Kentucky is more poorly represented, since there are more people per representative.

2. The absolute unfairness of the apportionments is 725,101 − 700,029 = 25,072
    The relative unfairness is 25,072 / 700,029 = 0.03581... = 3.581...% ≈ 3.58%

3. Average constituency means number of crimes per policeman. The table below shows the average constituencies if the new policeman is given to each of the districts.

	Extra to District A	Extra to District B
District A Avg. Constituency	$\dfrac{631}{23+1} \approx 26.29$	$\dfrac{631}{23} \approx 27.43$
District B Avg. Constituency	$\dfrac{550}{20} = 27.5$	$\dfrac{550}{20+1} \approx 26.19$

So the relative unfairness under each scenario is:

District A gets extra policeman: $\dfrac{27.5 - 26.29}{26.29} \approx 0.046 = 4.6\%$

District B gets extra policeman: $\dfrac{27.43 - 26.19}{26.19} \approx .047 = 4.7\%$

Giving the new policeman to District A produces the smaller relative unfairness between their apportionments.

4. Possible good things not previously mentioned: (i) Campaigns would be cheaper, (ii) political value of donations would be decreased, (iii) importance of mobilizing citizens might be greater, (iv) influence of lobbyists would be lessened. Possible bad things: (i) Larger budget for Congress, (ii) More agendas and debates, (iii) Need for a larger meeting place, (iv) (?) Might require electronic meeting and voting.

Problems for Section 4.6

Sharpen Your Skills (Answers in back of text.)

1. A gallon of milk cost $2.99 two years ago; now it costs $3.49.
   (a) What is the absolute difference in the prices? Interpret your result.
   (b) What is the relative difference in the prices? Express your result as a percentage rounded to the nearest hundredth of a percent, and interpret its meaning.

2. Professor Marshall had a $60,000 salary last year, but this year he has a $66,000 salary.
   (a) What is the absolute difference in the salaries? Interpret your result.
   (b) What is the relative difference in the salaries? Express your result as a percentage rounded to the nearest hundredth of a percent, and interpret its meaning.

Communicate the Concepts: (Answers in back of text.)

3. Explain how to decide which of two states an apportionment favors.

4. Explain how to calculate the relative unfairness between two states' apportionments after an apportionment is done.

5. Explain how relative unfairness incorporates the idea of relative change.

6. Explain how the size of average constituencies for the House of Representatives has changed in the last 100 years, and what has caused this change.

Apply Your Knowledge: (Answers to odd-numbered problems in back of text.)

7. According to the 2011 apportionment, the population of Ohio was 11,568,495 and the population of Tennessee was 6,375,431. Ohio was apportioned 16 House seats and Tennessee received 9 House seats.
   (a) Find the average constituency (to nearest whole number) for each state. Which state is more poorly represented?
   (b) Find the relative unfairness in the apportionments of the two states, to the nearest hundredth of a percent. Interpret this in terms of this apportionment problem.
   (c) Suppose a seat were transferred from Tennessee to Ohio giving Ohio 17 seats and Tennessee 8. Find the new relative unfairness in the apportionments of the two states. Does this transfer increase the relative unfairness in the apportionments of the two states?

8. According to the 2011 apportionment the population of Pennsylvania was 12,734,905 and they were apportioned 18 House seats. The population of Washington was 6,753,369; it received 10 House seats.
   (a) Find the average constituency (to the nearest whole number) for each state. Which state is more poorly represented?
   (b) Find the relative unfairness in the apportionments of the two states to the nearest hundredth of a percent. Interpret this in terms of this apportionment problem.
   (c) Suppose a seat were transferred from Washington to Pennsylvania, giving Pennsylvania 19 seats and Washington 9. Find the new relative unfairness in the apportionments of the two states. Does this transfer increase the relative unfairness in the apportionments of the two states?

9. According to the 2011 apportionment Indiana had a population of 6,501,582 and 9 seats in the House, and Illinois had a population of 12,864,384 and 18 seats.
   (a) Show that the apportionment favors Illinois.
   (b) Show that the relative unfairness in the apportionments of the two states is smaller with the current apportionment than it would be if Illinois gave up one of its seats to Indiana.

10. According to the 2011 apportionment Missouri had a population of 6,011,478 and 8 seats in the House. Ohio had a population of 11,568,495 and 16 seats.
    (a) Show that the apportionment favors Ohio.
    (b) Show that the relative unfairness in the apportionments of the two states is smaller with the current apportionment than it would be if Ohio had 15 seats and Missouri had 9 seats.

11. The table below shows the number of firemen and the number of fire runs in two cities in the same fire district. The district wishes to allocate an additional fireman to one of the two cities based on the number of fire runs.

	Number of Firemen	Number of Fire Runs
Crestwood	13	1750
La Grange	15	2250

    (a) Find the relative unfairness that results from awarding the new fireman to Crestwood.
    (b) Find the relative unfairness that results from awarding the new fireman to La Grange.
    (c) To which city should the new fireman be given to minimize the relative unfairness of the apportioning of the firemen?

12. The table below shows the number of social workers and the number of cases (case load) handled by the caseworkers at two offices. A new social worker is to be hired for one of the offices.

	Social workers	Case load
Downtown office	20	584
Shively office	24	712

    (a) Find the relative unfairness that results from giving the new worker to the Downtown office.
    (b) Find the relative unfairness that results from giving the new worker to the Shively office.
    (c) To which office should the new social worker be given to minimize the relative unfairness of the apportioning of the social workers?

13. The table below shows the 2010 populations and resulting apportionments of several states.

State	Population	Apportionment	Average Constituency	
California	37,341,989	53		
Florida	18,900,773	27		
New York	19,421,055	27		
Texas	25,268,418	36		

    (a) Find the average constituency of each state, rounded to the nearest whole number. Which state is most poorly represented? Which state does the apportionment favor?
    (b) Find the largest absolute unfairness between two of these states, and the largest relative unfairness between two of these states, rounded to the nearest hundredth of a percent.
    (c) Take one of the seats from the state with the smallest average constituency and give it to the state with the largest average constituency. Then answer (a) and (b) again using this apportionment. Does transferring one seat in this fashion make the relative unfairness any less?

14. The table below shows the 2010 populations and resulting apportionments of several states.

State	Population	Apportionment	Average Constituency	
Indiana	6,501,582	9		
Kentucky	4,350,606	6		
Ohio	11,568,495	16		
Tennessee	6,375,431	9		
Virginia	8,037,736	11		

(a) Find the average constituency of each state, rounded to the nearest whole number. Which state is most poorly represented? Which state does the apportionment favor?

(b) Find the largest absolute unfairness between two of these states, and the largest relative unfairness between two of these states.

(c) Take one of the seats from the state with the smallest average constituency and give it to the state with the largest average constituency. Then answer (a) and (b) again using this apportionment. Does transferring one seat in this fashion make the relative unfairness any less?

15. A clinic has a nursing staff of 225 nurses working in 4 shifts: A (7am to 1pm); B (1pm to 7pm); C (7pm to 1 am); and D (1am to 7am). Shown below is the result of using Jefferson's method to apportion the nurses to the four shifts based on number of patients.

Shift	Average Number of Patients	Jefferson Apportionment	Average Constituency
A	823	83	
B	659	66	
C	482	48	
D	286	28	

(a) Find the average constituency for each shift using the Jefferson apportionment. Round each to three decimal places. Interpret the meaning of average constituency *in the context of this apportionment problem*. Which shift is most poorly represented? Which shift does this apportionment favor?

(b) Written as a percentage rounded to 2 decimal places, what is the largest relative unfairness between the apportionments of two shifts?

16. The following table shows an apportionment of 500 faculty positions among 5 different schools at Enormous State University. Using the Webster Method the positions are to be apportioned according to their enrollments given shown below.

School	Enrollment	Webster's Apportionment	Average Constituency
Agriculture	2472	82	
Business	1314	44	
Education	2886	96	
Humanities	3405	114	
Science	4923	164	

(a) Find a divisor that will give the above apportionment.

(b) Find the average constituency for each school. Round each to three decimal places. Interpret the meaning of average constituency *in the context of this apportionment problem*. Which school is most poorly represented by this apportionment? Which school does this apportionment favor?

(c) As a percentage rounded to two decimal places, what is the largest relative unfairness between the apportionments of two schools?

Section 4.7 The Search for an Ideal Apportionment Method

The research that Huntington and others conducted during the early twentieth century produced a mathematical argument, as opposed to emotional or empirical arguments, for eliminating all methods except for Huntington-Hill and Webster. After each of the 1920, 1930, and 1940 censuses, there was much argument in Congress as to which of these two methods to adopt. In 1921, gridlock occurred so that no apportionment was made and the 1911 apportionments remained. In 1931, the two methods produced the same apportionment so no decision was made as to which method to use. In 1941, Webster's Method and the Huntington-Hill Method agreed on the apportionment for every state except Michigan and Arkansas. According to the 1940 census, Michigan had a population of 5,256,106 and was apportioned 17 seats by the Huntington-Hill method, while Arkansas had a population of 1,949,387 and was apportioned 7. (The Webster Method would have given Michigan 18 seats and Arkansas 6.) To find the relative unfairness between the Huntington-Hill apportionments of these two states we first find the average constituency for each state:

$$\text{Arkansas: } 1,949,387 / 7 \approx 278,484 \qquad \text{Michigan: } 5,256,106 / 17 \approx 309,183$$

$$\text{Relative unfairness} = \frac{309,183 - 278,484}{278,484} \approx 0.1102 = 11.02\%$$

So Michigan has about 11% more people per representative than Arkansas using the Huntington-Hill apportionment. If the Webster Method were used, Michigan would have 18 seats and Arkansas 6. Let us now find the relative unfairness using the Webster Method apportionment:

$$\text{Average constituency: } \text{Michigan: } 5,256,106 / 18 \approx 292,006 \qquad \text{Arkansas: } 1,949,387 / 6 \approx 324,898$$

$$\text{Relative unfairness} = \frac{324,898 - 292,006}{292,006} \approx 0.1126 = 11.26\%$$

Notice that the relative unfairness is higher under the Webster method than under the Huntington-Hill method. This theme will be repeated throughout this section.

In 1941, Michigan was predominantly Republican, Arkansas predominantly Democrat, and the Democrats controlled Congress. Partly because the Huntington-Hill method gave Arkansas (and hence the Democrats) an extra seat, it was the method chosen for the apportionment of the 1942 House of Representatives. It is the method that has been used for apportioning the House of Representatives ever since.

The Huntington-Hill Apportionment Method

The Huntington-Hill apportionment method uses a rounding rule that seems very strange at first. Recall that with the Webster Method, a quotient q that lies between two consecutive whole number n and $(n+1)$ is compared to the number that is half way between n and $(n+1)$, namely $n + 0.5$. Thus with the Webster Method, if $n < q < n + 0.5$, q is rounded down to n, and if $n + 0.5 \, q < n + 1$ then q is rounded up to $n+1$. With the <u>Huntington-Hill</u> Method, a quotient q that lies between two consecutive whole number n and $(n+1)$ is compared to $\sqrt{n \times (n+1)}$:

Huntington-Hill Rounding Rule

To round a quotient q that lies between two consecutive integers n and $n + 1$, compare q to $\sqrt{n \times (n+1)}$. If $q < \sqrt{n \times (n+1)}$ then q rounds down to n; otherwise q rounds up to $n + 1$.

We call $\sqrt{n \times (n+1)}$ the **Huntington-Hill rounding cutoff** for quotients between n and $n+1$.

Here are some Huntington-Hill rounding cutoffs for quotients in certain ranges:

Range of quotient q: $n \le q < n+1$	Huntington-Hill rounding cutoff
$0 \le q < 1$	$\sqrt{0 \times 1} = \sqrt{0} = 0$
$1 \le q < 2$	$\sqrt{1 \times 2} = \sqrt{2} \approx 1.414$
$2 \le q < 3$	$\sqrt{2 \times 3} = \sqrt{6} \approx 2.449$
$3 \le q < 4$	$\sqrt{3 \times 4} = \sqrt{12} \approx 3.464$
$4 \le q < 5$	$\sqrt{4 \times 5} = \sqrt{20} \approx 4.472$
$5 \le q < 6$	$\sqrt{5 \times 6} = \sqrt{30} \approx 5.477$

Table 4.44

Notice that, except for the cutoff for quotas between 0 and 1, all cutoffs have fractional part between 0.4 and 0.5, and the fractional part gets closer and closer to 0.5 as n increases. So:

> **Tip: *To round a quotient q by the Huntington-Hill rounding rule, only compute the rounding cutoff if the fractional part of q is between 0.4 and 0.5*.** *If the fractional part of q is less than 0.4, then q must round down, and if the fractional part of q is greater than 0.5, then q must round up.*

Once the Huntington-Hill rounding rule is mastered, the Huntington-Hill apportionment method is like all divisor methods:

> ### Huntington-Hill Method of Apportionment
> Select a divisor D that creates for each state a quotient $= \dfrac{\text{state population}}{D}$ so that, **when rounded according to the Huntington-Hill rounding rule**, these sum to the house size. Then apportion to each state its rounded quotient. Such a divisor is called a **valid divisor** for this method

A valid divisor for the Huntington-Hill Method may be found by "Guess, Check, and Adjust" or by using algebra. We will discuss both techniques in the examples below. In practice, often the standard divisor will be a valid divisor for the Huntington-Hill Method. (This also happens frequently with the Webster Method.)

Example 1 A corporation wants to set up a union board of 9 members proportional to the number of workers in the 3 divisions, shown in Table 4.45. Use the Huntington-Hill Method to apportion the 9 seats.

Division	Workers	Standard Quota	H-H cutoff	H-H rounded
A	255	1.393	$\sqrt{1 \times 2} \approx 1.414$	1
B	621	3.393	$\sqrt{3 \times 4} \approx 3.464$	3
C	771	4.213	$\sqrt{4 \times 5} \approx 4.472$	4
Total:	1647			8

Table 4.45

Solution: The standard divisor is $1647 / 9 = 183$. Table 4.45 also shows the standard quotas and their Huntington-Hill cutoffs. Since each standard quota is less than the cutoff, each rounds down, and the sum of the rounded quotas is only 8 so another seat must be awarded. To do this with a divisor method requires a *smaller* divisor. We will guess $D = 180$. The quotients for this divisor are shown in Table 4.46 below. Now the quotient for division A, 1.417, is greater than its cutoff, $\sqrt{1 \times 2} = 1.414$, and so is rounded up to 2. Now the sum of the rounded quotients is 9 as desired.

Division	Workers	Quotient for $D = 180$	H-H cutoff	H-H rounded
A	255	1.417	$\sqrt{1 \times 2} \approx 1.414$	2
B	621	3.450	$\sqrt{3 \times 4} \approx 3.464$	3
C	771	4.283	$\sqrt{4 \times 5} \approx 4.472$	4
Total:	1647			9

Table 4.46

Quiz Yourself (Answers at end of the of this section, before the problems.)
1. Round each of these according to the Huntington-Hill rounding rule: (a) 1.45   (b) 5.45
2. A county wants to apportion 12 police cars among 3 districts according to their populations shown below. Use the Huntington-Hill Method to make the apportionment.

District	Popul.	Standard Quota	H-H cutoff			
A	62,000					
B	44,000					
C	14,000					
Total:						

In Example 1 our guess of $D = 180$ turned out to be a valid divisor for the Huntington-Hill apportionment of this problem. Let's now see how algebra could be used to find a valid divisor.

Recall that the rounded standard quotas summed to 8, so we needed to *decrease* the divisor until a division's quotient grew enough to reach its Huntington-Hill cutoff and be rounded up. Here are the requirements for a divisor D to cause each division's quotient to grow to its Huntington-Hill cutoff:

A: $\dfrac{255}{D} = \sqrt{1 \times 2}$,   or $255 = D\sqrt{2}$,   or $D = \dfrac{255}{\sqrt{2}} \approx 180.312$

B: $\dfrac{621}{D} = \sqrt{3 \times 4}$,   or $621 = D\sqrt{12}$,   or $D = \dfrac{621}{\sqrt{12}} \approx 179.267$

C: $\dfrac{771}{D} = \sqrt{4 \times 5}$,   or $771 = D\sqrt{20}$,   or $D = \dfrac{771}{\sqrt{20}} \approx 172.42$

These are the divisors for each division to receive an additional representative. As D decreases from the standard divisor of 183, it first crosses 180.312, the divisor of division A to receive a representative.

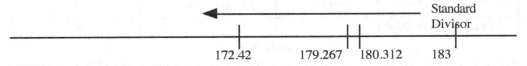

As long as $179.267 < D < 180.312$, D will cause division A to receive an additional representative on the board without either B or C receiving an extra representative. Our calculations for $D = 180$ verify this.

Quiz Yourself (Answers at end of the of this section, before the problems.)
3. Show how to use algebra and critical divisors to find the range of valid divisors in Quiz Yourself problem 2.

Example 2 In a number of countries seats in the legislative body are awarded to political parties in proportion to the votes they get in a general election. For example, in an election in Germany there were four parties who received the votes shown in Table 4.47 below. Apportion the 50 seats in the legislature to these four parties by (a) the Huntington-Hill Method, and (b) the Webster Method.

Party	Votes	Standard Quota	H-H cutoff	H-H rounded
CDU	40,980,000	20.49	$\sqrt{20 \times 21} \approx 20.4939$	20
SPD	39,100,000	19.55	$\sqrt{19 \times 20} \approx 19.494$	20
FDP	12,980,000	6.49	$\sqrt{6 \times 7} \approx 6.48074$	7
Green	6,940,000	3.47	$\sqrt{3 \times 4} \approx 3.464$	4
Total:	100,000,000			51

Table 4.47

<u>Solution:</u> The standard divisor is $100,000,000 / 50 = 2,000,000$. Dividing each party's vote by the standard divisor gives the standard quotas shown in the third column of Table 4.47.

(a) The standard quotas of the SPD, FDP, and Green parties are above their Huntington-Hill cutoff, and so round up. The rounded standard quotas sum to 51, one too many. We must increase D, which decreases the quotients until one of them is below its cutoff. The values of D for this to happen are:

$$\text{SPD: } \frac{39,100,000}{D} = \sqrt{19 \times 20} \text{ yields } D = \frac{39,100,000}{\sqrt{19 \times 20}} \approx 2,005,788$$

$$\text{FDP: } \frac{12,980,000}{D} = \sqrt{6 \times 7} \text{ yields } D = \frac{12,980,000}{\sqrt{6 \times 7}} \approx 2,002,857$$

$$\text{Green: } \frac{6,940,000}{D} = \sqrt{3 \times 4} \text{ yields } D = \frac{6,940,000}{\sqrt{3 \times 4}} \approx 2,003,405$$

As D increases from 2,000,000, it first crosses 2,002,857, the critical divisor that causes FDP to lose a seat, and then 2,003,405, the critical divisor that causes the Green party to lose a seat. As long as D is between these, say at $D = 2,003,000$, then FDP should lose a seat but the Green party should not. Table 4.48 below shows the calculations for $D = 2,003,000$. Notice the need for enough decimal places in the quotients and cutoffs to be able to compare them. Now the FDP's quotient is below its cutoff and so rounds down. The rounded quotas now sum to 50, so these give the Huntington-Hill apportionment.

Party	Votes	Quotients for $D = 2,003,000$	H-H cutoff	H-H rounded & Apportionment
CDU	40,980,000	20.4593	$\sqrt{20 \times 21} \approx 20.4939$	20
SPD	39,100,000	19.52		20
FDP	12,980,000	6.4803	$\sqrt{6 \times 7} \approx 6.48074$	6
Green	6,940,000	3.4648	$\sqrt{3 \times 4} \approx 3.464$	4
Total:	100,000,000			50

Table 4.48

(b) For this problem the Webster Apportionment differs from the Huntington-Hill apportionment. If we round the Standard Quotas according to the Webster rounding rule, as shown in Table 4.49, they sum to 49. So we must *decrease* the divisor until one party's quotient rounds up instead of down.

Party	Votes	Standard Quota	Webster rounded
CDU	40,980,000	20.49	20
SPD	39,100,000	19.55	20
FDP	12,980,000	6.49	6
Green	6,940,000	3.47	3
Total:	100,000,000		49

Table 4.49

The values of D at which this happens are (we omit SPD as it is just above its cutoff now):

$$\text{CDU: } \frac{40,980,000}{D} = 20.5 \text{ yields } D = \frac{40,980,000}{20.5} \approx 1,999,024 \text{ ,}$$

$$\text{FDP: } \frac{12,980,000}{D} = 6.5 \text{ yields } D = \frac{12,980,000}{6.5} \approx 1,996,923 \text{ ,}$$

$$\text{Green: } \frac{6,940,000}{D} = 3.5 \text{ yields } D = \frac{6,940,000}{3.5} \approx 1,982,857$$

As D decreases from 2,000,000, it first crosses 1,999,024, the divisor that causes CDU to gain a seat, and then 1,996,923, the divisor that causes FDP to gain a seat. Any divisor between these, say $D = 1,998,000$, should cause the quotient of the CDU to round up while that of the FDP still rounds down. Table 4.50 on the next page shows the actual calculations that verify this.

Party	Votes	Quotients for $D = 1,998,000$	Webster Apportionment
CDU	40,980,000	20.51051	21
SPD	39,100,000	19.56957	20
FDP	12,980,000	6.496496	6
Green	6,940,000	3.473473	3
Total:	100,000,000		50

Table 4.50

While the Huntington-Hill Method may seem strange, it evolved from the idea of creating an apportionment whose relative unfairness was as small as possible. In fact, Huntington and Hill proved:

Huntington-Hill Theorem The Huntington-Hill Apportionment method always produces an apportionment with the following property:

If a seat is transferred from one state to another, this transference cannot decrease the relative unfairness in the two states' apportionments.

We now verify that the conclusion of this theorem is true in the election shown in Example 2. Suppose, starting from the Huntington-Hill apportionment in Table 4.47, we transfer a seat from the Green Party to the CDU, thereby creating the Webster apportionment. Table 4.51 gives the average constituency of these two parties under each apportionment. (In this problem, average constituency represents the average number of votes represented by each of the party's seats.)

Party	Votes	Hunt. - Hill Apportion.	Avg. Constituency With H-H	Webster Apportion.	Avg. Constituency With Webster
CDU	40,980,000	20	2,049,000	21	1,951,429
Green	6,940,000	4	1,735,000	3	2,313,333
Total:	100,000,000	50		50	

Table 4.51

The relative unfairness of the Huntington-Hill apportionments of the two parties is:
$$\frac{2,049,000 - 1,735,000}{1,735,000} = 0.1809798... \approx 18.10\%$$
The relative unfairness of the Webster apportionments of the two parties is:
$$\frac{2,313,333 - 1,951,429}{1,951,429} = 0.1854559... \approx 18.55\%$$
The relative unfairness is slightly smaller with the apportionment determined by the Huntington-Hill Method than with the apportionment determined by the Webster Method.

Quiz Yourself (Answer at end of the of this section, before the problems.)
4. Shown below are the Huntington-Hill and Webster apportionments of the 12 police cars in Quiz Yourself problem 3 and populations of the districts.

District	Popul.	H-H Appor.	Webster Appor.	Avg. Constituency With H-H Appor.	Avg. Constituency With Webster Appor.
A	62,000	6	6		
B	44,000	4	5		
C	14,000	2	1		
Total:					

Determine the average constituencies with each apportionment. Find the largest relative unfairness between two states with the Huntington-Hill apportionment, and then again with the Webster apportionment. Do your calculations support the Huntington-Hill Theorem above?

The Results of Balinski and Young

In the 1970s and 1980s Michel L. Balinski and H. Peyton Young performed even further analyses searching for an ideal apportionment method. We now discuss briefly some of their considerations.

In Section 4.5 we noted that an ideal apportionment method should always produce an apportionment that satisfies the Quota Rule, for it seemed unreasonable to have a state receive either more than the standard quota of seats, to which is entitled, rounded either up or down to the next whole number. For clarity, we recall that rule:

> **The Quota Rule: Each state should be apportioned its standard quota rounded up or down; that is, its lower quota or 1 more than its lower quota.**

Hamilton's Method always produces an apportionment that satisfies the Quota Rule. Jefferson's Method does not because when it was applied to the apportionments of the U. S. House in 1820 and 1830 the resulting apportionments violated the Quota Rule. Balinski and Young proved that:

> **Theorem 4:** *No divisor method always produces apportionments that satisfy the Quota Rule.*

Example 3 Suppose we have 4 states whose populations are shown in Table 4.46 below. One is very large, the other three are small. (If this seems unlikely in America, think of the situation in many European countries, where the seats in the legislature are awarded to *parties*, rather than states, based on the vote that the party wins in a general election. In that situation small parties still may be awarded a seat or two.) Also, suppose there are 100 seats in the house to be apportioned. With a total population (or number of votes in the other scenario) of $P = 10,000$, the standard divisor is $D = 100$.

State	Popul.	S Quota	L Quota	LQ+1	D=98	Jeff	D=101	Web and H-H
A	9510	95.10	95	96	97.04	97	94.16	94
B	170	1.70	1	2	1.73	1	1.68	2
C	165	1.65	1	2	1.68	1	1.63	2
D	155	1.55	1	2	1.58	1	1.53	2
Total	10000	100	98			100		100

Table 4.52

Table 4.52 shows the apportionments resulting from the Jefferson (Jeff), Webster (Web), and Huntington-Hill (H-H) methods. For the Jefferson Method $D = 98$ gives rounded quotients that add up to 100. Note that with this apportionment the state A gets more than one more than its lower quota. For the Webster and Huntington-Hill Methods $D = 101$ gives rounded quotients that add up to 100. Note that with the latter two apportionments, state A gets less than its lower quota. If you try the Adams Method (another divisor method discussed in the problems for Section 4.6) on this example, $D = 102$ will lead to the same apportionment as Webster above. Thus this one example can be used to show that all four divisor methods we have discussed can produce an apportionment that does not satisfy the Quota Rule.

Some divisor methods produce apportionments that violate the Quota Rule with less frequency than other methods. Balinski and Young analyzed the 1970 and 1980 census data used to apportion the U. S. House of Representatives, varying the populations slightly and computing the apportionments for various divisor methods. For that data they found that the Huntington-Hill Method apportionment violates the Quota Rule about 3% of the time, and the Webster Method about 1% of the time. So violation of the Quota Rule by the Huntington-Hill and Webster Methods seems to be fairly rare. On the other hand, we know that the Hamilton Method <u>always</u> produces apportionments that satisfy the Quota Rule. So why not use it? The answer is the Alabama and Population paradoxes we saw in Section 4.4. Do divisor methods avoid these paradoxes? Balinski and Young proved that they do:

> **Theorem 5:** *No* divisor method can exhibit the Alabama Paradox in any apportionment.

This means that no method *we have studied* always produces apportionments that both satisfy the Quota Rule and avoid the Alabama Paradox. But maybe there is a method *we have not studied* that does. Balinski and Young were able to prove that in order for an apportionment method to avoid the Population Paradox, the method <u>must</u> be a divisor method:

> **Theorem 6:** An apportionment method never exhibits the Population Paradox in any apportionment if and only if the method is a divisor method in which the rounding rule may depend on the house size and the number of states. Combining this with Theorem 4, this means:

> **Theorem 7 ("Balinski and Young's Theorem"):** **No apportionment method always produces apportionments that both satisfy the Quota Rule and avoid the Population Paradox.**

The second theorem above is usually interpreted as saying that *there is no "ideal" apportionment method.* Our current method, the Huntington-Hill Method, which avoids the paradoxes and only rarely produces apportionments that violate the Quota Rule, seems about as good as we can do. However, it is not "perfect", and so occasional challenges to its use still occur, usually when the apportionment it produces differs from the apportionment produced by the Webster Method. Balinski and Young argued that the Webster method is slightly better than the Huntington-Hill method, for the Webster Method is less biased toward small states, and, as was noted above, seems to less frequently produce apportionments that violate the Quota Rule. But the fight over how to apportion Congress still occasionally flares:
- Before the 1950 census, Congress appointed a blue-ribbon panel of mathematicians to try to settle the question as to which is the best apportionment method. Their work confirmed what Huntington and Hill had shown, but again this depended on how you measured "best".
- In 1950, California would have gained a seat and Kansas lost a seat if the Webster method had been used, but no serious attempt to change to it occurred.
- In 1960, North Dakota would have lost a seat to Massachusetts if Webster had been used.
- In 1970 Kentucky and Colorado would have gained a seat and South Dakota and Montana lost a seat if Webster had been used.
- In 1980 Indiana would have gained and New Mexico lost a seat if Webster had been used.
- In 1990 both H-H and Webster reduced Montana from 2 to 1 seat. Montana sued, asking that a method we have not studied be used. The case went all the way to the Supreme Court, which said Congress had the right to choose to use Huntington-Hill.
- In 2000 the two methods agreed.
- In 2010 a court order was sought for Congress to increase the size of the House's voting membership and then reapportion the seats in accordance with the population figures of the 2010 Census. The intent was to rectify the disparity of congressional district population sizes among the states at present. The U.S. Supreme Court in December 2010 remanded the case to the U.S. District Court with instructions that the district court dismiss the case for lack of jurisdiction.

An interesting proposal called the Wyoming Rule proposes that the size of the House be increased until the average constituency overall equals the average constituency of the smallest state. Current that state is Wyoming, hence the name. According to published calculations, this would currently require a House size of 567 to make the average constituency overall equal to the 495,000 people in Wyoming, rather than the 710,000 it currently is. The argument is that people in Wyoming, who are guaranteed a representative by the Constitution, are much better represented than the people in most other states, where there is only about one representative for each 710,000 people on average!

> *Quiz Yourself* (Answer on the next page.)
> 5. Is there an apportionment method we have studied in the previous sections that avoids the Population Paradox and always produces apportionments that satisfy the Quota Rule? If so, name one; if not, state a Theorem from this section that insures that none exists.
> 6. True or False: (a) The Jefferson Method avoids the Population Paradox.

Quiz Yourself Answers:

1. Round each of these according to the Huntington-Hill rounding rule:

    (a) 1.45 is compared to the cutoff $\sqrt{1 \times (1+1)} = \sqrt{2} = 1.414$. Since $1.45 > 1.414$, 1.45 rounds up to 2.

    (b) 5.45 compares to the cutoff $\sqrt{5 \times (5+1)} = \sqrt{30} = 5.477$. Since $5.45 < 5.477$, 5.45 rounds down to 5.

2. A county wants to apportion 12 police cars among 3 districts according to their populations shown below. Use the Huntington-Hill Method to make the apportionment.

District	Population	Stan. Quota	H-H cutoff	H-H round	Quotients D=9850	H-H round
A	62,000	6.2	$\sqrt{42} = 6.48$	6	6.2944	6
B	44,000	4.4	$\sqrt{20} = 4.472$	4	4.467	4
C	14,000	1.4	$\sqrt{2} = 1.414$	1	1.4213	2
Total:	120,000			11		12

Standard divisor = 120,000 / 12 = 10,000. Divisor must decrease to get larger quotients. One valid divisor is D = 9850; its quotients are shown above. (See problem 3 for the range of valid divisors.) The quotients of A and B are below their H-H cutoffs and so round down, but C's quotient is above its cutoff and rounds up. The total of rounded quotients is now 12.

3. Show how to use algebra and critical divisors to find the range of valid divisor for problem 2.

    Here are the critical divisors for each state to gain a seat:

    A: $\dfrac{62,000}{D} = \sqrt{42}$ yields $D = \dfrac{62,000}{\sqrt{42}} \approx 9567$, B: $\dfrac{44,000}{D} = \sqrt{20}$ yields $D = \dfrac{44,000}{\sqrt{20}} \approx 9839$,

    C: $\dfrac{14,000}{D} = \sqrt{2}$ yields $D = \dfrac{14,000}{\sqrt{2}} \approx 9900$

    As D decreases from 10,000 it first crosses 9900, the critical divisor of C, then 9839, the critical divisor of B. Any divisor in the range $9839 < D < 9900$ produces quotients which, when rounded by the Huntington-Hill method, add up to 12, 1 more than the original 11. We saw 9850 did in problem 2.

4. The average constituencies based on the results of the two methods are shown in the table below. (The range of valid divisors for the Webster apportionment is $953.8 < D < 933.333$.)

District	Popul.	H-H Appor.	Webster Appor	Avg. Constituency With H-H Appor.	Avg. Constituency With Webster Appor.
A	62,000	6	6	10333.33	10333.33
B	44,000	4	5	11,000	8,800
C	14,000	2	1	7,000	14,000
Total:					

With the both apportionments, the largest relative unfairness is between B and C.

With H-H: $\dfrac{11,000 - 7,000}{7,000} = .57142857 \approx 57.14\%$ Webster: $\dfrac{14,000 - 8,800}{8,800} = .590909 \approx 59.01\%$

So the Huntington-Hill method's apportionment has a smaller relative unfairness than does Webster's. This supports the Huntington-Hill Theorem.

5. Is there an apportionment method we have studied in the previous sections that avoids the Alabama Paradox and always produces apportionments that satisfy the Quota Rule? If so, name one; if not, state a Theorem from this section that insures that none exists.

    No – this is part of Balinski and Young's Theorem

6. True or False: (a) The Jefferson Method avoids the Population Paradox.

    True; all divisor methods avoid the Population paradox.

    (b) The Jefferson Method always produces apportionments that satisfy the Quota Rule.

    False: Examples were seen in Section 4.5, and also in the congressional apportionments of 1820 and 1830.

Problems for Section 4.7

Sharpen Your Skills (Answers in back of the text.)   *In problems 1 - 4, find the Huntington-Hill cutoff for each quotient q, and round the quotient according to the Huntington-Hill rounding rule.*

1. $q = 5.45$ 2. $q = 2.46$ 3. $q = 0.23$ 4. $q = 7.49$

5. A state with a population of 2,500,000 has a standard quota of 4.4 seats. What is the critical divisor for the state to get 5 seats using the Huntington-Hill Method?

6. A state with a population of 2,500,000 has a standard quota of 3.5 seats. What is the critical divisor for the state to get 3 seats using the Huntington-Hill Method?

7. Mark each of the following true of false: (a) The Hamilton Method avoids the Population Paradox.
   (b) The Webster Method avoids the Alabama Paradox.
   (c) The Huntington-Hill Method avoids the Alabama Paradox.

8. Mark each of the following true of false:
   (a) The Hamilton Method always produces apportionments that satisfy the Quota Rule.
   (b) The Webster Method always produces apportionments that satisfy the Quota Rule.
   (c) The Huntington-Hill Method always produces apportionments that satisfy the Quota Rule.

9. Is there an apportionment method that avoids both the Alabama and Population Paradoxes? If so, name one; if not, state a Theorem from this section that insures none exists.

10. Is there an apportionment method that avoids the Population Paradox and always produces apportionments that satisfy the Quota Rule? If so, name one; if not, state a Theorem from this section that insures none exists.

Communicate the Concepts: (Answers in back of the text.)

11. Explain how to round a quotient q using the Huntington-Hill rounding rule.

12. Give at least one reason that supports the statement that the Huntington-Hill Method is better than the Webster Method, and one reason that the Webster Method is better than the Huntington-Hill Method.

13. Suppose a state with population P has a standard quota of 10.3 in a legislative apportionment. Explain how to find the critical divisor D so that P/D rounds to 11 using the Huntington-Hill rounding rule.

14. Suppose a state with population P has a standard quota of 10.6 in a legislative apportionment. Explain how to find the critical divisor D so that P/D rounds to 10 using the Huntington-Hill rounding rule.

Apply Your Knowledge: (Answers to odd-numbered problems in back of text.)

15. A small university consists of three colleges having enrollments shown in the table below.
    (a) Apportion five Student Senate seats to the colleges using the Huntington-Hill method. Give a divisor that yields appropriate quotients and the Huntington-Hill rounding cutoffs used.

College	Enrollment	Stan. Quotas	H-H cutoffs			H-H Apportionment
Arts	420					
Science	375					
Business	705					
Total	1500					

(b) Find the Webster Method apportionment and a valid divisor for that method.

College	Enrollment	Stan. Quotas				Webster Apportionment
Arts	420					
Science	375					
Business	705					
Total	1500					

(c) Determine the relative unfairness of those two schools' apportionments under each method. Which method produces the least relative unfairness?

16. A small country consists of three states whose populations are shown in the table below and has a legislature with 100 seats.
    (a) Apportion the 100 seats to the three states using the Huntington-Hill method. Give a valid divisor that yields appropriate quotients, the Huntington-Hill rounding cutoffs used in rounding the quotients, and the resulting apportionment.

State	Population	Stan. Quotas				H-H Apportionment
A	3,480					
B	46,010					
C	50,510					
Total						

    (b) Find the Webster Method apportionment and a valid divisor for that method.

State	Population	Stan. Quotas				Webster Apportionment
A	3,480					
B	46,010					
C	50,510					
Total						

    (c) The apportionments in (a) and (b) are different for two of the states. Determine the relative unfairness of those two states' apportionments under each of the two methods. Which method produces the least relative unfairness?

17. A city has three districts whose populations are shown in the chart below.
    (a) Use the Huntington-Hill method to apportion 25 city council seats among these three districts. Give a divisor that yields appropriate quotients, the Huntington-Hill rounding cutoffs used in rounding the quotients, and the resulting apportionment. Show your work in the chart below.

District	Population	Stan. Quotas				H-H Apportionment
A	2295					
B	895					
C	1810					
Total						

    (b) Find the Webster Method apportionment and a valid divisor for it. Show your work in the chart below.

District	Population	Stan. Quotas				Webster Apportionment
A	2295					
B	895					
C	1810					
Total						

    (c) The apportionments in (a) and (b) are different for two of the districts. Determine the relative unfairness of those two districts apportionments under each of the two methods. Which method gives the least relative unfairness?

18. The table below shows the populations of 5 states according to the 1970 census.
    (a) Use the Huntington-Hill method to apportion to these states the 57 seats they had in the U. S. House of Representatives. Give a divisor that yields this apportionment.

State	Population	Standard Quotas			H-H Apportionment	Average Constituency
Cal.	20,098,863					
Conn.	3,050,693					
Montana	701,573					
Oregon	2,110,810					
S. Dak.	673,247					
Total						

    (b) Using your apportionment from a), find the average constituency of each state. Fill these in the chart above
    (c) Find the largest *absolute* unfairness among two of the states' apportionments.
    (d) If a seat were transferred from the state with the smallest average constituency to the state with the largest average constituency, would the *absolute* unfairness of those two states' apportionments be less? Justify your answer.
    (e) Find the largest *relative* difference in constituency among the states' apportionments in (a).
    (f) If a seat were transferred from the state with the smallest average constituency to the state with the largest average constituency, would the *relative* unfairness of those two states' apportionments be less? Justify your answer.

19. A junior college expects the enrollments in its mathematics courses to be as given in the table below. Since the college has 9 faculty who teach 4 sections each, a total of 36 sections may be offered. Apportion the 36 sections to the 5 courses using the methods below. For each, give a valid divisor, the quotients for that divisor, and the resulting apportionment.
    (a) The Huntington-Hill Method

Course	Enrollment	Standard Quotas			H-H Apportionment
Alg.	286				
Trig.	133				
PreCal.	678				
Cal. I	568				
Cal. II	295				
Total					

    (b) The Webster Method

Course	Enrollment	Standard Quotas			Webster Apportionment
Alg.	286				
Trig.	133				
PreCal.	678				
Cal. I	568				
Cal. II	295				
Total					

    (c) The apportionments in (a) and (b) are different for two of the courses. Compare the relative unfairness of those two courses' apportionments under the two methods.

20. A bank with 6 branches wants to set up a total of 11 ATM machines at the branches according to the average numbers of customers per day at each branch, which are shown in the table below. Apportion the ATMs using the Huntington-Hill Method, giving a valid divisor.

Branch	Average # Customers Per Day	Standard Quotas				H-H Apportionment
Churchill Downs	157					
Dixie Highway	298					
Downtown	68					
Hurstbourne Pkwy	354					
Iroquois Park	100					
St. Matthews	167					

21. Suppose a country has a 110-member legislature and 4 states whose populations are given in the table below.

(a) Find the apportionment by the **Webster Method.** Give the standard divisor and a valid divisor.

State	Population	Stand. Quotas				Appor.
A	10,099					
B	430					
C	330					
D	141					
Total:						

(b) Explain how this apportionment violates the Quota Rule.

22. Suppose a country has a 37-member legislature and 5 states whose populations are given in the table below.

(a) Find the apportionment by the Jefferson Method. Give the standard divisor and a valid divisor.

State	Population	Stand. Quotas				Appor.
A	14,978					
B	9,260					
C	5,453					
D	4,624					
E	2,753					
Total:						

(b) Explain how this apportionment violates the Quota Rule.

Section 4.8   Overview and Review Problems for Chapter 4

Part 1: Voting Theory

A **preference ballot** is a ranking of all the candidates in order. A **preference schedule** is a chart showing how many voters submitted the various possible preference ballots.

We studied four voting methods (ways to decide the winner of a preference schedule):
1. The **Plurality Method**: The candidate with the most first place votes wins.
2. The **Borda Count Method:** If there are n candidates, then each first place ranking is worth n points, each second place ranking is worth n-1 points, and so on down to each last place ranking being worth 1 point. The points awarded in this fashion are totalled, and the candidate with the most points is declared the winner.
3. The **Plurality with Elimination Method:** If a candidate has a majority of the first place votes they win. Otherwise, eliminate the candidate (or candidates if there is a tie) that has the fewest first place votes. Redraw the preference schedule, moving up candidates that were ranked below the eliminated candidate(s). Repeat this process until a candidate has a majority of first place votes.
4. The **Method of Pairwise Comparisons**: Perform a two-person pairwise comparison between each pair of candidates, counting how many voters prefer the first candidate to the second and how many prefer the second to the first in each pairing. For each such pairing award 1 point to the winner, or award 1/2 point to each if there is a tie. The winner is the candidate that receives the most points.

We studied four fairness criteria:
1. The **Majority Fairness Criterion:** If there is a majority candidate (one with more than half the first place votes) the voting method must choose that candidate as the winner of the election.
2. The **Condorcet Fairness Criterion**: If there is a candidate that beats every other candidate in pairwise comparison (a *Condorcet candidate*), then the voting method must choose that candidate as the winner.
3. The **Monotonicity Fairness Criterion:** Suppose candidate X wins an election using a voting method. If a second election is done with the only change in the preference schedule being that some voters rank X higher in the second election that the first, then X must win the second election if the same method is used.
4. The **Independence of Irrelevant Alternatives Criterion**: Suppose candidate X wins an election using a voting method. If a second election is held, but one of the losing candidates drops out, then X must still win if the voters do not change their preferences.

The table below summarizes which of our four voting methods satisfy which fairness criteria.

	Majority Criterion	Condorcet Criterion	Monotonicity Criterion	Independence of Irrelevant Alternatives
Plurality	Y	N	Y	N
Borda Count	N	N	Y	N
Plurality With Elimination	Y	N	N	N
Pairwise Comparisons	Y	Y	Y	N

If a particular voting method does satisfy a particular fairness criterion, you should be able to explain why. You should be able to decide whether a given preference schedule is or is not an example of a violation of one of the Fairness Criteria by one of the voting methods, and explain your answer.

Arrow's Impossibility Theorem says that that it is impossible for there to be a voting method that satisfies all four of our fairness criteria.

Part 2: Apportionment

Although apportionment ideas and methods may be used to apportion any collection of indivisible objects, the terms and definitions are usually stated in terms of the problem of apportioning a representative body.

If the state i has population p_i, and if P is the total of all these populations and M is the number of seats to be apportioned, we define:

The *standard divisor* is the quotient $D = P / M$. It represents the ideal number of people per seat.
The *standard quota* of state i is p_i / D. It represents the number of seats to which state i is entitled.
The sum of these standard quotas equals M.

The **Hamilton Method** of apportionment is to
   (1) Tentatively allocate to each state the whole part of its standard quota; this is its Lower Quota.
   (2) Compare the sum of these tentative allocations to the total number of things to be allocated. If the difference is k, award one additional seat to the k states with the largest fractional parts in their standard quotas.

The Hamilton Method can suffer from the **Alabama Paradox**, which is when an increase in the number of things to be apportioned causes the apportionment of a state to decrease, and also from the **Population Paradox**, which is when changing populations causes a state whose population increased to lose a seat and one whose population decreased to gain a seat. Examples of these after the 1880 and 1900 censuses caused the U. S. House to abandon the Hamilton Method forever.

The other apportionment methods we studied are all divisor methods of apportionment:
   A *divisor method* is one in which a divisor D is found so that, when each state's population is divided by D and these quotients are rounded in a manner prescribed by the apportionment method, those rounded quotients add up to M, the number of items to be apportioned. A divisor that causes these rounded quotients to add up to M is called a *valid divisor*.

The three divisor methods we studied, with their rounding methods, are:
   (1) The **Jefferson Method**, in which each quotient is rounded to its whole part;
   (2) The **Webster Method**, in which each quotient is rounded in the conventional method (any fractional part less than 0.5 is dropped; if the fractional part is ≥ 0.5 the quotient is rounded up.)
   (3) The **Huntington-Hill Method**, in which a quotient between two consecutive whole numbers n and $n + 1$ is compared to the **Huntington-Hill rounding cut-off** $\sqrt{n \times (n+1)}$; if the quotient is less than this cutoff the quotient is rounded down, otherwise it is rounded up.

In any divisor method, the key is to find a valid divisor for the problem. Two ways to find a valid divisor are:
   A. The first, called "**guess, check, and adjust**", is an iterative process in which, if the current divisor is not valid, we adjust that divisor down if the sum of the rounded quotients for the current divisor is too small, whereas if that sum is too large we increase the current divisor. The new divisor is then checked and adjusted similarly, if necessary, iteratively until a valid divisor is reached.
   B. Algebra may be used to find the **critical divisor** for a state to gain or lose a seat. By comparing these divisors for the states to the current divisor one can tell which state will gain or lose a seat first as the divisor is adjusted up or down. This can be used to avoid the guessing in the first method.

The **Quota Rule** says that each state should get its standard quota rounded either up or down. This is reasonable since the standard quota is the number of seats to which the state is entitled. In 1820 and 1830 the Jefferson Method produced apportionments of the U. S. House of Representatives in which this rule was violated, causing the House to abandon the Jefferson Method. The Hamilton Method is the only one of our apportionment methods that always produces apportionments that satisfy the Quota Rule. This is a point in favor of the Hamilton Method, and was the major reason the Hamilton Method was used to apportion the U. S. House in the second half of the nineteenth century.

No divisor method can exhibit the Alabama Paradox. Moreover Balinski and Young proved mathematically a result that has come to be known as "**Balinski and Young's Theorem**": No apportionment method can always produce apportionments that satisfy the Quota Rule and avoid the Population Paradox.

The **average constituency** of a state is its population divided by the number of seats it is apportioned. A state with a larger average constituency is said to be **more poorly represented** since it has, on average, more people represented by each of its representatives. The **absolute unfairness** between the apportionments of two states is the absolute difference between their average constituencies. The **relative unfairness** between the apportionments of two states is the absolute unfairness between their apportionments divided by the smaller of their two average constituencies.

Huntington and Hill were able to prove that their method produces an apportionment in which the transfer of a seat from one state to another cannot decrease the relative unfairness of the states' apportionments. This, along with political reasons, caused their method to be adopted in 1942 for apportioning the U. S. House, and it is used to this day.

Review Problems for Chapter 4 (Answers in back of text)

1. A 26-member team must choose a Captain from among four candidates A, B, C, and D. Their preference schedule is:

Number of Votes:	5	6	5	3	2	3	2
First	A	B	C	D	C	A	D
Second	B	D	A	C	B	D	A
Third	C	C	B	B	D	B	C
Fourth	D	A	D	A	A	C	B

(a) Who wins if the Plurality Method is used? Is there a majority candidate?

(b) Who wins if Plurality with Elimination is used?

2. A 25-member selection committee must choose from among three candidates X, Y, and Z. Their preference schedule is:

Number of Votes:	9	7	5	4
First	X	Y	Z	X
Second	Y	Z	Y	Z
Third	Z	X	X	Y

(a) Find the winner using the Borda Count Method. Show your work.

(b) Is there a majority candidate? Explain why or why not.

(c) Is this an example of a violation of the Majority Fairness Criterion by the Borda Count Method? Explain why or why not.

3. A selection committee must choose between Atlanta (A), Boston (B), and Chicago (C) as the site of a convention. Their preference schedule is:

Number of Votes:	7	4	3	5
First	A	B	C	B
Second	C	A	A	C
Third	B	C	B	A

(a) Find the winner using the Method of Pairwise Comparisons.

(b) Does this example show a violation of the Condorcet Fairness Criterion by the Plurality Method? Explain why or why not.

4. The preference schedule for an election is:

Number of voters:	7	4	2
First	P	C	M
Second	C	M	P
Third	S	S	S
Fourth	M	P	C

(a) Is there a Majority Candidate?   (b) Is there a Condorcet Candidate?

(c) Find the winner using the Borda Count Method.

(d) Suppose S drops out of the race. Who wins the election then, still using the Borda Count Method?

(e) Based on the results of parts (a) - (d), of which of our four fairness criteria does this preference schedule show a violation by the Borda Count Method? *Explain*.

5. Mark each of the following True or False and *explain*:
   (a) Any majority candidate is also a Condorcet candidate.
   (b) Any Condorcet candidate is also a majority candidate.
   (c) The Plurality Method satisfies the Monotonicity Fairness Criterion.

6. Suppose you are a candidate in a three-person election and you have commitments for first place votes from more than half of the voters. Which voting methods we studied guarantee that you will win? Explain.

7. Show that in a country with 5 states whose populations are shown below, one of the paradoxes we studied occurs when the size of the legislature increases from 24 to 25 if the Hamilton Method is used. Name the paradox, and explain how this is an example of it.
   (a) **Hamilton** Apportionment when legislature has 24 seats:

State	Population	Stand. Quotas			Apportionment
A	1676				
B	1454				
C	925				
D	778				
E	615				
Totals					

   (b) **Hamilton** Apportionment when legislature has 25 seats:

State	Population	Stand. Quotas			Apportionment
A	1676				
B	1454				
C	925				
D	778				
E	615				
Totals					

   (c) Name the paradox that occurs, and explain how this is an example of it.

8. Suppose a town has four districts A, B, C, and D, and a force of 40 police officers that will be apportioned to the districts using the Hamilton Method.
   (a) Hamilton Apportionment with old population:

State	Old Population	Standard Quotas			Hamilton Appor.
A	1865				
B	1269				
C	712				
D	594				
Totals					

   What does the standard divisor represent in this problem? What do the standard quotas represent?
   (b) Hamilton Apportionment with new population:

State	New Population	Standard Quotas			Hamilton Appor.
A	1924				
B	1272				
C	710				
D	594				
Totals					

   (c) Show that one of the paradoxes we studied occurs, and explain how this is an example of it.

9. A school can offer a total of 20 sections of mathematics. Students have registered for 4 courses according to the table below. Apportion the 20 sections among the 4 courses using the methods listed below. For each method, show your calculations and give a divisor that yields the apportionment.

Course	Students
Geometry	980
Algebra	820
Precalculus	670
Calculus	530

   (a) Jefferson Method
   (b) Webster Method
   (c) Is either of the apportionments above a violation of the Quota Rule? Explain why or why not.

10. A country has 3 states whose populations are shown below. Use the Huntington-Hill method to apportion 25 house seats among these three states. Show a divisor D that yields the apportionment, the quotas it yields, the cutoffs used, and the resulting apportionment.

State	Population in thousands					Huntington-Hill Apportionment
A	880					
B	1,850					
C	2,270					
Total						

   Divisor that yields the Huntington-Hill Apportionment: _____

11. A small country consists of four states A, B, C, and D. The total population of this country is 10,000,000. Suppose the standard quotas for the states are as shown in the table below:

State	A	B	C	D
Standard Quota	0.84	4.14	3.66	1.36

   (a) Find the standard divisor for this apportionment problem.

   (b) Find the population of State C

12. The table below shows the populations and apportionments of Kentucky, Indiana, and Ohio according to the 1990 Census.

State:	Kentucky	Indiana	Ohio
Population	3,698,969	5,564,228	10,877,325
Apportionment	6	10	19

   (a) Find the average constituency of each state.
   (b) Which benefits a state, having a large average constituency or a small average constituency? Explain
   (c) For these states, what is the largest absolute unfairness between two states?
   (d) For these states, what is the largest relative unfairness between two states?

13. (a) State the Quota Rule.
    (b) Which apportionment method(s) we studied always produce(s) apportionments that satisfy the Quota Rule?

14. State Balinski and Young's Theorem.

15. Which Apportionment Method favors large states the most?

16. Which apportionment methods that we studied are Divisor Methods? What are the advantages of a divisor method? What are the disadvantages of a divisor method?

Review of the History of the Apportionment of the U. S. House of Representatives

Fill in the blanks below using the phrases listed at the bottom to supply some of the highlights of the history of the apportionment methods considered and/or used by the U. S. Congress to apportion the House of Representatives. (Some phrases may need to be used more than once, some not at all; the blank by 1911 requires a number, not a phrase.)

1792. Congress proposes that _____ be used, but President

Washington vetoes this proposal. In its place, _____ is adopted.

1842. Congress abandons _____, primarily because

_____, and adopts

_____.

1852. Congress adopts _____ under a new name.

1880. _____ surfaces as a serious flaw in

_____.

1902. _____ resurfaces as the same serious flaw in

_____, and

_____ is readopted.

1911. The size of the House of Representatives is fixed at its current size of _____ ˇ

1942. The method currently used, _____, is adopted.

Phrases:

The Hamilton Method   It favors small states

The Huntington-Hill Method   It favors large states

The Jefferson Method   It violates the Quota Rule

The Webster Method   It produces paradoxes

It minimizes the absolute unfairness   The Alabama Paradox

The Population Paradox

Answers to Problems

Section 1.1

	Percent	Decimal	Fraction
1.	40%	0.4	$\frac{4}{10} = \frac{2}{5}$
2.	60%	0.6	$\frac{6}{10} = \frac{3}{5}$
3.	15%	0.15	$\frac{3}{20}$
4.	5.85%	0.0585	$\frac{585}{10000} = \frac{117}{2000}$
5,	6.53%	0.0653	$\frac{653}{10000}$
6	0.75%	0.0075	$\frac{3}{40} = \frac{15}{200} = \frac{75}{1000}$

7. $0.28(350) = 98$ 8. $20 = 0.16(Base)$; Base = $20 / 0.16 = 125$

9. $(percent)(40) = 6$; percent = $6/40 = 0.15 = 15\%$ 10. $0.12(125) = 15$

11. $84 = 0.15(Base)$; Base = $84 / 0.15 = 560$ 12. $8.4 = (percent)(48)$; percent = $8.4 / 48 = 0.175 = 17.5\%$

13. Amount Change = 7; percent change = $7/140 = 0.05 = 5\%$

14. Amount Change = $78; percent change = $78 / $1200 = 0.065 = 6.5\%$

15. Amount Change = $30; percent change = $30 / $15,000 = 0.002 = 0.2\%$

16. Amount Change = $0.1 billion; percent change = $0.1 billion / $1 billion = 0.1 / 1 = 0.1 = 10\%$

17. "Percent" means per hundred"   18. See bottom of page 4 of text.

19. $(percent)(Base) = Amount$ (See bottom of page 4 of text.)

20. Amount of Interest = (Monthly Interest rate)(Amount of Unpaid Balance)

21. Percent change = (Amount change) / (Smaller amount)   (Convert quotient to percent)

22. Amount of change = larger - smaller

23. Base = Number of people in the U. S. who do not have health insurance = 44 million
     Amount = Number of people in the U. S. who do not have health insurance and are between 18 and 24
     = 15.4 million. Percent = Amount / Base = (15.4 million) / (44 million) = 15.4 / 44 = 0.35 = 35\%.

25. Amount = 360 students. $360 = 45\%(Base)$, so Base = $360 / 0.45 = 800$ students in the survey.

27. Base = number who e-filed in 2013. Since 20% is a percent change,
          Number who e-filed in 2014 = $(100 + 20)\%$ of (Number who e-filed in 2013)
               54.3 million = 1.20(Number who e-filed in 2013)
          Number who e-filed in 2008 = (54.3 million) / 1.20 = 45.25 million.
          So 54.3 million – 45.25 million = 9.05 million more people e-filed in 2014 than in 2013.

29. Base = price of shoes. $59.34 = (100 + 6)\%$(price of shoes)
          Price of shoes = $59.34 / 1.06 = $55.98.

31. Unpaid balance = $630 – $200 = $430. Monthly interest rate = $18\% / 12 = 1.5\%$.
          Amount of Interest = $(1.5\%)($430) = (0.015)($430) = 6.45.

33. Unpaid balance = $980 – $500 = $480. Monthly interest rate = $13.5\% / 12 = 1.125\%$.
          Amount of Interest = $(1.125\%)($480) = (0.01125)($480) = 5.40.

35. $1000 = Base - 20\% of Base = 80\% of Base. Base = $1000 / 0.80 = $1250.

Section 1.2

1. $40 = ($800)(2.5)r$ $40 = $2000r; $r = 40 / 2000 = .02 = 2\%$

2. $33 = $1500r; $r = $33 / $1500 = 0.022 = 2.20\%$

3. $3300 = P + P(0.1)$ Factor: $3300 = P(1 + 0.1)$ $P = $3300 / 1.1 = 3000

4. $2075 = P + P(0.0375)$ Factor: $2075 = P(1+ 0.0375)$ $P = $2075 / 1.0375 = 2000

5. Subtract $1200: $100 = ($1200)(1.5)r$ Simplify: $100= $1800r$ Divide: $r = 100/1800 = 0.05555... \approx 5.56\%$

Section 1.2

6. Subtract \$800: $31 = (\$800)(0.5)r;$ Simplify: $31 = \$400r;$ Divide: $r = 31 / 400 = 0.0775 = 7.75\%$

7. Amount I of simple interest = (Principal)(annual interest rate)(time in years)

8. $I = F - P$

9. In 1 year the amount of interest is Pr; in 2 years it is $2Pr$; in 3 years it is $3Pr$, etc. Each year the account earns another Pr worth of interest.

10. $P + Pr = P(1) + Pr = P(1 + r)$

11. t = 8/12 year; I = \$1500 ×0.15 ×(8/12) = \$150; $F = P + I = \$1500 + \$150 = \$1650.$

13. Feb. 1 to June 1 is 4 months, so $t = (4/12) = 1/3$ year. $I = P \times (0.18) \times (1/3) = 0.06P$

Using $F = P + I,$ Solve $\$800 = P + 0.06P$ $\$800 = (1 + 0.06)P$

$P = \$800 / 1.06 = 754.71698....$ which rounds to \$754.72 to the nearest penny.

15. $F = \$500,$ $P = \$500 - \$40 = \$460,$ so $I = \$40.$ $t = 2 / 12 = 1/6.$ r is unknown.

Substitute in $I = Prt$ and solve: $40 = 460 \times r \times (1/6)$

Multiply by 6: $6 \times 40 = 460r$

Divide by 460: $r = \dfrac{240}{460} = 0.521739 \ldots \approx 52.17\%$

17. $F = \$160, t = 2/12 = 1/6, I = \$18.$ So $P = F - I = \$160 - \$18 = \$142.$ Substitute into $I = Prt$:
$\$18 = \$142(r)(1/6)$ Multiply by 6: $108 = 142r$
Divide: $r = 108 / 142 = 0.76056... = 76.056...\% \approx 76.06\%$

19. Your brother is earning $I = \$50$ on his \$600 investment over 3 months = 1/4 year = 0.25 year
Use $I = Prt$: Solve $\$50 = \$600(r)(0.25)$ $r = 50 / (600 \times 0.25) = 0.33333.. \approx 33.33\%$

Section 1.3

1. 1200 × 1.08 ^ 12 yields \$3021.80

2. 900 × 1.07 ^ 9 yields \$1654.61

3. With simple interest you only earn interest on the original principal, never on the previously earned interest. With compound interest you earn interest at each compounding based on the current balance including all previously earned interest.

4. F is the Future value at the end of the growth
   P is the original principal invested
   r is the annual compound interest rate
   t is the time measured in years.

5. (a) $t = 50 - 21 = 29$ years, so $F = \$2000(1 + 0.062)^{29} = \$11,445.66.$
   (b) $t = 65 - 21 = 44$ years, so $F = \$2000(1 + 0.062)^{44} = \$28,216.86.$

7. Bob: $t = 55 - 21 = 34$ years so $F = \$1000(1 + 0.055)^{34} = \$6174.24$
   Sam: $t = 55 - 40 = 15$ years so $F = \$3000(1 + 0.055)^{15} = \$6697.43$

9. After $t = 35$ years, John's account will be worth $F = P + Prt = \$2000 + \$2000(0.07)(35) = \$6900.$
   Jane's account will be worth $F = P(1 + r)^{t} = \$1000(1.07)^{35} = \$10,676.58$

11. After $t = 3$ years he will have $F = \$2400(1 + 0.05)^{3} = \$2778.30.$
   This becomes the principal of the next investment.
      After $t = 2$ more years he will have $F = \$2778.30(1 + 0.061)^{2} = \$3127.59.$
      So the total interest earned is \$3127.59 - \$2400 - \$727.59.

13. $P = \$28;$ $r = 0.095;$ $F = \$28(1 + 0.095)^{4} = \$40.25,$ or \$40 per square foot to the nearest dollar.

15. Cost in 25 years = \$3.55(1.0350 ^ 25 = \$8.38519... \approx \$8.39

17. It will be $t = 4$ years from 2014-15 until 2018-19. The tuition per year should be

$F = \$10236(1 + .085)^{6} = \$14,185.65$ which yields \$14,186 when rounded to the nearest dollar.

19. $I = \$19,$ so $P = \$400 - \$19 = \$381.$ Solve $\$19 = \$381(r)(1/6)$ $r = (6 \times 19)/381 = 29.92\%.$

20. Amount change = \$300; Percent change = 300 / 2500 = 0.12 = 12\%.

Section 1.4

1. Keystrokes: $1200 \times 1.012 \wedge 36 =$ $1843.66   2. Keystrokes: $360 \times (1+.05/365) \wedge 730 =$ $397.86

3. Percent change $= 10/250 = 0.04 = 4\%$ 4. Percent change $= 33/550 = 0.06 = 6\%$

5. Keystrokes: $(1+.04/365) \wedge 365 - 1 = 0.04080.... \approx 4.08\%$

6. Keystrokes: $(1+.05/12) \wedge 12 - 1 = 0.05116... \approx 5.12\%$

7. (a) P means *Present Value* or *Principal*; its unit is *dollars*
   (b) t means the *time*; its unit is *years*
   (c) i means the *periodic interest rate*, or *rate per compounding*; its form is a *decimal*
   (d) m means the total number of compoundings; its form is a *whole number*.

8. (a) F means *Future Value*, which is the value after last compounding; its unit is *dollars*
   (b) Y means the *Annual Percentage Yield*; its form is *percent* rounded to the nearest hundredth
   (c) r means the *annual interest rate*; its form is a *decimal*

9. The variable r is the annual interest rate, but i is the periodic interest applied at each compounding.
   $i = r / $ (number of compoundings per year)

10. The variable t is time measured in *years*, whereas m is the number of total number of compoundings that occur. $m = t \times$ (number of compoundings per year)

11. The variable Y is the percent change over 1 year; r is the annual rate that is divided by the number of compoundings per year, with the quotient giving the rate applied at each compounding.

12. $F = P + I$, or $I = F - P$

13. $t = 18 - 10 = 8$ years; $m = 8 \times 12 = 96$ compoundings; $r = 0.054$; $i = 0.054 / 12 = 0.0045$

    $P = \$7000$ $F = \$7000(1+0.0045)^{96} = \$10,771.90$, $I = \$10,771.90 - \$7000 = \$3771.90$.

15. The investment earns at a quarterly rate of $i = 0.069 / 4 = 0.01725$; $m = nt = 4 \times 1.5 = 6$ compoundings.

    Using the Compound Interest Formula: $F = 4000(1.01725)^6 = \$4432.27$, or $432.27 in interest.

17. APY = percent change $= (1370 - 1325) / 1325 = 0.03396... \approx 3.40\%$

19. (a) $n = 2$ compoundings per year, so $Y = (1 + 0.054/2)^2 - 1 = (1.027)^2 - 1 = .054729 \approx 5.47\%$
    (b) $n = 4$ compoundings per year, so $Y = (1 + 0.054/4)^4 - 1 = (1.0135)^4 - 1 = .055103.. \approx 5.51\%$
    (c) $n = 12$ compoundings per year, so $Y = (1 + 0.054/12)^{12} - 1 = (1.0045)^{12} - 1 = 0.0553567... \approx 5.54\%$
    (d) $n = 365$ compoundings per year, so $Y = (1 + 0.054/365)^{365} - 1 = (1.000147945)^{365} - 1 = .05548 \approx 5.55\%$
    (e) It seems that as the number of compoundings per year increases, the APY increases.

21. Bank A: $Y = \$29.16 / \$500 = 0.05832 \approx 5.83\%$
    Bank B: $Y = (1 + 0.0568/365)^{365} - 1 = 0.0584394 \approx 5.84\%$. Bank B is the better investment.

23. (a) First we compute the value after the first 3 months. $n = 12$ compoundings per year, and $t = 0.25$ years, $r = 0.054$, so $i = 0.054 / 12 = 0.0045$ and $m = 3$ monthly compoundings. So
    $F = \$1500(1 + 0.0045)^3 = \$1520.34$ is the value after the first 3 months.
    For the second 9 months $t = 0.75$, $m = 9$ monthly compoundings, $r = 0.057$, $i = 0.057/12 = 0.00475$.
    So $F = \$1520.34(1.00475)^9 = \$1586.58$ is the value at the end of the year.
    (b) This gives $I = \$1586.58 - \$1500 = \$86.58$ interest for the year.
    (c) This interest is the amount of change. It represents a percent increase in value of $86.58 / 1500 = 0.05772 = 5.77\%$. The formula on page 27 cannot be used because there is not a single value of r that applies throughout the year.

Review Problems

25. Sue is paying $I = \$1600 - \$1500 = \$100$ in interest for $t = 4/12 = 1/3$ years.
    Using $I = Prt$ $100 = 1500(r)(1/3)$ Solve for r: Multiply by 3: $300 = 1500r$.
    Divide by 1500: $(1/5) = r$. So $r = 0.2 = 20\%$ annual interest.

26. Cost in 10 years $= \$400(1.095)\wedge 10 \approx \$991$.

Section 1.5

1. $P = \dfrac{2000}{(1.02)^{20}} = \$1345.94$ 2. $P = \dfrac{4500}{(1.045)^{35}} = \$964.14$

3. Keystrokes:2500 / (1 + .05 / 12) ^ 48 = $2047.68 4. Keystrokes: 358 / (1 + .04 / 365) ^ 1460 = $305.07

5. An amount at the start of growth is a Principal; an amount at the end of the growth is a Future Value.

6. As interest rates rise, you are able to start with a smaller principal (price today) and still end up with

   the same future value. This is because when you solve $F = P(1+r)^t$ for P you obtain $P = \dfrac{F}{(1+r)^t}$. If

   r rises then the denominator rises and so the value of the quotient (the price P today) falls.

7. $F = \$20,000;\ \ r = 0.033;\ \ t = 17 - 3 = 14$ years; P unknown

   (a) $m = 14 \times 1 = 14$ compoundings; $i = r / 1 = 0.033$; solve $\$20,000 = P(1+0.033)^{14}$

   $P = 20,000 / (1.033)^{14} = \$12,694.79$ $I = \$20,000 - \$12,694.79 = \$7305.21$

   (b $m = 14 \times 4 = 56$ compoundings; $i = 0.033/4 = 0.00825$; solve $\$20,000 = P(1.00825)^{56}$

   $P = 20,000 / (1.00825)^{56} = \$12,642.35$ $I = \$20,000 - \$12,642.35 = \$7,357.65$

9. $F = \$7,500;\ \ t = 6$ years 9 months $= 6.75$ years; $r = 4.35\%$; $n = 12$ compoundings per year;

   $m = 12 \times 6.75 = 81$ compoundings; (or $m = 6 \times 12 + 9 = 81$ months) $i = 0.0435 / 12 = 0.003625$

   Solve $\$7500 = P(1+0.003625)^{81}$; $P = \dfrac{7,500}{(1+0.003625)^{81}} = \$5594.64$; $I = \$7500 - \$5594.64 = \$1905.36$

11. $F = \$20,000;\ m = 35(12) = 420$ monthly compoundings; $i = 0.048 / 12 = 0.004$ Solve

    $\$20,000 = P(1.004)^{420}$; $P = 20,000 \div (1.004)^{420} = \$3,739.99$; $I = \$20,000 - \$3739.99 = \$16,260.01$

13. Solve $\$10,000 = P(1+0.015)^{10}$ Obtain $P = \$10,000 / (1+0.015)^{10} = \$8616.67$

15. (a) Solve $\$5000 = P(1+0.0175)^{20}$ Obtain $P = \$5000 / (1+0.0175)^{20} = \$3534.12$

    (b) 13 years remain. Solve $\$5000 = P(1+0.025)^{13}$ Obtain $P = \$5000 / (1.025)^{13} = \$3627.10$

17. $F = \$200, i = r = 0.11, t = m = 6$. Solve $\$200 = P(1.11)^6$ $P = \$200 / (1.11)^6 = \$107$ to the nearest dollar.

19. <u>Step I</u> In 6 years, the cost will grow at 5.0% per year to $F = 35000(1.05)^6 = \$46,903$.

    <u>Step II</u> The investment needed today in account paying 8.2% annually so as to have this

    cost in 6 years is the solution of $\$46,903 = P(1.082)^6$, namely $P = \$46,903 \div (1.082)^6 = \$29,231$.

    Rounded to the nearest thousand dollars, the investment needed today is $29,000.

Review Problems

21. Four years and 8 months of monthly compoundings means $m = 4 \times 12 + 8 = 56$ compoundings. So $5000

    will grow to $F = \$5000 \left(1 + \dfrac{0.042}{12}\right)^{4 \times 12 + 8} = \$5000(1.0035)^{56} = \$6080.55$.

22. $I = \$2950 - \$2500 = \$450$; $\$450 = \$2500(0.09)(t) = 225t$ $t = 450/225 = 2$ years.

Challenge Problem

23. Cost of UofL in 13 years: $F = \$36,000(1.085)^{13} = \$103,965.46$. The amount you need to invest to day

    is found by solving $\$103,965.46 = P(1.003)^{156}$ since $i = 0.036 / 12 = 0.003$ and $m = 12(13) = 156$.

    So $P = \dfrac{\$103,965.46}{(1.003)^{156}} = \$65,154.37$. This is much more than the current cost!

Section 1.6

1. Keystrokes: 1.73 ^ (1 / 3) − 1 = 0.20046... $\approx 20.05\%$

2. Keystrokes: (13 / 5) ^ (1 / 9) − 1 = 0.1120086... $\approx 11.20\%$

3. Take 5th root: $(2.31)^{1/5} = 1 + r$; subtract 1: $r = 2.31^{1/5} - 1 = 0.18228...\ \approx 18.23\%$

Section 1.6

4. $(38/30) = (1+r)^7$; Take 7th root: $\left(\dfrac{38}{30}\right)^{1/7} = 1+r$; $r = \left(\dfrac{38}{30}\right)^{1/7} - 1 = 0.034346... \approx 3.43\%$

5. In this case the APY Y satisfies $F = P(1+Y)^t$. Solve this for Y.

6. First divide both sides by P, then raise both sides to the $1/t$ power, finally subtract 1.

7. One-third is not exactly 0.33, but one-fifth is exactly 0.2.

8. The calculator evaluates the keystrokes from left to right. It will calculate $2 \wedge 1$, which is 2, then calculate $2 / 9 = 0.22222....$ But $(0.2222....) \wedge 9$ is not equal to 2.

9. $P = \$10,000$; $F = \$14,000$; $t = 18 - 13 = 5$ years

   Solve $\$14,000 = \$10,000(1 + r)^5$; obtain $r = (1.4)^{1/5} - 1$ Calculate $r = 1.4 \wedge (1/5) - 1 = 0.06961... \approx 6.96\%$

11. $P = \$5000$, $F = \$15000$, $t = 18$ years. Solve $\$15000 = \$5000(1 + r)^{18}$ Divide by $\$5000$: $3 = (1 + r)^{18}$

    Take 18th root: $1 + r = (3)^{1/18}$ Subtract 1: $r = (3)^{1/18} - 1$. Calculate $r = 3 \wedge (1/18) - 1 = 0.062935... \approx 6.29\%$

13. $P = 0.27$ grows to $F = 3.50$ in $2014 - 1968 = 46$ years. Solve $3.50 = 0.27(1 + r)^{46}$

    Obtain $r = \left(\dfrac{3.50}{0.27}\right)^{1/46} - 1$ Calculate $(3.50 / 0.27) \wedge (1/46) - 1 = 0.057278... \approx 5.73\%$ per year.

15. APY $= 0.031$, $P = \$2000$. For 6 months $t = 0.5$, so $F = 2000 (1 + 0.031)^{0.5} = \$2030.76$

    For 2 years 3 months $t = 2.25$, so $F = 2000 (1.031)^{2.25} = \$2142.21$

17. $F = \$7000$, APY $= 0.0228$, $t = 3.5$, P is unknown.   Solve $\$7000 = P(1.0228)^{3.5}$

    $P = \$7000 \div (1.0228)^{3.5} = \$6468.90$. $I = \$7000 - \$6468.90 = \$531.10$.

19. (a) (i) For the first six months the account earns at a rate of $i = 0.02/4 = 0.005$ per quarter for

    $m = 2$ quarters. After that 6 months the account is worth $F = \$1000(1.005)^2 = \$1010.03$.

    (ii) For the next six months $i = 0.025/4 = 0.00625$ per quarter for $m = 2$ quarters. The $\$1010.03$

    will grow to $F = \$1010.03(1.00625)^2 = \$1022.69$ by the end of the second six months.

    (iii) For the second year the account earns at a rate of $i = 0.036/4 = 0.009$ per quarter

    for $m = 4$ quarters. In that time the $\$1022.69$ at the end of the first year will grow to

    $F = \$1022.69(1.009)^4 = \$1060.01$ by the end of the second year.

    (b) From part (a) the $\$1000$ investment has grown to $\$1060.01$ in two years. So the APY Y for

    this investment satisfies $\$1060.01 = \$1000(1 + Y)^2$ Solving for Y:

    Divide by 1000: $1.06001 = (1 + Y)^2$ Take square roots: $(1.06001)^{1/2} = 1 + Y$

    Subtract 1: $Y = (1.06001)^{1/2} - 1 = .02956787..... = 02.956787..... \% \approx 2.96\%$

21. (a) Solve $2400 = 2000(1 + r)^3$; $1.2 = (1 + r)^3$, $r = (1.2)^{1/3} - 1 = 0.0626585.. \approx 6.27\%$

    (b) Solve $2400 = 2000 + 2000(r)3$; Subtract 2000, evaluate $(2000)3$, to obtain: $400 = 6000r$,

    Divide by 6000: $r = 400 / 6000 = 0.06666666... \approx 6.67\%$

    (c) the annual interest rate r is applied at a rate of $r / 4$ each of the 12 quarters.

    Solve $2400 = 2000\left(1 + \dfrac{r}{4}\right)^{12}$;   Divide by 2000: $1.2 = \left(1 + \dfrac{r}{4}\right)^{12}$;

    Raise to (1/12)th power: $(1.2)^{1/12} = \left(1 + \dfrac{r}{4}\right)$;   Subtract 1: $\dfrac{r}{4} = (1.2)^{1/12} - 1$

    Multiply by 4: $4((1.2)^{1/12} - 1) = r = 0.061237882.. \approx 6.12\%$ (compounded quarterly)

Review Problems

23. (a) $Y = \left(1 + \dfrac{0.062}{4}\right)^4 - 1 = 0.63456... \approx 6.35\%$ (b) $Y = \left(1 + \dfrac{0.061}{365}\right)^{365} - 1 = 0.062893... \approx 6.29\%$

(c) $Y = \$19.08\,/\,\$300 = 0.636 = 6.36\%$ (c) has highest APY.

24. $F = \$3,000$, $i = 0.027\,/\,12 = 0.00225$, $m = 12(5) = 60$ monthly compoundings.

Solve $\$3,000 = P(1.00225)^{60}$ $P = 3,000 \div (1.00225)^{60} = \$2,621.55$

25. Solve $2500 = P(1 + 0.0268)^6$ Obtain $P = 2500\,/\,1.0268 \wedge 6 = \$2133.17$

Section 1.7

1. Keystrokes: $\log(2.3)\,/\,\log(1.04) = 21.23646....$

2. Keystrokes: $\log(5340\,/\,1320)\,/\,\log(1 + 0.05\,/\,12) = 336.12....$

3. Divide by P: $4 = (1 + 0.03)^m$ Apply logs: $\log(4) = \log((1 + 0.03)^m) = m\log(1.03)$

Divide by $\log(1.03)$: $m = \log(4)\,/\,\log(1.03) = 46.89...$ which rounds up to 47.

4. Divide by 500: $\dfrac{\$2750}{\$500} = (1 + 0.0035)^m$ Apply logs: $\log\left(\dfrac{275}{50}\right) = \log((1.035)^m) = m\log(1.035)$

Divide by $\log(1.035)$: $m = \dfrac{\log\left(\dfrac{275}{50}\right)}{\log(1.035)} = 49.55...$ which rounds up to 50.

5. Guess and check solution: Guess values of m and substitute them into the right hand side:

$m = 100$: $\$500(1.0025)^{100} = \$641.81$ too low. $m = 150$: $\$500(1.0025)^{150} = \$727.16$ still too low

$m = 170$: $\$500(1.0025)^{170} = \$764.39$ almost! $m = 180$: $\$500(1.0025)^{180} = 783.72$ may be correct

Check: $m = 179$ gives $\$500(1.0025)^{179} = \$781.76$ is too low. So $m = 180$ is the smallest.

6. $\log(B^m) = m\log(B)$

7. Because interest is only added to the account at the end of a compounding period. So the value of an account jumps at the end of each compounding period after staying constant through the period.

8. Divide M by 12 since there are 12 months in a year. The whole number part of the result is the number of years. Convert the decimal part to a number of months by multiplying it by 12. (Other methods are possible.)

9. Divide Q by 4 since there are 4 quarters in a year. The whole number part of the result is the number of years. Convert the decimal part to a number of months by multiplying it by 4. (Other methods are possible.)

10. Guess values for the number m of compoundings until you find an m so that after m compoundings P grows to at least F, but after $m - 1$ compoundings P grows to less than F.

11. $P = \$12,000$; $F = \$35,000$; $r = 0.093$; $m = t$ unknown number of yearly compoundings.

(a) Solve $35,000 = 12,000(1 + 0.093)^m$; Divide by 12000: $\dfrac{35,000}{12,000} = (1.093)^m$ Simplify: $\dfrac{35}{12} = (1.093)^m$

Take logs: $\log\left(\dfrac{35}{12}\right) = \log(1.093)^m = m\log(1.093)$

Divide by $\log(1.093)$: $m = \log\left(\dfrac{35}{12}\right) \div \log(1.093) \approx 12.037$ which means 13 years are required.

(b) at the end of 13 years $F = \$12,000(1.093)^{13} = \$38,127.94$

$I = \$38,127.94 - \$12,000 = \$26,127.94$

Section 1.7

13. $P = \$3{,}750$; $F = \$15{,}000$; number m of quarters is unknown; $i = 0.04 / 4 = 0.01$

   (a) Solve $\$15{,}000 = \$3750\left(1+0.01\right)^{m}$;   Divide by $\$3750$: $\dfrac{15{,}000}{3750} = \left(1.01\right)^{m}$

      Take logs: $\log\left(\dfrac{15000}{3750}\right) = \log\left(1.01\right)^{m} = m\log\left(1.01\right)$

      Divide by $\log(1.01)$: $m = \log\left(\dfrac{15{,}000}{3{,}750}\right) \div \log\left(1.01\right) \approx 139.32.....$ so 140 quarters are needed.

      This is $140/12 = 11.666..$ years $= 11$ years 8 months

   (b) At the end of 140 quarters, $F = \$3750(1.01)^{140} = \$15{,}101.62$.

      $I = F - P = \$15{,}101.62 - \$3{,}750 = \$11{,}351.62$

15. Marla has $P = \$2800$ and wants $F = \$4000$. Her account earns $i = 0.063 / 12 = 0.00525$ per month.

    Letting m be the unknown number of months, Solve: $4000 = 2800(1.00525)^{m}$

    Divide by 2800: $40/28 = (1.00525)^{m}$ Take logs & use property: $\log(40/28) = m\log(1.00525)$

    Divide by $\log(1.00525)$: $m = \log\left(\dfrac{40}{28}\right) \div \log\left(1.00525\right) \approx 68.1$. So it will take 69 months,

    or 5 years, 9 months.

17. Solve $50 = 45\left(1+\dfrac{0.027}{365}\right)^{m}$; $\dfrac{50}{45} = \left(1+\dfrac{0.027}{365}\right)^{m}$; $\log\left(\dfrac{50}{45}\right) = m\log\left(1+\dfrac{0.027}{365}\right)$

    $m = \log\left(\dfrac{50}{45}\right) \div \log\left(1+\dfrac{0.027}{365}\right) = 1424.37$ It takes 1425 days, or 3 years 330 days.

19. (a) $i = 0.072 / 12 = 0.006$ Solve $1{,}000{,}000 = 400{,}000(1.006)^{m}$ ($m = $ # of months)

    Divide by 400,000: $2.5 = (1.006)^{m}$

    Take logs & use property: $\log(2.5) = m\log(1.006)$

    Divide by $\log(1.006)$: $m = \dfrac{\log\left(2.5\right)}{\log\left(1.006\right)} \approx 153.17$ It takes 154 months, or 12 years 10 months.

   (b) If he invested in a simple interest account, he would reach a million dollars when t solved

    $1{,}000{,}000 = 400{,}000 + 400{,}000(0.072)t$ or $600{,}000 = 400{,}000(0.072)t$,   or

    $600{,}000 = 28{,}800t$ $t = 600{,}000 / 28{,}800 = 20.833333...$ years, or 20 years, 10 months.

21. Solve $2P = P(1.06)^{m}$; obtain $m = \dfrac{\log\left(2\right)}{\log(1.06)} \approx 11.9$ years   Doubling would require 12 years.

23. $i = 0.06/4 = 0.015$.   Solve $2P = P\left(1+0.015\right)^{m}$ or $2 = \left(1.015\right)^{m}$ ($m = $ number of quarters)

    Obtain $m = \dfrac{\log\left(2\right)}{\log(1.015)} \approx 46.56$.   Thus 47 quarters, or 11 years 9 months, are needed to double.

Section 1.7 Review Problems

25. $F = \$800\left(1+\dfrac{0.071}{365}\right)^{365\times5} = \$1140.91$. $I = \$1140.91 - \$800 = \$340.91$.

26. The time is $t = 7.25 = $ years. Solve $2P = P\left(1+Y\right)^{7.25}$

    Divide by P: $2 = \left(1+Y\right)^{7.25}$ Raise to the $\frac{1}{7.25}$ power: $2^{1/7.25} = \left(1+Y\right)$

    Subtract 1 and switch sides: $Y = 2^{1/7.25} - 1 = .100326... = 10.03\%$ is the APY.

27. $i = 0.054 / 4 = 0.0135$; $m = 5.75$ years x 4 compoundings per year $= 23$ compoundings; $F = \$7500$.

    Solve $\$7500 = P\left(1.0135\right)^{23}$ $P = \$7500 \div \left(1.0135\right)^{23} = \$5509.53$

28. $t = 3 / 52$. $I = \$280 - \$250 = \$30$. Substitute into $I = Prt$: $\$30 = \$250(r)(3/52)$

    Multiply both sides by 52: $(30)(52) = (250)(3)r$ Perform calculations: $1560 = 750r$

    Divide by 750 and switch sides: $r = 1560 / 750 = 2.08 = 208\%$ (!!)

Section 1.7 Review Problems

29. Cruise cost m months in the future is $\$4000(1.003)^m$ since $i = 0.036 / 12 = 0.03$. Value of the investment

is $\$1800(1.00525)^m$ since $i = 0.063/12 = 0.00525$. Solve $\$4000(1.003)^m = \$1800(1.00525)^m$

Divide by 1800 and by $(1.003)^m$: $\dfrac{4000}{1800} = \dfrac{(1.00525)^m}{(1.003)^m} = \left(\dfrac{1.00525}{1.003}\right)^m$

Take logs: $\log\left(\dfrac{40}{18}\right) = m\log\left(\dfrac{1.00525}{1.003}\right)$; $m = \log\left(\dfrac{40}{18}\right)\Big/\log\left(\dfrac{1.00525}{1.003}\right) \approx 356.356$ months

It takes 357 months, or 29 years, 9 months.

Section 1.8

1. $(90.4 - 83.9) / 83.9 = 0.07747\ldots \approx 7.75\%$

2. $(215 - 217) / 217 = (-2) / 217 = -0.0092165899.. \approx -0.922\%$

3. $(90.9 - 82.4) / 82.4 = 0.103155\ldots \approx 10.3\%$

4. $(214.5 - 215.3) / 215.3 = -0.8 / 215.3 = -0.0037157\ldots = -0.4\%$ (0.8 has only 1 significant digit.)

5. Divide the given value by the reference value, then multiply by 100.

6. $\dfrac{\text{Adjusted Price in Year A dollars}}{\text{Price in Year B dollars}} = \left(\dfrac{\text{Year A CPI}}{\text{Year B CPI}}\right)$ so

   $\text{Adjusted Price in Year A dollars} = \left(\dfrac{\text{Year A CPI}}{\text{Year B CPI}}\right) \times (\text{Price in Year B dollars})$

7. If there is inflation, then the cost of goods is increasing. To purchase the same goods you will for your salary to grow at the same rate of inflation.

8. Each dollar will purchase a smaller amount of goods since it costs more to purchase a given amount of goods.

9. Using Table 1, $\dfrac{\text{Cost in 2014}}{\$25} = \left(\dfrac{3.40}{1.88}\right)$ so Cost in 2014 $= \left(\dfrac{3.40}{1.88}\right) \times \$25 = \$45.21 \approx \$45.20$ to 3

   significant digits.

11. $\dfrac{\text{Purchasing Power in 1970 dollars}}{\$68,000} = \left(\dfrac{1970\ \text{CPI}}{1990\ \text{CPI}}\right)$ so

   Purchasing Power in 1970 dollars $= \dfrac{38.8}{130.7} \times \$68,000 = \$20,187 \approx \$20,200$.

13. $\dfrac{\text{Purchasing Power in 2014 dollars}}{\$28,000} = \left(\dfrac{2014\ \text{CPI}}{1975\ \text{CPI}}\right)$ so

   Purchasing Power in 2014 dollars $= \dfrac{2014\text{CPI}}{1975\text{CPI}} \times \$28,000 = \dfrac{236.7}{53.8} \times \$28,000 = \$123,189.59 \approx \$123,000$

15. Convert the 1978 salary to year 2010 dollars. $\dfrac{\text{Purchasing Power in 2014 dollars}}{\$14,000} = \left(\dfrac{2014\ \text{CPI}}{1978\ \text{CPI}}\right)$ so

   Purchasing Power in 2014 dollars $= \dfrac{2014\text{CPI}}{1978\text{CPI}} \times \$14,000 = \dfrac{236.7}{65.2} \times \$14,000 = \$50,825.15 \approx \$50,800$

   Since a 1978 salary of $14,000 would adjust for inflation to a salary of $50,800 in the year 2014, the 1978 salary had a smaller purchasing power than a $51,000 salary in the year 2014.

17. Cost in 2010 dollars $= \dfrac{2014\text{CPI}}{1965\text{CPI}} \times \$4.98 = \dfrac{236.7}{31.5} \times \$4.98 = \$37.40$ to 3 significant digits, much more

   than a CD costs today.

Section 1.8

19. The 1985 price adjusts to $\dfrac{2014\text{CPI}}{1985\text{CPI}} \times \$2.61 = \dfrac{236.7}{107.6} \times \$2.61 = \$5.74$ This is less than the \$6.00 average

     cost of a pound of coffee in 2014. The price of coffee has grown faster than inflation.

21. The required salary is the future value of the present \$35,000 salary under 3.0% growth per year for 10 years. Thus $F = \$35,000(1.03)^{10} = \$47,037$ which is \$47,000 to the nearest thousand dollars.

23. Use Formula (B): Solve $\dfrac{\$50,000}{(1.045)^{m}} = \$30,000$, obtain $m = \log\left(\tfrac{5}{3}\right)\big/\log(1.045) = 11.6$ years.

Section 1.8 Review Problems:

25. Solve $109.6 = 29.6(1 + r)^{26}$; obtain $r = \left(\dfrac{109.6}{29.6}\right)^{1/26} - 1 = 0.0516376 \approx 5.16\%$

26. Solve $109.6 = 56.9(1 + r)^{10}$; obtain $r = \left(\dfrac{109.6}{56.9}\right)^{1/10} - 1 = 0.06775\ldots \approx 6.78\%$

27. $i = 0.06 / 12 = 0.005$. $m = 3(12) + 5 = 41$ monthly compoundings.

    (a) $F = \$2350(1.005)^{41} = \$2883.21$

    (b) Solve $\$10,000 = \$2350(1.005)^{m}$ $\dfrac{10000}{2350} = (1.005)^{m}$

    $\log\left(\dfrac{10000}{2350}\right) = \log(1.005)^{m} = m\log(1.005)$ $m = \log\left(\dfrac{10000}{2350}\right) \div \log(1.005) \approx 290.357$

    It takes 291 months, which is 24 years 3 months.

28. $I = \$25, P = \$500, t = 2/12 = 1/6$ years. Solve $\$25 = \$500(r)(1/6)$
    Multiply by 6: $\$150 = \$500r$ Divide by \$500: $.3 = r$ $r = 30.00\%$

29. Solve $\$4,000 = P(1 + 0.022)^{6}$ $P = \$4,000 / (1.022)^{6} = \$3510.38$

Answers to Chapter 1 Review Problems

1. a) F means *Future Value*; its unit is dollars
   b) P means *Present Value*; its unit is dollars
   c) m means the *total number of compoundings*; it is a *whole number*
   d) t means *time*; its unit is *years*
   e) i means *interest rate per compounding*; its form is a *decimal* (in the formulas)
   f) Y means *annual percentage yield*; its form is a decimal
   g) r means the *nominal annual interest rate*; its form is a decimal
   h) I means the *amount of interest*; its unit is dollars

2. $P = \$1,600$; $m = 16 \times 4 = 64$; $i = 0.0625 / 4 = 0.015625$; $F = 1600(1 + 0.015625)^{64} = \$4,315.75$

3. $F = 35,000$; $t = 18 - 5 = 13$ years; $m = 13(12) = 156$ $i = 0.093/12 = 0.00775$; $P = ?$
      Solve $35,000 = P(1 + 0.00775)^{156}$; obtain $P = \$35,000 / (1.00775)^{156} = \$10,496.15$

4. $P = \$10,000$; $F = \$35,000$; $m = 13$; $i = ?$ Solve $35,000 = 10,000(1 + i)^{13}$

   $3.5 = (1 + i)^{13}$ $(3.5)^{1/13} = 1 + i$ $i = (3.5)^{1/13} - 1 = 0.1011624\ldots \approx 10.12\%$

5. Purchasing power in 1995 $= \dfrac{152.4}{38.8} \times \$12,000 = \$47,134.02 \approx \$47,100$

6. $F = \$5,500$; $t = 4$ years 9 months; $i = 0.084/12 = 0.007$; $m = 4 \times 12 + 9 = 57$ monthly compoundings
      Solve $5500 = P(1 + 0.007)^{57}$; $P = \$5500 / (1.007)^{57} = \$3,695.58$

Answers to Chapter 1 Review Problems

7. $P = \$13,590$; $m = 10 \times 365 = 3650$ daily compoundings; $i = 0.0436 / 365$

$$\text{So } F = \$13,590\left(1 + \frac{0.0436}{365}\right)^{3650} = \$21,016.51$$

8. The 2014 price after adjusting for inflation would be $\dfrac{236.7}{31.5} \times \$0.15 = \$1.13$, less than most loaves

of bread cost in 2014.

9. $i = 0.054 / 12 = 0.0045$; $P = \$3500$; $F = \$6500$; $m =$ unknown number of monthly compoundings

Solve $6500 = 3500(1 + 0.0045)^m$ $\qquad \dfrac{6500}{3500} = (1.0045)^m \qquad \log\left(\dfrac{6500}{3500}\right) = m\log(1.0045)$

$m = \log\left(\dfrac{65}{35}\right) \div \log(1.0045) \approx 137.87..$ so 138 months are needed. This is 11 years 6 months.

At the end of 138 months the balance would be $\$3500(1.0045)^{138} = \$6503.69$.

10. 1975 CPI = 53.8, 1990 CPI = 130.7, $m = 15$. $\qquad$ Solve $130.7 = 53.8(1 + i)^{15}$

$$\frac{130.7}{53.8} = (1+i)^{15} \qquad \left(\frac{130.7}{53.8}\right)^{1/15} = 1+i \qquad i = \left(\frac{130.7}{53.8}\right)^{1/15} - 1 \approx 0.06096 \approx 6.10\%$$

11. $Y = \left(1 + \dfrac{0.092}{12}\right)^{12} - 1 \approx 0.09598 \approx 9.60\%$

12. (a) Solve $2000 = 1000\left(1 + \dfrac{.03}{2}\right)^m$, where $m =$ number of six-month periods.

Divide by 1000: $2 = (1.015)^m$

Take logs and use property: $\log(2) = m\log(1.015)$

Divide by $\log(1.015)$: $m = \log(2) \div \log(1.015) \approx 46.555$

So 47 six month periods are needed, or 23 years and 6 months.

(b) At the end of that time you will have $F = \$1000(1.015)^{47} = \$2013.28$

13. APY = percent change = $\$13.73 / \$400 = 0.034325 = 3.43\%$

14. (a) $F = \$36,000(1 + 0.04)^5 = \$43,799.50 \approx \$44,000$ is what the RX-7 will cost in 5 years.

(b) Solve $\$44,000 = P(1 + 0.092)^5 \qquad P = \dfrac{\$44,000}{(1.092)^5} = \$28,336.06 \approx \$28,000$ $\quad$ must be invested today.

15. The interest paid is $\$320 - \$300 = \$20$. The time is 3 months, or $t = 1/4$ years. Using $I = Prt$:

$\$20 = (\$300)(r)(1/4)$. Multiply both sides by 4: $80 = 300r$

Divide by 300: $r = 80 / 300 = 0.26666666.. = 26.6666666...\% \approx 26.67\%$

16. $t = 14$ years. Solve $\qquad 7,500 = 2500(1 + Y)^{14} \qquad \dfrac{7,500}{2,500} = (1 + Y)^{14}$

$(3)^{1/14} = 1 + Y \qquad Y = (3)^{1/14} - 1 = 0.0816334 \ldots \approx 8.16\%$

17. Nine months = $9 / 12$ year = 0.75 of a year, so $t = 0.75$. Since we know the APY is $Y = 0.051$

we use $F = P(1 + Y)^t$ to compute: $F = \$1000(1.051)^{0.75} = \$1038.01$

18. Use Formula (B) on p. 57. If you receive a $\$70,000$ benefit m years from now, the current amount

equivalent to it is $\dfrac{\$70,000}{(1.036)^m}$. So solve $\dfrac{\$70,000}{(1.036)^m} = \$40,000$.

$\dfrac{\$70,000}{\$40,000} = (1.036)^m \qquad \log\left(\dfrac{7}{4}\right) = m\log(1.036) \qquad m = \log\left(\dfrac{7}{4}\right) \div \log(1.036) \approx 15.8$ years.

Answers to Chapter 1 Review Problems

19. (1995 value) / (reference value) = \$2.35 / \$3.05 = 0.77049 = 77.0%, so 1995 index is 77.0.

20. Solve $\$2{,}000 = P(1+.032)^5$ Obtain $P = \$2{,}000 / (1+.032)^5 = \$1708.57$

Section 2.1

1. Keystrokes: $300 \times (1.005 \wedge 54 - 1) \div 0.005 = \$18{,}545.01$

2. Keystrokes: $50 \times (1.004 \wedge 176 - 1) \div 0.004 = \$12{,}737.33$

3. *FA* means the total of the future value of the payments in the sequence, just after the last payment. *PMT* means the amount of each individual payment.

4. It is assumed that the payments are made at the ends of the payment intervals. The first payment is made at the end of the first payment interval, the second payment is made at the end of the second interval, etc.

5. The amount of interest earned is the difference between *FA* and total of all the payments made.

6. Add together the *FV* of the current value plus the *FA* of the sequence of payments.

7. (a) Total future value = $1500 (1.06)^4 + 1500 (1.06)^3 + 1500 (1.06)^2 + 1500 (1.06)^1 + 1500$
   $= \$1893.72 + 1786.52 + 1685.40 + 1590 + 1500 = \$8455.64$

   (b) Total future value = $FA = \$1500 \dfrac{\left((1.06)^5 - 1\right)}{0.06} = \$8455.64$

9. (a) $FA = \$600 \dfrac{\left((1.04)^{12} - 1\right)}{0.04} = \$9015.48$

   (b) $i = 0.06/12 = 0.005$; $m = 6\times12 + 3 = 75$ compoundings; $FA = \$250 \dfrac{\left((1.005)^{75} - 1\right)}{0.005} = \$22{,}681.63$

   (c) $i = 0.06/4 = 0.015$; $m = 8\times4 + 3 = 35$ compoundings; $FA = \$500 \dfrac{\left((1.015)^{35} - 1\right)}{0.015} = \$22{,}796.04$

11. $PMT = \$80$; $m = 15\times12 = 180$; $i = 0.03 / 12 = 0.0025$; $FA = \$80 \dfrac{\left((1.0025)^{180} - 1\right)}{0.0025} = \$18{,}157.82.$

   Amount of interest = $\$18{,}157.82 - 180\times\$80 = \$3757.82$.

13. We must deal with the situation in two steps as in Example 4 of this section. Here is the time line:
   From age 20 to 35, $PMT = \$1000$, $i = 0.07$, and $m = 15$. So the total value of the 15 deposits at age 35 is

   $FA = \$1000 \dfrac{\left((1.07)^{15} - 1\right)}{0.07} = \$25{,}129.02$. From age 35 to 65 this value is treated as a *lump sum*

   invested at 7% compound interest for 65 - 35 = 30 years. Its value at the end of that time will be $F = \$25{,}129.02(1.07)^{30} = \$191{,}288.51$ All of this except for the 15($1000) = \$15,000 in deposits is interest: Amount of Interest = $\$191{,}288.51 - \$15{,}000 = \$176{,}288.51$

15. At age 60 the value of the account is $FA = \$1000 \dfrac{\left((1.07)^{25} - 1\right)}{0.07} = \$63{,}249.04$. At age 65 it will be worth

   $F = \$63{,}249.04 (1.07)^5 = \$88{,}710.05$. Interest earned = $\$88{,}710.05 - 25(\$1000) = \$63{,}710.05$

Section 2.1

17. Here is the time line:

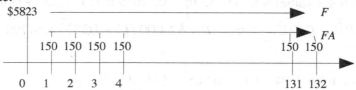

Time is 18 - 7 = 11 years, $m = 11 \times 12 = 132$ payments, $i = 0.066 / 12 = 0.0055$ per month.

His current savings will grow to $F = \$5823(1 + 0.0055)^{132} = \$12,011.04$

The additional monthly deposits of \$150 per month have $FA = \$150 \dfrac{\left(1.0055^{132} - 1\right)}{0.0055} = \$28,982.45$

So the total value of his account will be the sum of these, \$12,011.04 + \$28,982.45 = \$40,993.49.

The interest earned by his original savings is \$12,011.04 - \$5823 = \$6188.04

The interest earned by his deposits is \$28,982.45 – 132×\$150 = \$9182.45

His total interest is the sum of these, \$15,370.49.

19. (a) i) $i = 0.09/12 = 0.0075$; $t = 70 – 22 = 48$ years, $m = 48(12) = 576$ compoundings (and deposits).

$$FA = \$100 \frac{\left((1.0075)^{576} - 1\right)}{0.0075} = \$973,151.26 \quad \text{is the total value of George's account at age 70.}$$

ii) Interest Earned = $FA – m(PMT) = \$973,151.26\text{-}576(\$100) = \$915,551.26$

(b) i) $i = 0.0075$, $t = 70 – 32 = 38$; $m = 38(12) = 456$ compoundings (and deposits).

$$FA = \$200 \frac{\left((1.0075)^{456} - 1\right)}{0.0075} = \$778,181.07 \quad \text{is the total value of Frank's account.}$$

ii) Interest earned = $FA – m(PMT) = \$778,181.07 – 456(\$200) = \$686,981.07.$

(c) Frank's plan does not work; George has accumulated about \$195,000 more than Frank.

Section 2.2

1. If you have a (-) key, press it before you enter the number. If you have a +/- key, press it after the number.

2. $175 \times (\ 1 – 1.0135 \wedge (\text{-}) \, 24 \ ) \div 0.0135$ or $175 \times (\ 1 – 1.0135 \wedge 24 \, \text{+/-} \ ) \div 0.0135$ Value: 3567.15

3. $65 \times (1 – (1 + 0.07 \div 12) \wedge (\text{-}) \, 36 \ ) \div (0.07 \div 12)$ or

   $65 \times (1 – (1 + 0.07 \div 12) \wedge 36 \, \text{+/-} \ ) \div (0.07 \div 12)$ Value: 2105.12

4. *PV* is the sum of the present values of the individual payments. It is also the principal of a loan paid off by making the sequence of payments.

5. Determine the total of all the payments ($m \times PMT$). This is all the principal and interest paid over the life of the loan. Subtract the original principal *PV* to leave the total amount of interest paid.

6. Payments are assumed to be made at the ends of the payment intervals.

7. The cash value is the present value of the amortized loan (which is the principal of the loan), plus the down payment.

8. Formula (2) assumes the payments are made at the ends of the payment intervals. The first payment is made at the start of the first interval, so is like a down payment.

9. These are the same sequences of payments as in 2.1 #9. Using formula (2):

   a) $PV = \$600 \dfrac{\left(1 - (1.04)^{-12}\right)}{0.04} = \$5,631.04$ b) $PV = \$250 \dfrac{\left(1 - (1.005)^{-75}\right)}{0.005} = \$15,603.41$

   c) $PV = \$500 \dfrac{\left(1 - (1.015)^{-35}\right)}{0.015} = \$13,537.80$

Section 2.2

11. $i = 0.052 / 4 = 0.013$; $m = 15$; $PMT = \$500$. The time line is:

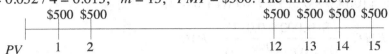

$$PV = \$500 \frac{\left(1-(1.013)^{-15}\right)}{0.013} = \$6774.26.$$ Total interest is $15 \times \$500 - \$6774.26 = \$725.74$

13. Cash value = down payment + present value of the sequence of payments.

    $i = 0.057 / 12 = 0.00475$; $m = 5 \times 12 = 60$ compoundings; $PMT = \$250$.

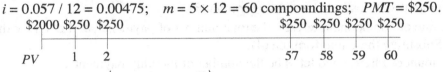

$$PV = \$250 \frac{\left(1-(1.00475)^{-60}\right)}{0.00475} = \$13,025.17$$

   Cash value = $\$2000 + \$13,025.17 = \$15,025.17$.   Total interest= $60 \times \$250 - \$13,025.17 = \$1974.83$

15. For the payments $i = 0.063 / 12 = 0.00525$ and $m = 4 \times 12 = 48$.

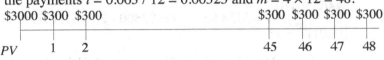

$$PV = \$300 \frac{\left(1-(1.00525)^{-48}\right)}{0.00525} = \$12,699.59.$$ The total cash value of the deal is this plus

   the \$3000 down, or \$15,699.59. This is more than the \$15,500 the dealer says you are paying.

17. Each payment is $\$190,000,000 / 25 = \$7.6$ million. The cash value is the first payment plus the PV of the other 24 payments.

   Cash value $= \$7,600,000 + \$7,600,000 \frac{\left(1-1.035^{-24}\right)}{0.035} = \$7,600,000 + \$122,043,593.80 = \$129,643,593.80$

19. There are $25 \times 12 = 300$ payments, but the first one is made at the start of the first payment interval. The company will have to pay the bank the first payment of \$3000 plus the PV of the sequence of 299 other payments at the ends of the 299 months. $i = 0.042 / 12 = 0.0035$.

   Lump Sum $= \$3000 + \$3000 \dfrac{\left(1-(1.0035)^{-299}\right)}{0.0035} = \$555,594.10$

21. There will be $22 \times 12 + 7 = 271$ payments. $i = 0.03 / 12 = 0.0025$

   Cash Value $= \$2350 \dfrac{\left(1-(1.0025)^{-271}\right)}{0.0025} = \$462,184.18$

Section 2.3

1. $20000 \times 0.003 \div (1.003 \wedge 120 - 1) =$ Calculated Value: \$138.71

2. $9000 \times 0.004 \div (1 - 1.004 \wedge (-) 40) =$ or $9000 \times 0.004 \div (1 - 1.004 \wedge 40 +/-) =$ Value: \$243.93

3. Multiply both sides by 0.025: $\$15,000 \times 0.025 = PMT(1 - (1 + 0.025)^{-72})$

   Divide by the coefficient of PMT: $\dfrac{\$15,000 \times 0.025}{(1 - (1 + 0.025)^{-72})} = PMT$

   Calculate: $PMT = \$15,000 \times 0.025 \div (1 - (1 + 0.025) \wedge (-)72) = \$451.26$

Section 2.3

4. Multiply both sides by 0.013: $\$10,000 \times 0.013 = PMT((1+0.013)^{120} - 1)$

   Divide by the coefficient of PMT: $\dfrac{\$10,000 \times 0.013}{((1+0.013)^{120} - 1)} = PMT$

   Calculate: $PMT = \$10,000 \times 0.013 \div ((1+0.013)^{120} - 1) = \$35.03$

5. Determine the periodic rate of compound interest, i, and the total number of deposits, m. Let FA be the future value to be accumulated. Substitute these into formula (3).

6. Determine the periodic rate of compound interest i, the total number of payments, m. Let PV be the principal of the loan. Substitute these into formula (4).

7. Compute $I = Prt$, the amount of interest and let m be the number of monthly payments.
    Then calculate $PMT = (P + I) / m$,

8. Determine the periodic rate of compound interest i, the total number of withdrawals, m. Let PV be the current sum of money. Substitute these into formula (4).

9. The $\$3500$ is the future accumulation FA of the sequence. $i = 0.04 / 4 = 0.01$; $m = 4 \times 5 = 20$.

   By formula (3) $PMT = \dfrac{3500 \times 0.01}{\left((1.01)^{20} - 1\right)} = \$158.95$ $I = \$3500 - 20 \times \$158.95 = \$321.00$

11. There are $7 \times 2 = 14$ deposits, so $m = 14$, $i = 0.05 / 2 = 0.025$, $FA = \$50,000$. Using formula (3),

   $PMT = \dfrac{\$50,000 \times 0.025}{\left((1.025)^{14} - 1\right)} = \$3026.83$

   Amount of Interest is $I = FA - m \times PMT = \$50,000 - 14 \times \$3026.83 = \$7624.38$

13. (a) $i = 0.042 / 12 = 0.0035$; $m = 3 \times 12 = 36$. The present value of the loan to be paid off by the sequence of payments is the $\$19000$ price less the $\$6200$ trade-in, or $\$12,800$.

   Using (4), $PMT = \dfrac{\$12800 \times 0.0035}{\left(1-(1.0035)^{-36}\right)} = \$379.05$.   (b) Total interest is $36 \times \$379.05 - \$12800 = \$845.80$.

   (c) Using the Add-On Interest Method the total interest is $I = \$12800(0.042)(3) = \$1612.80$. His monthly payment will be $(\$12800 + \$1612.80) / 36 = \$400.36$, which is more than the $\$379.05$ with amortization. The $\$1612.80$ in interest is almost twice the $\$845.80$ with amortization.

15. The $\$250$ trade-in reduces the amount she must finance to $PV = \$1500$.
   (a) $i = 0.12 / 12 = 0.01$; $m = 18$ payments and $PV = \$1500$. By formula (4),

   $PMT = \dfrac{\$1500 \times 0.01}{\left(1-(1.01)^{-18}\right)} = \$91.47$

   (b) Total Interest is $18 \times \$91.47 - \$1500 = \$146.46$

   (c) Using the Add-On Interest Method (and simple interest) the total interest is $I = \$1500(0.12)(1.5) = \$270$. The monthly payment will be $(\$1500 + \$270) / 18 = \$98.33$, which is more than the $\$91.47$ with amortization. The $\$270$ in interest is almost twice the $\$146.46$ with amortization.

17. This is like Example 5 in this section. $i = 0.05 / 2 = 0.025$, and $m = 2 \times 7 = 14$ compoundings.

   <u>Step 1:</u> The original $\$10000$ grows to $F = 10000(1.025)^{14} = \$14,129.74$

   <u>Step 2:</u> The 14 payments must accumulate $\$50,000 - \$14,129.74 = \$35,870.26 = FA$

   Using formula (3) $PMT = \dfrac{\$35870.26 \times 0.025}{\left((1.025)^{14} - 1\right)} = \$2171.46$

Section 2.3

19. This is like Example 5 in this section. $i = 0.054 / 12 = 0.0045$, and $m = 4(12) = 48$ compoundings.

Step 1 Her $923 in saving will grow to $F = \$923(1.0045)^{48} = \$1144.98$.

Step 2 So the 48 payments must accumulate $\$6000 - \$1144.98 = \$4855.02$. This is the *FA* of the sequence of payments. Using formula (3) the *PMT* needed to accumulate that *FA*

is $PMT = \dfrac{\$4855.02 \times 0.0045}{\left((1.0045)^{48} - 1\right)} = \$90.84$. Amount interest = $\$6000 - \$923 - 48 \times \$90.84 = \$716.68$

21. This is like Example 6. Here $PV = \$800,000$, (a) $i = 0.06 / 12 = .005$, $m = 12 \times 20 = 240$ withdrawals.

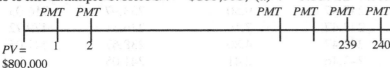

Using formula (4) the amount of each withdrawal is $PMT = \dfrac{\$800,000 \times 0.005}{\left(1 - (1.005)^{-240}\right)} = \$5731.45$

(b) Total interest = $240(\$5731.45) - \$800,000 = \$575,548$.

Review Problems

23. $i = 0.054/12 = 0.0045$, $m = 5 \times 12 = 60$, PV of loan $= \$260 \dfrac{\left(1 - (1.0045)^{-60}\right)}{0.0045} = \$13,644.68$.

Cash value $= \$13,644.68 + \$3000 + \$2500 = \$19,144.68$.

24. $i = 0.03 / 4 = 0.0075$, $m = 4 \times 8 = 32$. F of original $\$1200 = \$1200(1.0075)^{32} = \$1524.13$

FA of payments $= \$200 \dfrac{\left((1.0075)^{32} - 1\right)}{0.0075} = \$7202.97$. Total value $= F + FA = \$8727.10$.

Section 2.4

1. $i = 0.09 / 12 = 0.0075$ First Amount of Interest = 0.0075($700) = $5.25

Period	Current Balance at start of period	Payment Amount	Amt Interest paid	Principal repaid	Balance after payment
1	$700.00	$90.48	$5.25	$85.23	$614.77
2	$614.77	$90.48	$4.61	$85.87	$528.90

2. $i = 0.105 / 12 = 0.00875$ First Amount of Interest = 0.00875($4800) = $42.00

Period	Current Balance at start of period	Payment Amount	Amt Interest paid	Principal repaid	Balance after payment
1	$4800.00	$342.86	$42.00	$300.86	$4499.14
2	$4499.14	$342.86	$39.37	$303.49	$4195.65

3. $I = \$1400(.09)(8/12) = \$84$. Payment = ($1400 + $84) / 8 = $185.50. Each payment contains $1400 / 8 = $175.00 in principal and $84 / 8 = $10.50 in Interest. (Compare to Problem 1.)

4. $I = \$2400(0.105)(15/12) = \$315$ Payment = ($2400 + $315) / 15 = $181.00. Each payment contains $2400 / 15 = $160 in principal and $315 / 15 = $21 in interest. (Compare to Problem 2.)

5. After 5 payments you have $8 - 5 = 3$ payments left. Current balance = PV of remaining 3 payments =

$\$90.48 \dfrac{\left(1 - (1.0075)^{-3}\right)}{0.0075} = \$267.42$

6. After 11 payments you have $15 - 11 = 4$ payments left. Current balance = PV of remaining 4 payments

$= \$342.86 \dfrac{\left(1 - (1.00875)^{-4}\right)}{0.00875} = \$1343.45$

7. New balance = $400 + I + New Charges − Payment = $400 + $400(0.18/12) + $30 - $35 = $401

8. New Balance = $400 + $400(0.18/12) + $110 - $120 = $396.00

9. The amount of interest in the next payment equals the Current Balance times the periodic interest rate.

Section 2.4

10. Total Interest equals the principal times the annual rate times the time in years.

11. One way is to create an amortization table. Another is to determine the *PV* of the remaining payments.

12. The new balance equals the old balance plus the interest plus the new charges minus the payment amount.

13. (a) $i = 0.12 / 12 = 0.01$ per month. (b) $m = 4$; $PV = \$950$, $PMT = \dfrac{\$950 \times 0.01}{\left(1 - (1.01)^{-4}\right)} = \$243.47$

(c)

Payment #	Balance at start	Payment Amount	Interest Amount	Principal Repaid	Balance After
1	950.00	243.47	9.50	233.97	716.03
2	716.03	243.47	7.16	236.31	479.72
3	479.72	243.47	4.80	238.67	241.05
4	241.05	243.46	2.41	241.05	0

(d) Final payment = \$2.41 interest + \$241.05 principal = \$243.46

15. (a) $i = 0.07 / 2 = 0.035$. (b) $m = 4$. $PV = \$6,000$ $PMT = \dfrac{\$6000 \times 0.035}{\left(1 - (1.035)^{-4}\right)} = \$1633.51$

(c)

Payment #	Balance before	Payment Amount	Interest Amount	Principal Repaid	Balance After
1	6,000	1,633.51	210.00	1,423.51	4,576.49
2	4,576.49	1,633.51	160.18	1,473.33	3,103.16
3	3,103.16	1,633.51	108.61	1,524.90	1,578.26
4	1,578.26	1,633.50	55.24	1,578.88	0
Total:			534.03		

(d) Final payment amount is \$55.24 interest + \$1,578.26 principal = \$1,633.50

17. Monthly rate: $i = 0.18 / 12 = 0.015$; $m = 12$ payments; $PMT = \dfrac{2500 \times 0.015}{\left(1 - (1.015)^{-12}\right)} = \$229.20$

Total interest = 12(\$229.20) - \$2500 = \$250.40

19. (a) Monthly rate: $i = 0.21 / 12 = 0.0175$; $m = 12$ payments; $PMT = \dfrac{\$2000 \times 0.0175}{(1 - (1.0175)^{-12})} = \$186.23$

Period	Current Balance	Payment	Amt Interest	Balance Repaid	New Purchases	New Balance at end of period
1	\$2000.00	\$200.00	\$35.00	\$165.00	\$50.00	\$1885.00
2	\$1885.00	\$200.00	\$32.99	\$167.01	\$50.00	\$1767.99
3	\$1767.99	\$200.00	\$30.94	\$169.06	\$50.00	\$1648.93
4	\$1648.93	\$200.00	\$28.86	\$171.14	\$50.00	\$1527.79

(b) Yes, your current balance is lower at the end of the four months than at the start.

(c) If you make \$175 in new purchases, your next balance will be \$2000 - \$200 + \$35 + \$175 = \$2010, larger than your original debt.

21. (a) The original loan had $m = 60$ payments of \$342.15 at $i = .069 / 12 = 0.00575$.

So the original loan amount was $PV = \$342.15 \dfrac{(1 - (1.00575)^{-60})}{0.00575} = \$17,320.50$.

(b) The interest in the *first* payment was $i \times PV = 0.00575 \times \$17320.50 = \$99.59$.
The principal repaid was thus \$342.15 - \$99.59 = \$242.56.

(c) After 23 payments there are $5(12) - 23 = 37$ payments remaining.

So the payoff amount is $PV = \$342.15 \dfrac{(1 - (1.00575)^{-37})}{0.00575} = \$11,374.20$.

(d) The interest in the *next* payment is $i \times current\ balance = 0.00575 \times \$11,374.20 = \$65.40$. The principal repaid will be \$342.15 - \$65.40 = \$276.75.

Section 2.4

23. (a) $i = 0.066 / 12 = 0.0055$; $PV = \$90,000$, $m = 12(15) = 180$ payments.

Using formula (4) $PMT = \dfrac{\$90,000 \times 0.0055}{(1 - 1.0055^{-180})} = \$788.95$

(b) $180 - 5 \times 12 = 120$ payments remain; Payoff amount is $\$788.95 \dfrac{(1 - (1.0055)^{-120})}{0.0055} = \$69,171.29$

25. $i = 0.07 / 2 = 0.035$. $PV = \$6,000$. $PMT = \$1800$ initially.

Period	Balance at start of period	Payment Amount	Amount Interest paid in period	Principal repaid at end of period	Balance after payment
1	$6000.00	$1800.00	$210.00	$1590.00	$4410.00
2	$4410.00	$1800.00	$154.35	$1231.65	$3178.35
3	$3178.35	$1800.00	$111.24	$1688.76	$1489.59
4	$1458.59	$1541.73	$52.14	$1489.59	$0
Total:		$6941.73	$518.73	$6000.00	

It takes 3 payments of $1800 and a last payment of $1541.73 ($= \$1489.59 + 0.035 \times \$1489.59$) to pay off the loan. In problem 15 the total interest paid was $534.03; in this problem the total interest is $518.73. So the savings is $15.30.

Review Problems

27. $m = 60$, $i = 0.03 / 12 = 0.0025$. The $15,000 will grow to

$FA = \$15,000(1 + 0.0025)^{60} = \$17,424.25$. The payments need to accumulate

$25,000 - $17,424.25 = $7575.75. This is the FA of the sequence of payments:

$PMT = \dfrac{\$7575.25 \times 0.0025}{\left(1.0025^{60} - 1\right)} = \$117.19$ Interest $= \$25,000 - 60(\$117.19) - \$15,000 = \$2968.60$

28. There are 240 payments, but the first payment is like a down payment and the others are at the ends of the next 239 months. $i = 0.024 / 12 = 0.002$. So $PV = \$4000 + \$4000 \dfrac{\left(1 - (1 + 0.002)^{-239}\right)}{0.002} = \$763,363.51$

Section 2.5

1. (a) $\$176,000 - 0.25 \times 176,000 = \$132,000$ is the loan amount.

(b) $i = 0.075 / 12 = 0.00625$; $m = 20 \times 12 = 240$; So $PMT = \dfrac{\$132,000 \times 0.00625}{(1 - (1.00625)^{-240})} = \$1063.38$

(c) Total amount of interest $= 240 \times \$1063.38 - \$132,000 = \$123,211.20$

(d) The amount of interest in the first payment is $132,000 times the monthly interest rate $i = 0.00625$, which is $825.00. The rest of the $1063.38 payment, or $238.38, goes to repay the principal.

3. (a) as in 1, $132,000 is owed after down payment. If L is the amount of the loan *including points*, then $L = \$132,000 + 2\%$ of L. So 98% of $L = 132,000$, so $L = \$132,000 / 0.98 = \$134,693.88$

(b) $i = 0.0726 / 12 = 0.00605$; $m = 240$; So $PMT = \dfrac{\$134,693.88 \times 0.00605}{\left(1 - (1.00605)^{-240}\right)} = \$1065.40$

(c) Total interest paid $= 240 \times \$1065.40 - \$134,693.88 = \$121,002.12$

(d) Interest Amount in first payment $= \$134,693.88 \times 0.00605 = \$814.90$
Principal repaid in first payment $= \$1065.40 - \$814.90 = \$250.50$.

Note: The loan in Problem 3 has a smaller total interest than the loan in Problem 1, but a larger monthly payment. This may seem strange, but the reason is that the loan in Problem 3 is also paying off the points which have become part of the principal of the loan.

Section 2.5

5. (a) You have 14 years, or $12 \times 14 = 168$ payments, of $1063.38 left. So with the original rate

of $i = 0.00625$ your payoff amount is $PV = \$1063.38 \dfrac{\left(1-(1.00625)^{-168}\right)}{0.00625} = \$110,407.24.$

(b) With a new loan the rate would be $i = 0.0705 / 12 = 0.005875$. The principal is $110,407.24 + $2500

$= \$112,907.24.$ Your monthly payment would be $PMT = \dfrac{\$112907.24 \times 0.005875}{\left(1-(1.005875)^{-168}\right)} = \$1059.25$

Since you are paying $4.13 less per month with the new loan, you should refinance. You will save $168 \times \$4.13 = \$693.84$ over the entire 14 years.

(c) (i) In 5 years you will make 60 payments and save $60 \times \$4.13 = \$247.80$ in payments.

(ii) You will have 9 years of payments, or $9 \times 12 = 108$ payments left. Payoff amounts are:

Original Mortgage at $i = 0.00625$: $\dfrac{\$1063.38\left(1-1.00625^{-108}\right)}{0.00625} = \$83,330.35$

New Mortgage at $i = 0.005875$: $\dfrac{\$1059.25\left(1-1.005875^{-108}\right)}{0.005875} = \$84,526.20$

(iii) Difference = $1195.85. This is the amount worse off you would be in principal with the new mortgage. It is more than the $247.80 you save in monthly payments. Do not refinance.

7. (a) You now have 25 years, or 300 payments, remaining. Currently $i = 0.078/12 = 0.0065$.

Thus Payoff Amount = $\$1079.81 \dfrac{(1-1.0065^{-300})}{0.0065} = \$142,339.78$

(b) $i = 0.069 / 12 = 0.00575$. The principal of the new loan is $142,339.78 + $2000. The new payment

is $\dfrac{\$144,339.78 \times 0.00575}{(1-1.00575^{-300})} = \$1010.97$, a savings of $68.84 per month. If you expect to make the

25 years of payments you should refinance. You will save $12(25)\$68.84 = \$20,652$ over the 25 years.

(c) Five years from now there will be $20 \times 12 = 240$ payments remaining on either mortgage.

(i) You will save $60 \times \$68.84 = \$4130.40$ in monthly payments over the 5 years.

(ii) Payoff amounts five years from now: Original Mortgage: $\dfrac{\$1079.81(1-1.0065^{-240})}{0.0065} = \$131,039.17$

New Mortgage: $\dfrac{\$1010.97(1-1.00575^{-240})}{0.00575} = \$131,412.94$

You will be $131,412.94 - $131,039.17 = $373.77 behind in principal with the new mortgage, but $4130.40 ahead in monthly payments. You should definitely refinance.

9. (a) You now have 22 years, or 264 payments, remaining. Currently $i = 0.051/12 = 0.00425$.

Thus Payoff Amount = $\$1085.90 \dfrac{(1-1.00425^{-264})}{0.00425} = \$172,108.00$

(b) $i = 0.045 / 12 = 0.00375$. The principal of the new loan is $172,108.00 + $2500. The new payment

is $\dfrac{\$174608 \times 0.00375}{(1-1.00375^{-264})} = \$1043.08$, a savings of $42.82 per month. If you expect to make the 22

years of payments you should refinance. You will save $12(22)\$42.82 = \$11,304.48$ over the 22 years.

(c) Five years from now there will be $17 \times 12 = 204$ payments remaining on either mortgage.

(i) You will save $60 \times \$42.82 = \$2569.20$ in monthly payments over the 5 years.

(ii) Payoff amounts five years from now: Original Mortgage: $\dfrac{\$1085.90(1-1.00425^{-204})}{0.00425} = \$147,942.25$

New Mortgage: $\dfrac{\$1043.08(1-1.00375^{-204})}{0.00375} = \$148,534.53$

You will be $148,534.53 - $147,942.25 = $592.28 behind in principal with the new mortgage, but $2569.20 ahead in monthly payments. You should definitely refinance.

Section 2.5

10. Determine the payoff amount of your current mortgage. To this add the closing costs on the new mortgage to get the loan amount (*PV*) of the new mortgage. Using this find the monthly payment for a mortgage with this *PV* and having as many payments as you have remaining on your current mortgage. If the new payment is greater than your current payment, you should not refinance. If the new payment is less than your current payment, decide how long you expect to remain in the house with the new mortgage. Use this to determine how much you will save in monthly payments during that time. Compare that savings to the payoff amounts on the two mortgages. If your savings in monthly payments outweighs the difference in the two payoff amounts, you should refinance.

11. If you must pay *p* points, and finance $D out of the price of the house, then solve $L = D + p\%$ of L.

Section 2.6

1. $(-) \log (1 - 20000 \times 0.004 / 450) / \log (1.004) = 49.03395145$

2. $\log (1 + 8000 \times 0.005 / 150) / \log (1.005) = 47.39585175$

3. Computing $m \times PMT$ determines the total of the payments on each mortgage. The difference in these for the two mortgages is the savings in interest, because both loans pay off the principal in full.

4. In Section 1.6 the number m stood for the number of compoundings needed, and it is not possible to perform a fraction of a compounding. In formulas (6) and (7) m stands for the number of payments required, and it is often possible to make a fraction of a payment.

5. (a) An extra $75 per month makes the payment $852.74. $i = 0.057 / 12 = 0.00475$.

   Using formula (6), $m = -\log\left(1 - \dfrac{134,000 \times 0.00475}{852.74} \right) \div \log(1.00475)$

   $= -\log(0.253582569) \div \log(1.00475) \approx 289.54$. So 289 payments at $852.74 per month, plus a final payment of about $0.54 \times \$852.74 = \$460.48$, are required. 290 months = 24 years, 2 months.
   (b) The total of the payments with the extra $75 per month is about $289.54 \times \$852.74 = \$246,902.34$. Making the original 360 payments at $777.74 per month would mean a total payments of about $360 \times \$777.74 = \$279,986.40$. The difference, about $33,084.06, is the total interest saved.

7. (a) $i = 0.165 / 12 = 0.01375$ In the first payment there will be $0.01375 \times \$1500 = \$20.63$ in interest and $30 - \$20.63 = \$9.47 in repaid principal.

   (b) By Formula (6), $m = -\log\left(1 - \dfrac{1500 \times 0.01375}{30} \right) \div \log(1.01375) = -\log(0.3125) \div \log(1.01375) \approx$

   85.17. So it will take 86 monthly payments, or 7 years and 2 months. The last payment will be about $0.17 \times \$30 = \$5.10$. The amount of interest paid will be about $I = 85.17 \times \$30 - \$1500 = \$1055.10$ (!)

9. The $900,000 is what they have "loaned" to the bank to be repaid to them in monthly payments of $6500 while earning interest at a monthly rate of $i = 0.072 / 12 = 0.006$. So $900,000 = PV$. Using formula (6),

   $m = -\log\left(1 - \dfrac{900000 \times 0.006}{6500} \right) \div \log(1.006) = -\log(0.169230769) \div \log(1.006) \approx 296.969$

   So it will take about 297 months, or about 24 years 9 months, to exhaust the account. The last payment will be about $0.969 \times \$6500 = \$6298.50$

11. First find m so that the *PV* is $100,000. Recall from Problem 5 that $i = 0.00475$. Using formula (6),

   $m = -\log\left(1 - \dfrac{100,000 \times 0.00475}{777.74} \right) \div \log(1.00475) = -\log(0.38925605) \div \log(1.00475) = 199.1$. The

   balance drops below $100,000 when 199 payments remain, that is, after $360 - 199 = 161$ monthly payments have been made, or after 13 years 5 months.

13. Since money is accumulating here we use formula (7), with $PMT = \$200$, $i = 0.063 / 12 = 0.00525$, and

   $FA = \$300,000$. This gives $m = \log\left(1 + \dfrac{300,000 \times 0.00525}{200} \right) \div \log(1.00525) = 416.9455875$. The 417

   months convert to 34 years, 9 months. The last payment will be about $0.9455875 \times \$200 = \$189.12$
   The interest amount is about $FA - m \times PMT = \$300,000 - 416.9455875 \times \$200 = \$216,610.88$

Section 2.6

15. $i = 0.0055$. Formula (6) yields $-\log\left(1 - \dfrac{1{,}000{,}000 \times 0.0055}{5500}\right) \div \log(1.0055).$

If you attempt to evaluate this in your calculator, you get an error message! Why? If you simplify the expression in first parentheses, $1 - \dfrac{1{,}000{,}000 \times 0.0055}{5500}$ becomes 0 since $1{,}000{,}000 \times 0.0055 = 5500$.

But log(0) does not exist! This is the reason the calculator gives an error message. But what is it about the problem that causes this? If they have $1,000,000 in their account then the account earns $0.0055 \times$ $1,000,000 = \$5,500$ each month. So when they withdraw $5500 each month they are only withdrawing interest, and never touch the principal. They never exhaust the account!

17. As in Example 3, use formula (6). $i = 0.045 / 12 = 0.00375$, $PV = \$750{,}000$

$m = -\log\left(1 - \dfrac{750000 \times 0.00375}{4000}\right) \div \log(1.00375) = 324.4586$ It will take about 325 monthly

payments, or 27 years 1 month. Last payment is $0.4586(\$4000) = \$1834.40$

19. $i = 0.042 / 12 = 0.0035$. How many payments of 978.03 each are needed to pay off a $150,000 mortgage

at this rate? Use formula (6): $m = -\log\left(1 - \dfrac{150000 \times 0.0035}{978.03}\right) \div \log(1.0035) = 220.265$ This is 18 years

and 5 months. The original 30 year mortgage will have 18 years 5 months left when 11 years 7 months of payments have been made. Answer: 11 years, 7 months after start of mortgage.

Challenge Problems

21. Let m be the number of the last deposit you make. The *FA* of the m deposits you make will be

$\$400\left(\dfrac{1.005^m - 1}{0.005}\right)$ at the time you make your last deposit. This amount will then grow for 480 - m

monthly compoundings before you reach age 65. Thus your deposits will be worth

$\$400\left(\dfrac{1.005^m - 1}{0.005}\right)\left(1.005^{480-m}\right)$. Solve for the value of m that makes this equal to $500,000:

$$\$400\left(\dfrac{1.005^m - 1}{0.005}\right)\left(1.005^{480-m}\right) = \$500{,}000$$

To Solve: Multiply by 0.005; divide by $400: $\left(1.005^m - 1\right)\left(1.005^{480-m}\right) = \dfrac{500{,}000 \times 0.005}{400}$

Use laws of exponents; simplify: $1.005^{480} - 1.005^{480-m} = 6.25$ $1.005^{480} - 6.25 = 1.005^{480-m}$

Use log property: $\log\left(1.005^{480} - 6.25\right) = (480 - m)\log(1.005)$

Divide: $\log\left(1.005^{480} - 6.25\right) \div \log(1.005) = (480 - m)$

Simplify and evaluate: $m = 480 - \log\left(1.005^{480} - 6.25\right) \div \log(1.005) = 169.4$

Check: If you make 170 monthly payments the value of your account will be $\$400\left(\dfrac{1.005^{170} - 1}{0.005}\right) =$

$106,775.75. This will be compounded 480 - 170 = 310 times before you reach age 65, and will then be worth $\$106{,}775.75\left(1.005\right)^{310} = \$501{,}131.58$

Section 2.6

22. The Future Value of the $20,000 + the *FA* of the monthly payments must total $500,000.

Solve:
$$20,000(1.005)^m + 400\left(\frac{1.005^m - 1}{0.005}\right) = 500,000$$

Multiply by 0.005 and divide by 400: $0.25(1.005)^m + \left(1.005^m - 1\right) = 6.25$

Simplify: $1.25(1.005)^m = 7.25$ Divide by 1.25: $(1.005)^m = 5.8$

Take logs and use property: $m\log(1.005) = \log(5.8)$

Divide by $\log(1.05)$ and evaluate: $m = \log(5.8) \div \log(1.005) = 352.45$ months, or 29 years, 5 months.

Check: $20,000 grows to $20,000(1.005)^{353} = \$116,318.77$ The monthly payments grow to

$$\$400\left(\frac{1.005^{353} - 1}{0.005}\right) = \$385.275.07$$ The total of these is $501,593.84, just over $500,000.

Section 2.7

1. Frank makes $4 \times 8 = 32$ quarterly deposits at $0.062 = 0.0155$ per quarter. At age 28 he has

accumulated $FA = \$300\dfrac{(1.0155^{32} - 1)}{0.0155} = \$12,307.81$

After age 28 this lump sum grows for $4 \times (65-28) = 4 \times 37 = 148$ quarters. The value of Frank's account

at age 65 is $F = \$12,307.81(1.0155)^{148} = \$119,897.49$.

Fran makes $4 \times 13 = 52$ deposits of $800 at same interest rate, so at age 65 she has accumulated

$FA = \$800\dfrac{(1.0155^{52} - 1)}{0.0155} = \$63,232.74$.

This supports Conclusion 1. Even though Fran deposits much more per quarter for a large number of quarters, she only ends up with about 50% as much money as Frank, who did his saving early in life.

3. The value of the original account is $FA = \$1500\dfrac{(1.06^{25} - 1)}{0.06} = \$82,296.77$.

(a) If each deposit is $2000, $FA = \$2000\dfrac{(1.06^{25} - 1)}{0.06} = \$109,729.02$.

(b) If i is 0.08, $FA = \$1500\dfrac{(1.08^{25} - 1)}{0.08} = \$109,658.91$.

Of these two choices, (a) is slightly larger.

5. (a) With a regular savings account and a 15% tax rate, only $0.85 \times \$200 = \$170$ can actually be deposited each month for $12 \times 20 = 240$ months. The annual rate of interest after taxes is $0.85 \times 0.0615 = 0.052275$, or at $i = 0.052275 / 12 = 0.00435625$ per month.

So $FA = \$170\dfrac{\left((1.00435625)^{240} - 1\right)}{0.00435625} = \$71,741.20$

(b) With a traditional IRA the tax on deposits and interest is deferred. The entire $200 per month is deposited and earns at $i = 0.0615 / 12 = 0.005125$.

The nominal value of the account will be $FA = \$200\dfrac{\left((1.005125)^{240} - 1\right)}{0.005125} = \$94,068.29$

However, since withdrawals at retirement are taxed at 15%, only 85% of this, or $79,958.04, is the actual after-tax value.

(c) With a Roth IRA, only $170 can be deposited each month, but no other taxes apply. So the after-tax

value is $FA = \$170\dfrac{\left((1.005125)^{240} - 1\right)}{0.005125} = \$79,958.04$

Section 2.7

7. (a) Only 68% of the $200 per month, or $136, is now available for deposit. Also interest is only at $0.68 \times 0.0615 = 0.04182$ after taxes. or $i = 0.04182 / 12 = 0.003485$ per mo.

$$\text{So } FA = \$136\frac{\left((1.003485)^{240} - 1\right)}{0.003485} = \$50,914.71 \text{ is the after-tax value.}$$

(b) Same as 5(b), $79,958.04.

(c) With a Roth only $136 per month may be deposited, but the other variables are as in 5(c). So

$$FA = \$136\frac{\left((1.005125)^{240} - 1\right)}{0.005125} = \$63,966.43 \text{ is the after-tax value.}$$

This supports Conclusion 4. When the tax rate on deposits and interest is greater than the tax rate on withdrawals, the Traditional IRA produces the highest after-tax value of these three options.

9. (a) Since the tax rate on deposits and interest have not changed, the value of the regular savings account is the same as it was in 5(a), $71,741.20.

(b) Since a Traditional IRA has deferred taxes on deposits and interest, the nominal value here is the same as in 5(b), $94,068.29. But now only 68% of that is available for withdrawal, or $63,996.44.

(c) Since the tax rate on deposits and interest have not changed, the value of the Roth IRA is the same as it was in 5(c), $79,958.04.

This supports Conclusion 3. When the tax rate on deposits and interest is less than the tax rate on withdrawals, the Roth IRA produces the highest after-tax value of these three options.

Answers to Chapter 2 Review Problems

1. (a) $i = 0.09 / 12 = 0.0075$, $m = 5$, $PV = \$4000$, so $PMT = \dfrac{\$4000 \times 0.0075}{\left(1 - (1.0075)^{-5}\right)} = \$818.09$

(b)

Period	Balance	Payment Amount	Amount Interest	Principal Repaid	Balance Remaining
1	$4000.00	$818.09	$30.00	$788.09	$3211.91
2	$3211.91	$818.09	$24.09	$794.00	$2417.91
3	$2417.91	$818.09	$18.13	$799.96	$1617.95
4	$1617.95	$818.09	$12.13	$805.96	$811.99
5	$811.99	$818.08	$6.09	$811.99	0

Last Payment = $6.09 + $811.99 = $818.08

(c) I = Total Payments - Principal = 4($818.09) + $818.08 - $4000 = $90.44

(d) I = $4000(.09)(5/12) = $150. Payment = (4000 + 150) / 5 = $830.

2. $t = 18 - 4 = 14$ years of deposits. $m = 14 \times 12 = 168$ months. $i = 0.066 / 12 = 0.0055$. When the

daughter reaches age 18 the account will have accumulated to $FA = \$25\dfrac{(1.0055^{168} - 1)}{0.0055} = \$6877.17.$

This sum then grows for 9 more monthly compoundings, to $F = \$6877.17(1.0055)^9 = \$7225.18$.
Total Interest = $7225.18 - 168 \times $25 = $3055.18

3. (a) Since the first payment is made today, the cash value is the first payment + the PV of the other 19

payments = $2,000,000 + 2,000,000 \dfrac{(1 - 1.03^{-19})}{0.03} = \$30,647,598$

(b) In a similar fashion, cash value = $24.316 million

Answers to Chapter 2 Review Problems

4.   (a) $i = .081 / 12 = 0.00675$, $m = 12 \times 10 = 120$ payments, $PMT = \dfrac{\$13500 \times 0.00675}{\left(1 - (1.00675)^{-120}\right)} = \$164.51$

(b) $120 \times \$163.79 - \$13500 = \$6154.80$

(c) $120 - 36 = 84$ payments remain; Payoff Amount $= \$164.51 \dfrac{(1 - 1.00675^{-84})}{0.00675} = \$10{,}521.18$

(d) $PMT = \$264.51$, $PV = \$13500$. Using (6): $m = -\log\left(1 - \dfrac{\$13500 \times .00675}{264.51}\right) \div \log(1.00675) \approx 62.78$.

It takes 63 months, or 5 years and 3 months. Last payment is about $0.78 \times \$264.51 = \$206.32$
(e) About $62.78 \times \$264.51 - \$13500 = \$3105.94$

5.   (a) $FA = 20{,}000$, $i = 0.07 / 4 = 0.0175$; $m = 4 \times 10 = 40$. Using formula (3),
$$PMT = \frac{\$20{,}000 \times 0.0175}{(1.0175^{40} - 1)} = \$349.44$$

(b) The \$6000 in the account will grow to $F = \$6000(1.0175)^{40} = \$12{,}009.58$ in 10 years.
So the payments now need to accumulate $FA = \$20{,}000 - \$12{,}009.58 = \$7990.42$ in 10 years.
Proceeding as in (a), $PMT = \dfrac{\$7990.42 \times 0.0175}{\left(1.0175^{40} - 1\right)} = \$139.61$

6. $27 \times 12 = 324$ payments. The first is a "down payment, the rest are at the end of the next 323 months.

$i = 0.033 / 12 = 0.00275$ Cash Value $= \$2300 + \$2300 \dfrac{\left(1 - (1.00275)^{-323}\right)}{0.00275} = \$494{,}184.82$

7.   (a) FA at age 25 $= \$2200 \dfrac{(1.10^{7} - 1)}{0.10} = \$20{,}871.78$. In $65 - 25 = 40$ years this grows to
$F = \$20{,}871.78(1.10)^{40} = \$944{,}641.23$.

(b) After 35 years of deposits $FA = \$2200 \dfrac{(1.10^{35} - 1)}{0.10} = \$596{,}253.61$.

You deposit \$15,400 in (a) versus \$77,000 in (b), but (a) yields over 50% more at age 65!

8.   (a) Since money is accumulating here we use formula (7), with $PMT = \$150$, $i = 0.048 / 12 = 0.004$,
and $FA = \$250{,}000$. This gives $m = \log\left(1 + \dfrac{250{,}000 \times 0.004}{150}\right) \div \log(1.004) = 510.238$ It will
take 511 months, which is 42 years 7 months.
(b) The last payment will need to be $0.238 \times \$150 = \$35.70$
(c) The interest amount will be $\$250{,}000.00 - 510.238 \times \$150 = \$173{,}464.30$.

9.   Cash Value $= \$5000 + PV$ of the sequence of 48 payments of \$400 each at $i = 0.057 / 12 = 0.00475$
per month.   Cash value $= \$5000 + \$400 \dfrac{\left(1 - (1.00475)^{-48}\right)}{0.00475} = \$5000 + \$17{,}132.28 = \$22{,}132.28$.

Total Interest $= m \times PMT - PV = 48 \times \$400 - \$17{,}132.28 = \$2067.72$.

Answers to Chapter 2 Review Problems

10.   (a) Finance $(.80) \times (140{,}000) = \$112{,}000$. Loan Amount L solves $L = \$112{,}000 + 0.015L$

   $L = \$112{,}00 \div (.985) = \$113{,}705.58$

   (b) $i = 0.081/12 = 0.00675$, $m = 30 \times 12 = 360$. So $PMT = \dfrac{\$113{,}705.58 \times 0.00675}{\left(1 - 1.00675^{-360}\right)} = \$842.27$

   (c) Interest $= 0.00675 \times \$113{,}705.58 = \$767.51$ Principal repaid $= \$842.27 - \$767.51 = \$74.76$

   (d) $360 \times \$842.27 - \$113{,}705.58 = \$189{,}511.62$

   (e) Since 240 payments remain, balance $= PV = \$842.27 \dfrac{(1 - 1.00675^{-240})}{0.00675} = \$99{,}952.02$.

   (f) How many payments of \$842.27 are needed to pay off an \$80,000 loan at 8.1% monthly?

   Using formula (6): $m = -\log\left(1 - \dfrac{\$80{,}000 \times 0.00675}{\$842.27}\right) \div \log(1.00675) = 137.15$

   When 137 payments remain the balance drops below \$80,000. This is after $360 - 137 = 223$ payments, which is 18 years 7 months.

11. $i = 0.042 / 12 = 0.0035$; $\$250{,}000 = PV$ of payments.

   (a) In order to have $m = 12 \times 20 = 240$ payments, the payment amount should be

   $$PMT = \frac{\$250{,}000 \times 0.0035}{(1 - 1.0035^{-240})} = \$1541.43$$

   (b) Using formula (6), withdrawals of \$3000 per month will exhaust the account in

   $$m = -\log\left(1 - \frac{250{,}000 \times 0.0035}{3000}\right) \div \log(1.0035) \approx 98.698 \text{ months.}$$

   99 months is 8 years and 3 months of payments. Last payment is about $0.698 \times \$3000 = \$2094$

12.   (a) Using Formula (1), the future value of the investment would be

   $$FA = \$3000 \frac{(1.075^{15} - 1)}{0.075} = \$78{,}355.09.$$

   However, using a 15% tax bracket at the time of withdrawal, the true value of the account after taxes is 85% of this (since any withdrawals from the account are taxable), or \$66,601.83.

   (b) Traditional IRA: each \$3000 investment would be taxed at 32% <u>before</u> it is invested, leaving 68%, or $(0.68) \times (\$3000) = \$2040$, to be invested each year. Also, each year's interest at 7.5% is taxed at 32%, leaving a true interest earning of $(0.68) \times (7.5\%) = 5.1\%$. After 15 years, the value

   of the account would be $FA = \$2040 \dfrac{(1.051^{15} - 1)}{0.051} = \$44{,}353.04$

   The Traditional IRA's after tax value is about 50% more than the traditional savings account.

   (c) Each \$3000 investment would be taxed at 32% <u>before</u> it is invested, leaving 68%, or $(0.68) \times (\$3000)$ = \$2040, to be invested each year. The interest and withdrawals are not taxed, so the actual value is

   $$FA = \$2040 \frac{(1.075^{15} - 1)}{0.075} = \$53{,}281.46.$$

   In this case the Roth IRA's value is about 20% more than the regular savings account, but still considerably less than the Traditional IRA.

Section 3.1

1. (a) $0.7P$ gallons of high-octane are in P gallons of premium, and $0.4R$ gallons of high-octane are in R gallons of regular, for a total of $0.7P + 0.4R$ gallons of high-octane. This must be $\leq 250{,}000$ gallons high-octane available. The constraint is $0.7P + 0.4R \leq 250{,}000$.gallons of high-octane.

   (b) $R \leq 100{,}000$ gallons regular

2. (a) $C \leq 30$

   (b) Making T tables uses $4T$ hours of labor, and making C chairs uses $5C$ hours of labor. A total of $4T + 5C$ hours of labor are used in T tables and C chairs, and this must be ≤ 240 hours available. Constraint: $4T + 5C \leq 240$ hours of labor.

3. Constraints: (1) $20x + 50y \leq 600$

                              (2) $40x + 30y \leq 800$

                              (3) $35x \qquad \leq 400$

                                   $x \geq 0, y \geq 0$

   Points: (a) $(15, 6)$ $20(15) + 50(6) = 600$ which is ≤ 600 True

                                     $40(15) + 30(6) = 780$ which is ≤ 800 True

                                     $35(15) = 525$ which is not ≤ 400 False; Point is not feasible.

            (b) $(10, 8)$ $20(10) + 50(8) = 600 \leq 600$ True   Slack $= 600 - 600 = 0$

                                   $40(10) + 30(8) = 640 \leq 800$ True   Slack $= 800 - 640 = 160$

                                   $35(10) = 350 \leq 400$ True   Slack $= 400 - 350 = 50$

      $(10, 8)$ is feasible.

4. Constraints: $250x + 400y \leq 32{,}500$

                              $350x + 200y \leq 28{,}000$

                              $500y \leq 25{,}000$ \qquad $x \geq 0, y \geq 0$

   Points: (a) $(60, 40)$ $250(60) + 400(40) = 31{,}000 \leq 32{,}500$ True   Slack $= 32{,}500 - 31{,}000 = 1{,}500$

                                        $350(60) + 200(40) = 29{,}000$ which is not $\leq 28{,}000$

          Point is not feasible.

            (b) $(50, 50)$ $250(50) + 400(50) = 32{,}500 \leq 32{,}500$ True   Slack $= 32{,}500 - 32{,}500 = 0$

                                        $350(50) + 200(50) = 27{,}500 \leq 28{,}000$ True   Slack $= 28{,}000 - 27{,}500 = 500$

                                        $500(50) = 25{,}000 \leq 25{,}000$ True   Slack $= 25{,}000 =- 25{,}000 = 0$

          Point is feasible.

5. Substitute the values for the production variables into the constraints. If the values make each constraint true, then the set of values is feasible.

6. The slack in a constraint is the amount of the resource available that exceeds the amount used by the given values of the production variables.

7. The non-negativity constraints state that all the production variables must be non-negative.

8. The objective function describes how the quantity to be maximized (usually profit) can be calculated from the values of the production variables.

9. The product-resource chart is:

	Regular Gasoline	Premium Gasoline	Available
low-octane fuel	0.75 gal	0.5 gal	60,000 gallons
high-octane fuel	0.25 gal	0.5 gal	50,000 gallons

   Let $R = \#$ gallons of regular gasoline to produce

         $P = \#$ gallons of premium gasoline to produce.

   Maximize $Profit = \$0.20R + \$0.30P$

   Subject to: $0.75R + 0.5P \leq 60{,}000$ gallons of low-octane fuel

                                   $0.25R + 0.5P \leq 50{,}000$ gallons of high-octane fuel

                                   $R \geq 0, P \geq 0$

   Is $R = 70{,}000, P = 40{,}000$ feasible? Test:

         Is $0.75(70{,}000) + 0.5(40{,}000) \leq 60{,}000$?

            $52{,}500 + 20{,}000 = 72{,}500 > 60{,}000$ **NO**. There is not enough low-octane fuel.

Section 3.1

11. The product-resource chart is:

	Each Shawl	Each Afghan	Available
spinning	1 hours	2 hours	14 hours
dying	1 hour	1 hour	11 hours
weaving	1 hour	6 hours	30 hours

Let $\quad$ x = # shawls to be made, $\quad$ y = # afghans to be made

Maximize $\qquad\qquad P = \$25\,x + \$40y$

Subject to: $\qquad\qquad$ (1) $x + 2y \le$ 14 hours spinning

$\qquad\qquad\qquad\qquad$ (2) $x + \ y \le$ 11 hours dying

$\qquad\qquad\qquad\qquad$ (3) $x + 6y \le$ 30 hours weaving

$\qquad\qquad\qquad\qquad\quad x \ge 0, y \ge 0$

Is $x = 6, y = 4$ feasible? Test: $6 + 2(4) = 14 \le 14$? Yes $\quad$ Slack = $14 - 14 = 0$

$\qquad\qquad\qquad\qquad\qquad\qquad\qquad 6 + 4 \ = 10 \ \le \ 11$? Yes $\qquad$ Slack = $11 - 10 = 1$

$\qquad\qquad\qquad\qquad\qquad\qquad\qquad 6 + 6(4) = 30 \le 30$? Yes. $\quad$ Slack = $30 - 30 = 0$ $\qquad x = 6, y = 4$ is feasible

13. Let S be the number of Standard tents, D be the number of Deluxe tents to be made this week.

The product-resource chart is:

	Standard	Deluxe	Available
Cut & Assemble	2 hrs/tent	1 hr/tent	420 hours
Fabric	2 yds/tent	2 yds/tent	500 yards
Finishing	2 hrs/tent	3 hrs/tent	660 hours

Reading the per tent profits listed in the problem leads to the formulation:

Maximize $\qquad P = \$30S + \$50D$

subject to $\quad$ (1) $2S + 1D \le$ 420 $\ $ hours of cutting and assembly time

$\qquad\qquad$ (2) $2S + 2D \le$ 500 $\ $ yards of fabric

$\qquad\qquad$ (3) $2S + 3D \le$ 660 $\ $ hours of finishing time

$\qquad\qquad\qquad\quad S \ge 0, D \ge 0$

Is $S = 100, D = 150$ feasible? Test:

$\qquad\qquad$ $2(100) + 1(150) = 350 \le 420$? True $\ $ Slack = $420 - 350 = 70$ hours of C&A time unused

$\qquad\qquad$ $2(100) + 2(150) = 500 \le 500$? True $\ $ Slack = $500 - 500 = 0$ yards of fabric unused

$\qquad\qquad$ $2(100) + 3(150) = 650 \le 660$? True $\ $ Slack = $660 - 650 = 10$ hours of finishing time unused

Yes it is feasible.

15. Let $\ x$ = number of boxes of Rick Pitino mix, y = number of boxes of Bobby Petrino mix.

The product-resource chart is:

	Boxes of RP	Boxes of BP	Available
chocolate	0.4 lbs/box	0.2 lbs/box	44 lbs
nuts	0.2 lbs/box	0.2 lbs/box	26 lbs
fruit	0.4 lbs/box	0.6 lbs/box	72 lbs

(a) $\ $ Profit on a box of RP: $\$12.95 - 0.4(\$6) - 0.2(\$4) - 0.4(\$3) = \$8.55$

$\qquad$ Profit on a box of BP: $\$9.95 - 0.2(\$6) - 0.2(\$4) - 0.6(\$3) = \$6.15$

(b) $\qquad$ So total profit is $\ P = \$8.55x + \$6.15y$

Formulation:

$\qquad$ Maximize $\qquad P = \$8.55x + \$6.15y$

$\qquad$ subject to $\quad$ (1) $\quad 0.4x + 0.2y \ \le \$ 44 lbs chocolate

$\qquad\qquad\qquad\quad$ (2) $\quad 0.2x + 0.2y \ \le \$ 26 lbs nuts

$\qquad\qquad\qquad\quad$ (3) $\quad 0.4x + 0.6y \ \le \$ 72 lbs fruit

$\qquad\qquad\qquad\qquad\qquad x \ge 0, y \ge 0$

Feasibility Test: $\ 0.4(60) + 0.2(70) = 38 \ \le 44$ True $\ $ Slack = $44 - 38 = 6$ lbs chocolate

$\qquad\qquad\qquad\quad 0.2(60) + 0.2(70) = 26 \le 26$ True $\ $ Slack = $26 - 26 = 0$ lbs. nuts

$\qquad\qquad\qquad\quad 0.4(60) + 0.6(70) = 66 \le 72$ True $\ $ Slack = $72 - 66 = 6$ lbs. fruit

$\qquad$ So $(60, 70)$ is feasible.

Section 3.1

17. Let x = Number of first type of table to be made, y = Number of second type of table to be made,
 z = Number of third type of table to be made   The product-resource chart is:

	Table #1	Table #2	Table #3	Amount Available
Assembly	1 hour	2 hour	3 hour	500 hours
Painting	2 hour	1 hour	2 hour	400 hours
Finishing	1 hour	3 hour	1 hour	600 hours

Then the constraints are: $1x + 2y + 3z \leq$ 500 hours Assembly
$2x + 1y + 2z \leq$ 400 hours Painting
$1x + 3y + 1z \leq$ 600 hours Finishing $x \geq 0, y \geq 0, z \geq 0.$

and the profit function is $P = 40x + 50y + 90z$ dollars

Feasibility: Test: $1(100) + 2(100) + 3(100) = 600$ which is not ≤ 500 hours Assembly. Not feasible.

19. Let C = number of cotton-filled jackets to make, W = number of wool-filled jackets to make, and
D = number of down-filled jackets to make. Convert pounds to ounces hours to minutes. Since all
the cotton needed is available, no constraint on the amount of cotton. The product-resource chart is:

	Cotton-filled	Wool-filled	Down-filled	Available
Sewing time	50 min	50 min	50 min	40,000 minutes
stuffing time	8 min	9 min	6 min	4,804 minutes
wool	0	12 ounces	0	3600 ounces
down	0	0	12 ounces	2160 ounces

Maximize $P = 24C + 32W + 36D$ dollars
Subject to: $50C + 50W + 50D \leq$ 40000 minutes of sewing time
$8C + 9W + 6D \leq$ 4804 minutes of stuffing time
$12W \leq$ 3600 ounces of wool
$12D \leq$ 2160 ounces of down. $C \geq 0, W \geq 0, D \geq 0$

Section 3.2

1. $5x + 2y = 40$
    $3y = 15$

The second line is $y = 5$,
which is a horizontal line.

The first line $5x + 2y = 40$
has intercepts shown
below.

To find the point of intersection substitute
5 into the first equation:
 $5x + 2(5) = 40$ simplifies to
 $5x + 10 = 40$
  which simplifies to
 $5x = 30$ so $x = 6$
So the intersection point is x = 6, y = 5

x	y
0	20
8	0

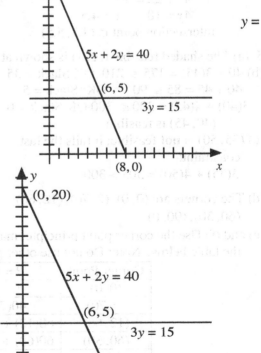

2. $6x + 4y = 48$
     $5x = 30$

The second line is $y = 5$,
which is a horizontal line.

The first line $5x + 2y = 40$
has intercepts shown
below.

From second equation $x = 6$
Substitute in first equation:
 $6(6) + 4y = 48$ which simplifies
to $4y = 12$,   so $y = 3$.
The intersection point is (6, 3)

x	y
0	20
8	0

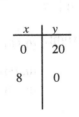
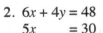
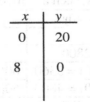

$y =$

Section 3.2

3. $3x + 4y = 24$ $x + 2y = 10$

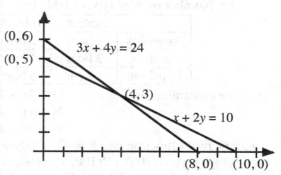

$3x + 4y = 24$		$x + 2y = 10$	
x	y	x	y
0	6	0	5
8	0	10	0

One solution is to multiply the second equation by 2: $3x + 4y = 24$
$$\underline{2x + 4y = 20}$$
Subtract: $x \qquad = 4.$
Substitute $x = 4$ in first equation: $3(4) + 4y = 24$
$$12 + 4y = 24$$
$4y = 12$, so $y = 3$.   The solution is $x = 4$, $y = 3$.

4. $4x + 4y = 40$
$2x + 6y = 42$
Multiply second by 2:
$$4x + 4y = 40$$
$$4x + 12y = 84$$
Subtract: $-8y = -44$
Divide: $y = 5.5$

Intercepts:

$4x + 4y = 40$

x	y
10	0
0	10

Substitute in first equation:
$4x + 4(5.5) = 40$
$4x + 22 = 40$
$4x = 18$ $x = 4.5$
Intersection point is $(4.5, 5.5)$

$2x + 6y = 42$

x	y
21	0
0	7

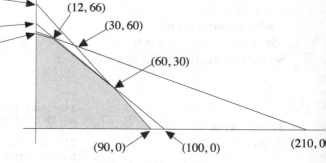

5. (a) The shaded feasible region is shown at right.
(b) $40 + 3(45) = 175 \le 210$ OK Slack = 35
   $40 + 45 = 85 \le 90$ OK Slack = 5
   $3(40) + 4(45) = 300 \le 300$ OK Slack = 0
      $(40, 45)$ is feasible
(c) $(35, 50)$ is **not** feasible; it fails the last
   constraint:
   $3(35) + 4(50) = 305 > 300$

(d) The corners are $(0, 0)$, $(0, 70)$, $(12, 66)$,
   $(60, 30)$, $(90, 0)$.

(e) and (f) Use the corner point principle; make a chart of the corner points and values of P and Q, as in
   the table below. Note: Do not use other points, such as $(30, 60)$, which are not corner points.

Corner Point	$P = 60x + 40y$	$Q = 60x + 90y$
$(0, 0)$	0	0
$(0, 70)$	$40(70) = 2800$	$90(70) = 6300$
$(12, 66)$	$60(12) + 40(66) = 3360$	$60(12) + 90(66) = 6660$
$(60, 30)$	$60(60) + 40(30) = 4800$	$60(60) + 90(30) = 6300$
$(90, 0)$	$60(90) = 5400$	$60(90) = 5400$

The maximum of P is 5400 at $(90, 0)$. The maximum of Q is 6660 at $(12, 66)$.

Section 3.2

6. (a) The feasible region is the part of the first quadrant below all the lines, as shown.

(b) Substitute $(50, 40)$ in all the constraints.

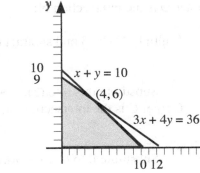

$50 + 2(40) = 130 \le 180$ OK Slack $= 50$

$2(50) + 2(40) = 180 \le 200$ OK Slack $= 20$

$3(50) + 2(40) = 230 \le 240$ OK Slack $= 10$

It satisfies them and hence is feasible.

(c) Substitute $(35, 70)$ in the constraints. It fails the second and third constraints:

$35 + 2(70) = 175 \le 180$ OK

$2(35) + 2(70) = 210$ is not ≤ 200 False

$3(35) + 2(70) = 245$ is not ≤ 240 False

So $(35, 70)$ is not feasible.

(d) Corner points are $(0, 90)$, $(20, 80)$, $(40, 60)$, $(80, 0)$, and $(0,0)$

(e) and (f) Substitute each corner point into the respective profits:

Corner Point	$P = 60x + 40y$	$Q = 60x + 90y$
$(0, 90)$	$40(90) = 3600$	$90(90) = 8100$
$(20, 80)$	$60(20) + 40(80) = 4400$	$60(20) + 90(80) = 8400$
$(40, 60)$	$60(40) + 40(60) = 4800$	$60(40) + 90(60) = 7800$
$(80, 0)$	$60(80) = 4800$	$60(80) = 4800$
$(0, 0)$	0	0

(e) For $P = 60x + 40y$ the maximum profit of 4800 is attained at the two corner points $(40, 60)$ and $(80, 0)$ (and along the segment joining them as well).

(f) For $P = 60x + 90y$ the maximum profit of 8400 is attained at $(20, 80)$.

7. Change the $\le$ to $=$ to obtain the equation of the constraint line. Graph this line. (Simplest way is to determine its intercepts. Each is found by setting one variable $= 0$ and solving for the other variable.) Once the constraint line is graphed, select a test point not on the line. Substitute the test point into the original inequality and determine whether the test point satisfies the inequality. If it does, the graph of the inequality consists of the line and the half-plane containing the point. If the test point does not satisfy the inequality, the graph consists of the line and the half-plane on the other side of the line.

8. The feasible region consists of all the points (x, y) that satisfy all the inequalities. Said another way, it consists of the intersection of all the graphs of the linear inequalities in the system.

9. The Corner Point Principle says that the maximum value of the objective function (usually the profit) must occur at one of the corner points of the feasible region for the system of constraints.

10. First determine the coordinates of all the corner points of the feasible region. Then determine the value of the objective function at each corner point. By the Corner Point Principle, the largest one of these values is the largest value of the objective function at any point in the feasible region. Any point that gives that largest value is a best course of action.

11. If two linear programming problems have the same system of constraints then their feasible regions are the same, and so the corner points are also the same.

12. The objective function is used to choose the best corner point of the feasible region, and that best corner point is the best course of action.

13. The intercepts and the feasible region are shown at right.

The corner points are the origin, the intercepts $(0, 9)$ and $(10, 0)$, and the intersection point of the two lines. One way to find that point is to multiply $x + y = 10$ by 3 and subtract it from $3x + 4y = 36$:

Intercepts

$3x + 4y = 36$ $x + y = 10$

x	y
0	9
12	0

x	y
0	10
10	0

$$3x + 4y = 36$$

Subtract: $\underline{3x + 3y = 30}$

$$y = 6$$

Substitute: $x + 6 = 10$, so $x = 4$

This corner point is $(4, 6)$.

Section 3.2

15. The intercepts are: For (1) $2x + y = 22$: (0, 22) and (11, 0).
　　 For (2) $x + y = 13$: (0, 13) and (13, 0). For (3) $2x + 5y = 50$: (0, 10) and (25, 0).
　　 The origin makes each inequality true, so we want the region in the first quadrant that is on the same
　　 side of all the lines as the origin.

Two of the corners are intercepts of
the lines: the y-intercept of
$2x + 5y = 50$, which is (0, 10), and
the x-intercept of $2x + y = 22$,
which is (11, 0).

One of the other corners is the
solution of (2) $x + y = 13$
　　　　　　　(3) $2x + 5y = 50$.

Multiply (2) by 2 to make both x
terms $2x$:　$2x + 2y = 26$
　　　　　　　$\underline{2x + 5y = 50}$
　　Subtract:　$-3y = -24$,
　　　so $y = 8$.
　　Substitute in (2): $x + 8 = 13$,
　　so $x = 5$. This gives (5, 8) as
　　　this corner.

The last corner is the solution of
　　　　(1) $2x + y = 22$
　　　　(2) $\underline{x + y = 13}$
　　Subtract:　　　$x \quad = 9$　Substitute in (2): $9 + y = 13$, so $y = 4$. This corner is (9, 4).

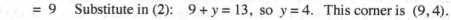

17. The intercepts are:
　　For (1) $x + 3y = 30$:
　　　　(30, 0) and (0, 30)
　　For (2) $3x + 4y = 48$:
　　　　(16, 0) and (0, 12)
　　For (3) $x + y = 14$:
　　(14, 0) and (0, 14)
　　(4) $2x = 20$ is a vertical line; $x = 10$.
The origin makes each inequality true, so we
want the region in the first quadrant that is
on the same side of all the lines as the origin.
　Corner A is (0, 0), Corner B is the y-
intercept of (1), so B is (0, 10), and Corner
F is the x-intercept of (4), so F is (10, 0).
Corner E is the intersection of (4) $2x = 20$ and (3) $x + y = 14$.　　Solving (4) gives the value of $x = 10$.
　Substituting this into (3) gives $10 + y = 14$, or $y = 4$. So E is (10, 4).
　Corner D is the intersection of:　　　　　(2) $3x + 4y = 48$
　　　　　　　　　　　　　　　　　　　(3) $x + y = 14$
　　　　Multiply (3) by 3 and subtract the result from (2);　　(2) $3x + 4y = 48$
　　　　　　　　　　3 x (3):　　　　$\underline{3x + 3y = 42}$
　　　　　　　　　Subtract:　　　　　　$y = 6$
　　Substitute this into (3): $x + 6 = 14$, which gives $x = 8$. So D is (8, 6).
　　Corner C is the intersection of: (1) $x + 3y = 30$　times 3: $3x + 9y = 90$
　　　　　　　　　　　　(2) $3x + 4y = 48$　　　　　　　$\underline{3x + 4y = 48}$
　　　　　　　　　　　　　Subtract:　　　　　$5y = 42$, or $y = 8.4$
　　Substitute into (1): $x + 3(8.4) = 30$, $x + 25.2 = 30$, $x = 4.8$. So C is (4.8, 8.4).

Section 3.2

19. The intercepts are:

For (1) $x + 2y = 38$: (38, 0) and (0, 19)
For (2) $2x + y = 34$:   (17, 0) and (0, 34)
For (3) $5x + 4y = 100$: (20, 0) and (0, 25)

The feasible region (at right) consists of all points on the origin side of all three lines.

Corner <u>E is (0, 0)</u>. Corner A is the y-intercept of line (1), so <u>A is (0, 19)</u>. Corner D is the x-intercept of line (2), so <u>D is (17, 0)</u>.

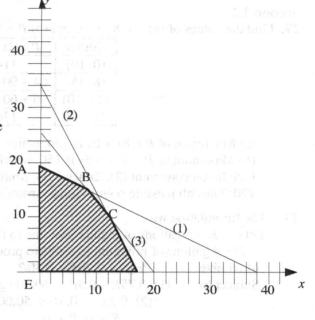

Corner B is the intersection of (1) and (3):

$$(1) \quad x + 2y = 38$$
$$(3) \quad 5x + 4y = 100$$

2 times (1): $2x + 4y = 76$
Subtract: $3x \quad\quad = 24$, so $x = 8$
Substitute in (1): $8 + 2y = 38$, so $2y = 30$,
 $y = 15$. Corner <u>B is (8, 15)</u>.

Corner C: (2) $2x + y = 34$
                (3) $5x + 4y = 100$
4 times (2): $8x + 4y = 136$
Subtract: $-3x \quad\quad = -36$, so $x = 12$.
Substitute in (2): $2(12) + y = 34$, so $y = 10$. Corner <u>C is (12, 10)</u>

21. Find the values of (a) $P = 5x + 6y$ and (b) $P = 6x + 4y$ at each corner found in Problem 13.

Corner	$P = 5x + 6y$	$P = 6x + 4y$
(0, 9)	54	36
(4, 6)	20 + 36 = 56	24 + 24 = 48
(10, 0)	50	60
(0, 0)	0	0

(a) Maximum of $P = 5x + 6y$ is 56, which occurs at $(x, y) = (4, 6)$.
(b) Maximum of $P = 6x + 4y$ is 60, which occurs at $(x, y) = (10, 0)$.

23. Find the values of (a) $P = 3x + 4y$ and (b) $P = 2x + 7y$ at each corner found in Problem 15.

Corner	$P = 3x + 4y$	$P = 2x + 7y$
(0, 10)	40	70
(5, 8)	15 + 32 = 47	10 + 56 = 66
(9, 4)	27 + 16 = 43	18 + 28 = 46
(11, 0)	33	22
(0, 0)	0	0

(a) Maximum of $P = 3x + 4y$ is 47 which occurs at $(x, y) = (5, 8)$.
(a) Maximum of $P = 2x + 7y$ is 70 which occurs at $(x, y) = (0, 10)$.

25. Find the values of (a) $P = 8x + 11y$ and (b) $P = 9x + 4y$ at each corner found in Problem 17.

Corner	$P = 8x + 11y$	$P = 9x + 4y$
(0, 10)	110	40
(4.8, 8.4)	38.4 + 92.4 = 130.8	43.2 + 33.6 = 76.8
(8, 6)	64 + 66 = 130	72 + 24 = 96
(10, 4)	80 + 44 = 124	90 + 16 106
(10, 0)	80	90
(0, 0)	0	0

(a) Maximum of $P = 8x + 11y$ is 130.8, which occurs at $(x, y) = (4.8, 8.4)$.
(b) Maximum of $P = 9x + 4y$ is 106, which occurs at $(x, y) = (10, 4)$.

Section 3.2

27. Find the values of (a) $P = 8x + 4y$ and (b) $P = 9x + 4y$ at each corner found in Problem 19.

Corner	$P = 8x + 6y$	$P = 10x + 5y$
(0, 19)	114	95
(8, 15)	64 + 90 = 154	80 + 75 = 155
(12, 10)	96 + 60 = 156	120 + 50 = 170
(17, 0)	136	170

(a) Maximum of $P = 8x + 6y$ is 156, which occurs at $(x, y) = (12, 10)$.

(b) Maximum of $P = 10x + 5y$ is 150, which occurs at both $(x, y) = (12, 10)$ and $(17, 0)$. These corners both lie on constraint (2): $2x + y = 34$. Multiply this equation by 5 on both sides to obtain $10x + y = 170$. Thus all feasible points along constraint line (2) give the maximum profit of 170.

29. The formulation was:

Let R = # gallons of regular gasoline to produce

     P = # gallons of premium gasoline to produce.

Maximize $Profit = 0.20R + 0.30P$

Subject to: (1) $0.75R + 0.5P \le 60{,}000$ gallons of low octane

           (2) $0.25R + 0.5P \le 50{,}000$ gallons of high octane

           $R \ge 0, P \ge 0$

The intercepts are: For (1) $0.75R + 0.5P = 60{,}000$:

If $R = 0$, then $P = 60{,}000 \div 0.5 = 120{,}000$ If $P = 0$, then $R = 60{,}000 \div 0.75 = 80{,}000$

        For (2) $0.25R + 0.5P = 50{,}000$:

If $R = 0$, then $P = 50{,}000 \div 0.5 = 100{,}000$ If $P = 0$, then $R = 50{,}000 \div 0.25 = 200{,}000$

The feasible region is shown below (the scales are in thousands).

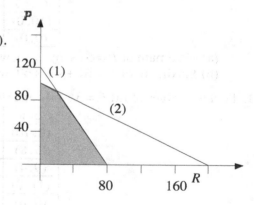

Two corners are the intercepts $(80{,}000, 0)$ and $(0, 100{,}000)$.

The corner where (1) and (2) meet is the solution of:

           (1) $0.75R + 0.5P = 60{,}000$

           (2) $0.25R + 0.5P = 50{,}000$

Subtract: $0.5R$ = 10,000, so $R = 20{,}000$

Substituting: $0.75(20{,}000) + 0.5P = 60{,}000$

  15,000 + $0.5P = 60{,}000$ $0.5P = 45{,}000$,

so $P = 90{,}000$.   That corner is $(20{,}000, 90{,}000)$

Which corner gives the largest profit = $0.20R + 0.30P$:

At $(80{,}000, 0)$, profit = $16,000

At $(0, 100{,}000)$, profit = $30,000

At $(20{,}000, 90{,}000)$, profit = $4,000 + $27,000 = $31,000

So the best production policy is to produce 20,000 gallons of regular and 90,000 gallons of premium. This produces a profit of $31,000.

Substitute $(20{,}000, 90{,}000)$ into the constraints to determine the slack in each resource constraint:

$0.75(20{,}000) + 0.5(90{,}000) = 60{,}000 \le 60{,}000$. There will be 0 gallons of low-octane left unused.

$0.25(20{,}000) + 0.5(90{,}000) = 50{,}000 \le 50{,}000$. There will be 0 gallons of high-octane left unused.

Solution: Make 20,000 gallons of regular and 90,000 gallons of premium. This will earn a profit of $31,000. There will be 0 gallons of low-octane and 0 gallons of high octane left unused (slack).

Section 3.2

31. The intercepts of the constraint lines, and feasible region, are shown below:

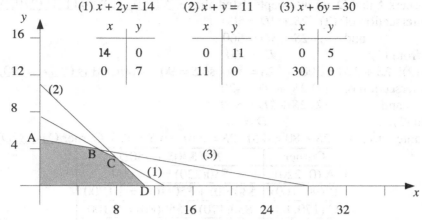

(1) $x + 2y = 14$ (2) $x + y = 11$ (3) $x + 6y = 30$

x	y		x	y		x	y
14	0		0	11		0	5
0	7		11	0		30	0

Corner A is the y-intercept of (3), or $(0, 5)$, and corner D is the x-intercept of (2), or $(11, 0)$.
Corner B is the intersection of: (1) $x + 2y = 14$
                                  (3) $x + 6y = 30$

   Subtract (1) from (3): $4y = 16$,   so $y = 4$.
   Substitute: $x + 2(4) = 14$,   so $x = 6$. So B is $(6, 4)$.

Corner C is the intersection of: (1) $x + 2y = 14$
                                  (2) $x + y = 11$

   Subtract: (2) from (1): $y = 3$
   Substitute: $x + 2(3) = 14$,   so $x = 8$. So C is $(8, 3)$.

Make a chart of the corner points and the value of P at each.

Corner	$P = \$25x + \$40y$
A $(0, 5)$	$\$40(5) = \$200$
B $(6, 4)$	$\$25(6) + \$40(4) = \$310$
C $(8, 3)$	$\$25(8) + \$40(3) = \$320$
D $(11, 0)$	$\$25(11) = \$275$

So the best production policy is to make 8 shawls and 3 afghans, for a profit of $320.
Substitute $(8, 3)$ into constraints to find slack: (1) $8 + 2(3) = 14 \leq 14$; 0 hours spinning time unused.
(2) $8 + 3 = 11 \leq 11$; 0 hours of dying time unused. (3) $8 + 6(3) = 26 \leq 30$; 4 hours weaving unused.

33. The mathematical formulation was: Let S = number of Standard tents,
      D = number of Deluxe tents to be made.

Maximize $P = \$30S + \$50D$
subject to   (1) $2S + 1D \leq 420$ hours of cutting and assembly time
              (2) $2S + 2D \leq 500$ yards of fabric
              (3) $2S + 3D \leq 660$ hours of finishing time $S \geq 0, D \geq 0$

The intercepts are: For (1): $(210, 0)$ and $(0, 420)$ For (2): $(250, 0)$ and $(0, 250)$
          For (3): $(330, 0)$ and $(0, 220)$

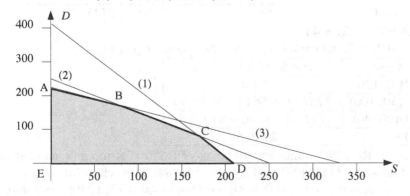

Section 3.2

33. (Continued) Corners A and D are intercepts listed above: <u>A is (0, 220) and D is (210, 0)</u>.
Corner B is the intersection of: (2) $2S + 2D = 500$
and (3) $2S + 3D = 660$
Subtract (2) from (3): $D = 160$
Substitute into (2): $2S + 320 = 500$ $2S = 180$, so $S = 90$.   Corner <u>B is $(S, D) = (90, 160)$</u>.
Corner C is the intersection of: (1) $2S + D = 420$
and   (2) $2S + 2D = 500$
Subtract (1) from (2): $D = 80$
Substitute this value into (1): $2S + 80 = 420$ $2S = 340$, so $S = 170$. Corner <u>C is $(S, D) = (170, 80)$</u>.

Corner	$P = \$30S + \$50D$
A (0, 220)	$\$50(220) = \$11,000$
B (90, 160)	$\$30(90) + \$50(160) = 10,700$
C (170, 80)	$\$30(170) + \$50(80) = 9,100$
D (210, 0)	$\$30(210) = 6,300$

The maximum profit of \$11,000 occurs if no Standard tents and 220 Deluxe tents are made.
Substitute (0, 220) into resources constraints: (1) $2(0) + 1(220) = 220 \leq 420$; 200 hours of c&a time unused
(2) $2(0) + 2(220) = 440 \leq 500$; 60 yards of fabric unused.
(3) $2(0) + 3(220) = 660 \leq 660$; 0 hours of finishing time unused.

35. Let $x = $ # boxes of Rick Pitino mix to make, $y = $ # boxes of Bobby Petrino mix to make.
Maximize $P = \$8.55x + \$6.15y$
subject to   (1) $0.4x + 0.2y \leq 44$ lbs chocolate
(2) $0.2x + 0.2y \leq 26$ lbs nuts
(3) $0.4x + 0.6y \leq 72$ lbs fruit $x \geq 0, y \geq 0$
The intercepts are:
For (1): (110, 0) and (0. 220)   For (2): (130, 0) and (0, 130) For (3): (180, 0) and (0, 120)
The constraint lines and feasible region are shown below.
<u>Corner B is the intercept (0, 120)</u>; <u>Corner E is the intercept (110, 0)</u>.
Corner C is the intersection of:
(2) $0.2x + 0.2y = 26$
and   (3) $0.4x + 0.6y = 72$
Multiply (2) by 2: $0.4x + 0.4y = 52$
Subtract this from (3): $0.2y = 20$,
so $y = 20 / 0.2 = 100$.
Substitute this value into (2): $0.2x + 20 = 26$
$0.2x = 6$, so $x = 6 / 0.2 = 30$.
So Corner <u>C is (30, 100)</u>.
Corner D is the intersection of:
(1) $0.4x + 0.2y = 44$
and   (2) $0.2x + 0.2y = 26$
Subtract (2) from (1): $0.2x$ $= 18$,
so $x = 18 / 0.2 = 90$

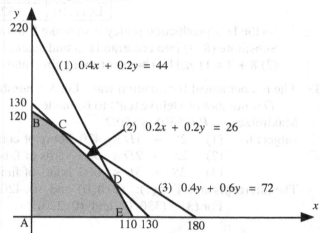

Substitute this value into (1): $0.4(90) + 0.2y = 44$
$36 + 0.2y = 44$ $0.2y = 8$, so $y = 8 / 0.2 = 40$. So Corner <u>D is (90, 40)</u>.

Corner	$P = \$8.55x + \$6.15y$
B(0, 120)	$\$738$
C(30, 100)	$\$256.50 + \$615 = \$871.50$
D(90, 40)	$\$769.50 + \$246 = \$1015.50$
E(110, 0)	$\$940.50$

The factory should make 90 boxes of Rick Pitino mix and 40 boxes of Bobby Petrino mix, and earn a
profit of \$1015.50. Substitute to find slack: (1) $0.4(90) + 0.2(40) = 44 \leq 44$; 0 lbs. chocolate unused
(2) $0.2(90) + 0.2(40) = 26 \leq 26$; 0 lbs nuts unused. (3) $0.4(90) + 0.6(40) = 60 \leq 72$; 12 lbs. fruit unused.

Section 3.3

1. (a) s_1 = number of pounds of cashews unused, s_2 = number of pounds of almonds unused

s_3 = number of pounds of peanuts unused, s_4 = number of minutes of labor unused.

(b) Using these slack variable to change the constraint inequalities into equalities, and rewriting the profit equation gives:

$$3x + 2y + 5z + s_1 = 23$$
$$2x + y + z + s_2 = 80$$
$$x + y + 2z + s_3 = 70$$
$$5x + 2y + 8z + s_4 = 250$$
$$-4x - 3y - 2z + P = 0$$

(c) The initial matrix is:

x	y	z	s_1	s_2	s_3	s_4	P	
3	2	5	1	0	0	0	0	23
2	1	1	0	1	0	0	0	80
1	1	2	0	0	1	0	0	70
5	2	8	0	0	0	1	0	250
-4	-3	-2	0	0	0	0	1	0

2. (a) s_1 = # yards fabric unused, s_2 = # board-feet of lumber unused, s_1 = # pounds padding unused

(b) Using these slack variable to change the constraint inequalities into equalities, and rewriting the profit equation gives:

$$2x + y + 2z + 2w + s_1 = 300$$
$$x + y + 3w + s_2 = 200$$
$$3x + 4y + 5z + 4w + s_3 = 600$$
$$-x - 2y - 3z - 4z + P = 0$$

(c) The initial matrix is:

x	y	z	w	s_1	s_2	s_3	P	
2	1	2	2	1	0	0	0	300
1	1	0	3	0	1	0	0	200
3	4	5	4	0	0	1	0	600
-1	-2	-3	-4	0	0	0	1	0

3. (a) The basic variables are x, y, s_3, and P. The non-basic variables are z, s_1, and s_2.

(b) The optimal solution is: Set the non-basic variables to zero: $z = 0$, $s_1 = 0$, $s_2 = 0$
Read off the values of the basic variables: $x = 15$, $y = 20$, $s_3 = 30$, $P = 820$.

4. (a) The basic variables are y, z, s_2, s_3, and P. The non-basic variables are x, s_1, and s_4.

(b) The optimal solution is: Set the non-basic variables to zero: $x = 0$, $s_1 = 0$, $s_4 = 0$
Read off the values of the basic variables: $y = 210$, $z = 300$, $s_3 = 240$, $s_3 = 180$, $P = 15250$.

5. (a) The basic variables are x, y, s_2, and P.   (b) The non-basic variables are z s_1, and s_3.

(c) The optimal solution is found by setting the non-basic variables equal to 0:

$z = 0$, $s_1 = 0$, and $s_3 = 0$.   Then solve for the values of the basic variables:

$x = 1000$, $y = 13,500$, $s_2 = 3000$, and $P = 56,000$ In the original problem, these mean:

(d) Make 1000 cans of mixture X, 13,500 cans of mixture Y, and 0 cans of mixture Z.

(e) This production policy will result in a profit of $P = \$56,000$.

(f) There will be $s_1 = 0$ pounds of peaches (resource 1) left unused, $s_2 = 3000$ pounds of pears

(resource 2) unused, and $s_3 = 0$ pounds of cherries (resource 3) left unused.

Section 3.3

6. (a) Basic variables: A, B, s3, P (b) Nonbasic: C, s1, s2
   (c) Set nonbasic = 0: C = 0, s1 = 0, s2 = 0. Solve for basic: A = 90, B = 20, s3 = 50, P = 310
   (d) This means make 90 of gift box A, 20 of gift box B, and none of gift box C
   (e) This yields a profit of $310.
   (f) There will be s1 = 0 apples left unused, s2 = 0 candy bars unused, and s3 = 50 dozen flowers left unused.

7. (a) The basic variables are R, S, s1, and P. (b) The non-basic variables are D, s2, and s3.
   (c) The optimal solution is found by setting the non-basic variables equal to 0:
       $D = 0, s2 = 0$, and $s3 = 0$.   Then solve for the values of the basic variables:
       $R = 1050, S = 212.5, s1 = 232.5$, and $P = 5475$ In the original problem, these mean:
   (d) Make 1050 lbs of Regular, 212.5 lbs of Supreme, and 0 lbs of Deluxe.
   (e) This will result in a profit of $P = \$5475$
   (f) There will be $s1 = 232.5$ pounds of peanuts (resource 1) left unused, $s2 = 0$ pounds of cashews (resource 2) unused, and $s3 = 0$ pounds of hazelnuts (resource 2) left unused.

8. (a) Basic variables: x, y, s2, P   (b) Nonbasic variables: z, s1, s3
   (c) Set nonbasic $z = 0, s1 = 0, s3 = 0$
       Solve for basic variables: $x = 250, y = 750, s2 = 1000, P = 10{,}750$
   (d) This means make 250 sacks of lawn, 750 sacks of garden, and 0 sacks of general purpose fertilizer.
   (e) This yields a profit of $10,750.
   (f) There will be $s1 = 0$ lbs. of phosphate, $s2 = 1000$ lbs. of nitrate, and $s3 = 0$ lbs of potash left over.

9. A slack variable stands for the amount of a resource that is unused by a production policy. It is the difference between the amount of the resource available and the amount used by the production policy.

10. The left hand side of the constraint computes the amount of the resource used. Add to that the slack variable and the result must equal the amount of the resource available. This is the equation. To insure the amount of the resource used is ≤ the amount available, we require the slack variable to be ≥ 0.

11. Change the equation $P = ax + by + \ldots\ldots$ to the equivalent equation $-ax - by - \ldots.. + P = 0$ by subtracting $ax + by + \ldots\ldots$ from both sides of $P = ax + by + \ldots\ldots$

12. A basic variable for a simplex matrix is one whose column contains a single 1 and the other entries 0.

13. Set all the nonbasic variables equal to 0. This will simplify the equations that go with the final matrix, because now all the terms involving nonbasic variables drop out (become 0). The remaining equations give the values of the basic variables in the optimal solution to the problem.

14. The values of the slack variables in the optimal solution tell the amounts of the various resources left unused when we produce the amounts of the products that generate the maximum profit.

15. The formulation obtained in Section 3.1 was:
       Let x = number of shawls to make, y = number of afghans to make.
    Maximize $P = \$25\, x + \$40y$
    Subject to: (1) $x + 2y \le 14$ hours spinning
                 (2) $x + y \le 11$ hours dying
                 (3) $x + 6y \le 30$ hours weaving $x \ge 0, y \ge 0$
    (i) Define slack variables: Let s_1 = number of unused hours of spinning available,

    s_2 = number of unused hours of dying available, s_3 = number of unused hours of weaving available.

    Using these the constraints become equations:

    $$x + 2y + s_1 \qquad\qquad = 14 \text{ hours spinning}$$
    $$x + y + \quad s_2 \qquad\quad = 11 \text{ hours dying}$$
    $$x + 6y + \qquad\quad s_3 \quad = 30 \text{ hours weaving}$$

    Rewriting the profit equation gives: $-25x - 40y \qquad\qquad + P = 0$

Section 3.3

15. (continued) Extract the initial simplex matrix of coefficients:

x	y	s1	s2	s3	P	
1	2	1	0	0	0	14
1	1	0	1	0	0	11
1	6	0	0	1	0	30
-25	-40	0	0	0	1	0

(ii) The final matrix from the software is:

x	y	s1	s2	s3	P	
1	0	-1	2	0	0	8
0	0	-5	4	1	0	4
0	1	1	-1	0	0	3
0	0	15	10	0	1	320

(iii) The basic variables are: x, y, s_3, and P. The non-basic variables are s_1 and s_2. The values of these variables in the optimal solution are: $s_1 = 0, s_2 = 0,\ x = 8, y = 3, s_3 = 4, P = 320$.

In the original problem, these mean: Kentucky Weavers should make 8 shawls and 3 afghans. All of their resource time will be used up except 4 hours of weaving (the third constraint), and they will make a profit of $320. This agrees with the graphical solution in 3.2 #31.

17. The mathematical formulation was: Maximize $P = \$30S + \$50D$

subject to   (1) $2S\ +\ 1D \le\ 420$ hours of cutting and assembly time
   (2) $2S\ +\ 2D \le\ 500$ yards of fabric
   (3) $2S\ +\ 3D \le\ 660$ hours of finishing time $S \ge 0, D \ge 0$

(i) Define slack variables: Let s_1 = number of unused hours of cutting and assembly available,

s_2 = number of unused yards of fabric available, s_3 = number of unused hours of finishing available.

Using these the constraints become equations:

$$2S + 1D + s_1 \qquad\qquad = 420 \text{ hours cutting and assembly}$$

$$2S + 2D + \quad s_2 \qquad\ = 500 \text{ yards fabric}$$

$$2S + 3D + \qquad\quad s_3\ = 660 \text{ hours finishing}$$

Rewritten profit equation: $-30S - 50D \qquad\quad + P = 0$

The initial simplex matrix is:

S	D	s1	s2	s3	P	
2	1	1	0	0	0	420
2	2	0	1	0	0	500
2	3	0	0	1	0	660
-30	-50	0	0	0	1	0

(ii) The software produces this final matrix:

S	D	s1	s2	s3	P	
1.33	0	1	0	-.33	0	200
0.67	0	0	1	-.67	0	60
0.67	1	0	0	0.33	0	220
3.33	0	0	0	16.67	1	11000

(iii) The basic variables are: $D, s1, s2$, and P. The non-basic variables are S and $s3$.
The values of these variables in the optimal solution are:
   $S = 0, s3 = 0,\ D = 220, s1 = 200, s2 = 60, P = 11{,}000.$
In the original problem, these mean: The company should make 220 Deluxe tents (and no Standard tents). This will leave 200 hours of cutting and assembly and 60 yards of fabric, but no finishing time, unused, and they will make a profit of $11,000. This agrees with the graphical solution in 3.2 #33.

Section 3.3

19. Let x = # boxes of Rick Pitino mix to make, y = # boxes of Bobby Petrino mix to make.

Maximize $P = \$8.55x + \$6.15y$

subject to   (1) $0.4x + 0.2y \le 44$ lbs chocolate

(2) $0.2x + 0.2y \le 26$ lbs nuts

(3) $0.4x + 0.6y \le 72$ lbs fruit $x \ge 0, y \ge 0$

(i) Define slack variables: Let s_1 = number of unused lbs. chocolate,

s_2 = number of unused lbs. nuts, s_3 = number of unused lbs. fruit.

Using these the constraints become equations:

$$0.4x + 0.2y + s_1 \qquad\qquad = 44 \text{ lbs chocolate}$$
$$0.2x + 0.2y \quad + s_2 \qquad = 26 \text{ lbs nuts}$$
$$0.4x + 0.6y \qquad + s_3 \quad = 72 \text{ lbs fruit}$$

Rewritten profit: $-8.55x - 6.15y \qquad + P = 0$

The initial simplex matrix is:

x	y	s_1	s_2	s_3	P	
0.4	0.2	1	0	0	0	44
0.2	0.2	0	1	0	0	26
0.4	0.6	0	0	1	0	72
-8.55	-6.15	0	0	0	1	0

(ii) The software produces this final matrix:

x	y	s_1	s_2	s_3	P	
1	0	5	-5	0	0	90
0	1	-5	10	0	0	40
0	0	1	-4	1	0	12
0	0	12	18.75	0	1	1015.50

(iii) The basic variables are: x, y, s_3, and P. The non-basic variables are s_1 and s_2.

The values of these variables in the optimal solution are:

$s1 = 0, s2 = 0, x = 90, y = 40, s3 = 12, P = 1015.50$

In the original problem, these mean: Make 90 boxes of Rick Pitino mix, 40 boxes of Bobby Petrino mix, for a profit of $1015.50. There will be no chocolate or nuts left over, but there will be 12 lbs. of fruit left unused. This agrees with the solution found in Section 3.2 #35.

21. The mathematical formulation was: Let x = number of arrangements to make

y = number of baskets to make z = number of centerpieces to make.

Maximize: $P = \$10x + \$25y + \$35z$

Subject to: $2x + 6y + 10z \le 4800$ minutes of Joan's time

$6x + 10y + 8z \le 12{,}000$ minutes of Beth's time

$4x + 8y + 16z \le 12{,}000$ minutes of Carol's time

$x \ge 0, y \ge 0, z \ge 0.$

(i) Define slack variables: Let s_1 = number of unused minutes of Joan's time,

s_2 = number of unused minutes of Beth's time,

s_3 = number of unused minutes of Carol's time.

Using these the constraints become equations:

$$2x + 6y + 10z + s_1 \qquad\qquad = 420 \text{ minutes of Joan's time}$$
$$6x + 10y + 8z \quad + s_2 \qquad = 500 \text{ minutes of Beth's time}$$
$$4x + 8y + 16z \qquad + s_3 \quad = 660 \text{ minutes of Carol's time}$$

Rewritten profit equation: $-10x - 25y - 35z \qquad\qquad + P = 0$

Section 3.3

27. Let x = number of boxes of apple muffins to make

     y = number of pies to make z = number of dozen cookies to make.

   Mixture Chart:

	boxes of muffins (x)	Pies(y)	Cookies(z dozen)	Available
apples	3	10	1	840
sugar	1 cup	2 cups	3 cups	630 cups
flour	2 cups	3 cups	1 cups	450 cups

Constraints: $3x + 10y + 1z \le 840$ apples

$1x + 2y + 3z \le 630$ cups sugar

$2x + 3y + 1z \le 450$ cups flour

$x \ge 0, y \ge 0, z \ge 0.$

(a) Each box of apple muffins costs $3(\$0.25) + \$0.10 + 2(\$0.15) = \$1.15$ to make, so they earn a profit of $\$1.95 - \$1.15 = \$0.80$ on each box of muffins.

(b) Each apple pie costs $10(\$0.25) + 2(\$0.10) + 3(\$0.45) = \$3.15$ to make, so they earn a profit of $\$3.75 - \$3.15 = \$0.60$ on each pie.

(c) Each dozen cookies costs $\$0.25 + 3(\$0.30) + (\$0.15) = \$0.70$ to make, so they earn a profit of $\$1.20 - \$0.70 = \$0.50$ on each dozen cookies.

So the profit function is $P = \$0.80x + \$0.60y + \$0.50z$

Define slack variables: Let s_1 = number of unused apples available,

s_2 = number of unused cups sugar available, s_3 = number of unused cups flour available.

Using these the constraints become equations:

$$3x + 10y + 1z + s_1 \qquad\qquad\qquad = 840 \text{ apples}$$
$$1x + 2y + 3z \qquad + s_2 \qquad\qquad = 630 \text{ cups sugar}$$
$$2x + 3y + 1z \qquad\qquad + s_3 \qquad = 450 \text{ cups flour}$$

Rewritten profit equation: $-0.80x - 0.60y - 0.50z \qquad\qquad + P = 0$

The initial simplex matrix is:

x	y	z	s1	s2	s3	P	
3	10	1	1	0	0	0	840
1	2	3	0	1	0	0	630
2	3	1	0	0	1	0	450
-0.80	-0.60	-0.50	0	0	0	1	0

The final matrix from the computer software is:

x	y	z	s1	s2	s3	P	
0	-3.4	0	1	0.2	-1.6	0	246
0	.2	1	0	0.4	-0.2	0	162
1	1.4	0	0	-0.2	0.6	0	144
0	0.62	0	0	0.04	0.38	1	196.2

The basic variables in this final matrix are: x, z, s_1, and P. The non-basic variables are y, s_2, and s_3.

The values of these variables are: Set $y = 0, s_2 = 0, s_3 = 0$. Then $x = 144, z = 162,$

$s_1 = 246$, and $P = 196.20$

The interpretation of this in the original word problem is: The troop should make 144 boxes of apple muffins, no pies, and 162 dozen cookies. The only resource left unused will be 246 apples; there will be no sugar or flour unused. They will make $196.20 if they follow this production policy.

Review Problems for Chapter 3

1. This is Problem 27 of Section 3.3. Its formulation is shown in the answer to that problem.

2. Here are the intercepts or points on the graphs of the lines associated with the inequalities:

line (1)		line (2)		line (3)		line (4)	
x	y	x	y	x	y	x	y
0	87	0	70	0	60	50	0
58	0	70	0	120	0	50	100

The lines are graphed below. The origin $(0, 0)$ makes each of the inequalities true, so the feasible region includes the side of each line that contains the origin. The feasible region is the region on the correct side of each line, which is shaded below. It has 6 corners labeled A, B, C, D, E, F.

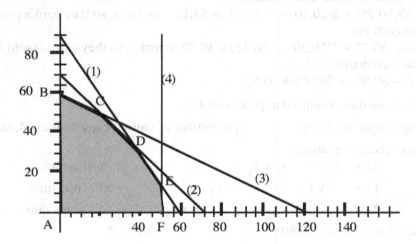

We already know these coordinates: $A = (0, 0)$, $B = (0, 60)$, $F = (50, 0)$

C is the intersection of lines (2) and (3): $x + y = 70$; multiply by 4: $\quad 4x + 4y = 280$

$$2x + 4y = 240 \qquad\qquad\qquad\qquad \underline{2x + 4y = 240}$$

$$\text{Subtract:} \qquad 2x \qquad = 40,$$
$$x = 20$$

Substitute: $20 + y = 70$; $y = 50$. **C is (20, 50)**

D is the intersection of (1) and (2): $3x + 2y = 174 \qquad\qquad 3x + 2y = 174$

$$x + y = 70; \text{ multiply by 2:}\quad \underline{2x + 2y = 140}$$

$$\text{Subtract:} \qquad x \qquad = 34$$

Substitute: $34 + y = 70$, $y = 36$. So **D is (34, 36)**

E is the intersection of (1) and (4): $3x + 2y = 174$

$$x \qquad = 50$$

Substitute: $3(50) + 2y = 174$, $150 + 2y = 174$, $2y = 24$, $y = 12$

So E is (50, 12)

3. (a) Is the point $(60, 60)$ feasible?

$60 + 60 = 120 \le 120$; slack $= 0$

$2(60) + 60 = 180 \le 200$; slack $= 200 - 180 = 20$

$2(22) = 44 \le 140$; slack $= 140 - 44 = 96$

This point satisfies all the constraints and so is feasible.

(b) Is the point $(90, 22)$ feasible?

$90 + 22 = 112 \le 120$; slack $= 8$

$2(90) + 22 = 202 > 200$; slack $= 200 - 202 = -2$.

This point is not feasible; it fails the second constraint; the slack in that constraint is negative.

Review Problems for Chapter 3

3. (c) Shade the feasible region.

$$x + y \le 120$$
$$2x + y \le 200$$
$$2y \le 140$$
$$x \ge 0, y \ge 0$$

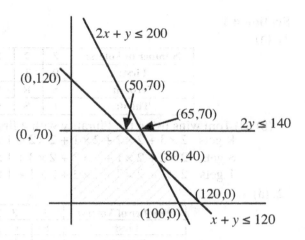

(d) Find the maximum value of $P = 2x + 3y$ on the feasible region. **(65, 70) is not a corner point; it is not feasible.**

Corner	P = 2x + 3y
(0, 0)	0
(0, 70)	210
(50, 70)	100 + 210 = 310 ** Best
(80, 40)	160 + 120 = 280
(100, 0)	200

4. Define a slack variable for each constraint:

Let s_1 = the number of unused skeins of yarn #1

s_2 = the number of unused skeins of yarn #2

s_3 = the number of unused hours of weaving.

With these the constraints become the equations:

$$3x + 5y + \ z + 2w + s_1 \qquad\qquad\quad = 300 \text{ skeins of yarn \#1}$$
$$5x + 3y + 7z + 6w \qquad + s_2 \qquad\quad = 400 \text{ skeins of yarn \#2}$$
$$2x + 3y + 4z + 5w \qquad\qquad + s_3 \qquad = 500 \text{ hours of weaving}$$

Rewriting the profit function gives:

$$-2x - 3y \ - 5z - 5w \qquad\qquad + P \ = 0$$

So the Initial Matrix is:

x	y	z	w	s1	s2	s3	P	
3	5	1	2	1	0	0	0	300
1	3	7	6	0	1	0	0	400
2	3	4	5	0	0	1	0	500
-2	-3	-5	-5	0	0	0	1	0

5. This is the last part of Problem 27 of Section 3.3. Its solution is shown in the answer to that problem.

Section 4.1

1. (a)

Number of Voters:	2	2	2	2	1
First:	R	T	T	S	R
Second:	S	R	S	R	T
Third:	T	S	R	T	S

(b) (i) Tom wins using the Plurality with 4 first place votes. (ii) Using Borda Count Ruth wins:

R gets $2 \times 3 + 2 \times 2 + 2 \times 1 + 2 \times 2 + 1 \times 3 = 6 + 4 + 2 + 4 + 3 = 19$ points

S gets $2 \times 2 + 2 \times 1 + 2 \times 2 + 2 \times 3 + 1 \times 1 = 4 + 2 + 4 + 6 + 1 = 17$ points

T gets $2 \times 1 + 2 \times 3 + 2 \times 3 + 2 \times 1 + 1 \times 2 = 2 + 6 + 6 + 2 + 2 = 18$ points

2. (a)

Number of Voters:	5	3	1	3
First:	S	C	P	C
Second:	P	P	M	P
Third:	C	S	C	M
Fourth:	M	M	S	S

(b) (i) C wins with 6 first place votes. (ii) Using Borda count P wins:

S gets $5 \times 4 + 3 \times 2 + 1 \times 1 + 3 \times 1 = 20 + 6 + 1 + 3 = 30$ points

P gets $5 \times 3 + 3 \times 3 + 1 \times 4 + 3 \times 3 = 15 + 9 + 4 + 9 = 37$ points

C gets $5 \times 2 + 3 \times 4 + 1 \times 2 + 3 \times 4 = 10 + 12 + 2 + 12 = 36$ points

M gets $5 \times 1 + 3 \times 1 + 1 \times 3 + 3 \times 2 = 5 + 3 + 3 + 6 = 17$ points

3. (a) (i) Z wins with 19 first place votes to 9 for Y and 7 for X.   (b) The Borda Count points are

W gets $8 \times 1 + 7 \times 2 + 9 \times 2 + 4 \times 1 + 7 \times 2 = 8 + 14 + 18 + 4 + 14 = 58$ points

X gets $8 \times 3 + 7 \times 4 + 9 \times 3 + 4 \times 2 + 7 \times 1 = 24 + 28 + 27 + 8 + 7 = 94$ points

Y gets $8 \times 2 + 7 \times 3 + 9 \times 4 + 4 \times 3 + 7 \times 3 = 16 + 21 + 36 + 12 + 21 = 106$ points

Z gets $8 \times 4 + 7 \times 1 + 9 \times 1 + 4 \times 4 + 7 \times 4 = 32 + 7 + 9 + 16 + 28 = 92$ points

Y wins if the Borda Count Method is used. Each of the 35 voters award 10 points, so a total of 350 points should be awarded. Since our points total 350, this checks.

4. (a) A has the most first place votes, 9, so A wins using the Plurality Method.

(b) The Borda Count points are:

A gets: $8 \times 1 + 6 \times 3 + 4 \times 1 + 4 \times 2 + 3 \times 3 = 8 + 18 + 4 + 8 + 9 = 47$ points

B gets: $8 \times 3 + 6 \times 2 + 4 \times 2 + 4 \times 1 + 3 \times 1 = 24 + 12 + 8 + 4 + 3 = 51$ points

C gets: $8 \times 2 + 6 \times 1 + 4 \times 3 + 4 \times 3 + 3 \times 2 = 16 + 6 + 12 + 12 + 6 = 52$ points

So C wins using Borda Count. Each of the 25 judges award $3 + 2 + 1 = 6$ points, so there should be a total of $25 \times 6 = 150$ points awarded. Since $47 + 51 + 52 = 150$, our work checks.

5. (a) W wins using Plurality with 12 first place votes.

(b) The Borda Count points are: W gets 74 points, X gets 55 points. Y gets 72 points, Z gets 69 points. W wins if the Borda Count Method is used. The 27 voters award 10 points each, so there should be 270 total points awarded, and our totals sum to 270.   Our work checks.

6. (a) D has the most first place votes with 13 and wins using the Plurality Method.

(b) The Borda Count points are: A gets 79 points, B gets 92 points, C gets 61 points, D gets 88 points, E gets 40 points. So B wins using Borda Counts. There should be $24(5+4+3+2+1) = 360$ points awarded here, and $79+92+61+88+40 = 360$.

7. (a) With six candidates the maximum any voter can award is 6 points, so the maximum that the 40 voters can give to a single candidate is $40 \times 6 = 240$ points.

(b) The minimum points that a voter can give to a candidate is 1 point, so the minimum that the 40 voters can give a candidate is $40 \times 1 = 40$.

(c) Each voter awards $6 + 5 + 4 + 3 + 2 + 1 = 21$ points. If there are 40 voters, a total of $40 \times 21 = 840$ points is awarded to all the candidates.

9. With four candidates each voter awards $4 + 3 + 2 + 1 = 10$ points. If there are 25 voters, a total of $25 \times 10 = 250$ points is awarded to all the candidates. Since A, B, and C receive a total of $63 + 52 + 45 = 160$, D must get the other $250 - 160 = 90$ points, the most. D wins.

Section 4.1

11. Tom has the most first place votes, 4, but that is not a majority of the 9 voters. So there is no majority candidate, and so no violation of the Majority Fairness Criterion is possible.

13. Z wins 19 first place votes out of 35, so Z is a majority candidate. But problem 3 shows Borda Count chooses Y as the winner. So this is a violation of the Majority Criterion by the Borda Count Method.

15. There are 27 voters, so 14 first place votes are needed for a majority. The most anyone has is 12. With no majority candidate no violation of the Majority Criterion is possible.

17. (a) C Wins (b) Borda Results are: A - 25 points, B - 23 points, C - 24
    (c) No violation since there is no majority candidate.

19. There are many possible correct answers. One is shown. The Borda Count points for this example are:

Number of voters:	9	6	6
First	A	B	C
Second	B	C	B
Third	C	A	A

A: $9 \times 3 + (6 + 6) \times 1 = 27 + 12 = 39$, B: $6 \times 3 + (9 + 6) \times 2 = 48$, C: $6 \times 3 + 6 \times 2 + 9 \times 1 = 39$. B wins.

21. If there is a majority candidate, that candidate has more than half the first place votes, and so must have more first place votes than anyone else.

23. If there is a majority candidate, the Plurality Method guarantees that they win, but the Borda Count Method does not.

Section 4.2

1. (a) Sue is eliminated with the fewest first place votes. The two voters in the fourth column now vote for Ruth giving her 5 votes to 4 for Tom, so Ruth wins using Plurality with Elimination.
   (b) The pairwise matches are:

      R vs S: R gets $2 + 2 + 1 = 5$, S gets $2 + 2 = 4$ Ruth gets 1 point
      R vs T: R gets $2 + 2 + 1 = 5$, T gets $2 + 2 = 4$ Ruth gets 1 point
      S vs T: S gets $2 + 2 = 4$, T gets $2 + 2 + 1 = 5$ Tom gets 1 point

    So Ruth wins using the Method of Pairwise Comparisons. She is also a Condorcet candidate.

2. (a) P is eliminated first. The voter in the third column then votes for M, but M is then eliminated with only 3 first place votes. Then C has all the first place votes except the first column, so C wins.
   (b) C beats M 11 to 3, P beats C 8 to 6, C beats S 9 to 5, P beats M 11 to 3, S beats M 8 to 6, P beats S 9 to 5. So C wins 2 points, M wins 0 points, P wins 3 points, and S wins 1 point. P has the most points, wins when the Method of Pairwise Comparisons is used, and is a Condorcet candidate.

3. (a) Since no candidate has a majority of first place votes, and X has the fewest (1), X is eliminated. The voter in the 4th column now has W in first, so W has 13 first place votes, Z 5, and Y 9. Since 13 is not a majority, Z is eliminated. The 5 voters in column 1 then have Y in first place. So now Y has 14 first place votes, a majority. So Y wins using Plurality with Elimination.
   (b) There are 6 pairwise matches: W defeats X 21 to 6, Y defeats W 14 to 13, Z defeats W 14 to 13, Y defeats X 18 to 9, Z defeats X 14 to 13, and Z defeats Y 14 to 13. So Z wins all his matches, wins by Method of Pairwise Comparisons, and also is a Condorcet candidate.

4. (a) Since D has a majority of first place votes it is declared the winner by Plurality with Elimination.
   (b) Since D has a majority of first place votes it wins all its pairwise comparisons and so is a Condorcet candidate, and also wins using the Method of Pairwise comparisons.

5. (a) After C is eliminated with the fewest first place votes, S and P each have 10 first place votes, a tie.
   (b) Here are the pairwise comparisons: P defeats C 11 to 9, C defeats S 11 to 9, and P and S tie 10 to 10. So P gets 1 1/2 points, C 1 point, S 1/2 point. P wins using the Method of Pairwise Comparisons.

6. (a) No majority candidate. Fox has the fewest first place votes and is eliminated. Still no majority candidate. ABC has the fewest first place votes, and is eliminated. Only CBS and NBC are left, with 60% preferring CBS. So CBS wins using Plurality with Elimination.
   (b) The 6 matches yield these results: ABC beats CBS 55 to 45, ABC beats Fox 90 to 10, ABC beats NBC 60 to 40, CBS beats Fox 65 to 35, CBS beats NBC 60 to 40, and Fox beats NBC 70 to 30. Since ABC wins all its pairwise matches it wins using the Method of Pairwise Comparisons.

7. (a) M is eliminated first, then L. Then A defeats H 14-13. So A wins using Plurality With Elimination.
   (b) In pairwise comparisons L defeats A 17 to 10, L defeats H 16 to 11, and L defeats M 19 to 8. So L wins using the Method of Pairwise Comparisons and also is a Condorcet candidate.

Section 4.2

8. (a) No majority candidate. F eliminated with 0 first place voters. Then D is eliminated. Then E is eliminated. Finally G defeats C. So G wins using Plurality with Elimination.

(b) Results of pairwise comparisons: D beats C 27-15; E defeats C 27-15; F defeats C 27-15; G defeats C 27 – 15; E defeats D 22-20; D defeats F 27 – 15; D defeats G 27-15; E defeats F 24 – 18; E defeats G 24 – 18; G defeats F 25 – 17. Total wins: C-0, D-3, E-4; F-1; G-2. E wins using the Method of Pairwise Comparisons and also is a Condorcet candidate.

9. (a) Since the Plurality with Elimination Method chooses the Condorcet candidate, R, no violation.

(b) Since the Plurality Method chooses Tom as the winner but Ruth is a Condorcet candidate, this is a violation of the Condorcet Criterion by the Plurality Method.

(c) Since the Borda Count Method chooses Ruth, who is also a Condorcet candidate, this is a no violation of the Condorcet Criterion by the Borda Count Method.

11. (a) Since Z is a Condorcet candidate but the Plurality with Elimination Method chooses Y as the winner, this is a violation of the Condorcet Fairness Criterion.

(b) Since Z is a Condorcet candidate but the Plurality Method chooses W as the winner, this is a violation of the Condorcet Fairness Criterion.

(c) Since Z is a Condorcet candidate but the Borda Count Method chooses W as the winner, this is a violation of the Condorcet Fairness Criterion.

13. (a) and (b) As shown in 5(b) no candidate wins all their pairwise matches, so there is no Condorcet candidate, so no violation of the Condorcet Criterion by any voting method is possible here.

15. (a) In problem 7 it was shown that L is a Condorcet candidate, but A wins by Plurality With Elimination. So this is a violation of the Condorcet Fairness Criterion by the Plurality With Elimination Method.

(b) L is a Condorcet candidate but H wins by the Plurality Method, so this is a violation of the Condorcet Fairness Criterion by the Plurality Method.

(c) The Borda Count points are: A: 70; H: 72; L: 79; M: 49. So the Borda Count Method chooses the Condorcet Candidate L as the winner. No violation.

17. There are many possible values of a and b. As long as $a > b$ is true there are more voters that prefer B to either A or C than vice versa, making B a Condorcet candidate. Note that A gets $3b + 2a$ Borda Count points, and B gets $3a + b$ points. To have B lose to A in Borda Count would require $3b + 2a > 3a + b$. Subtracting $2a + b$ from both sides yields $2b > a$. So to have B be a Condorcet candidate but lose to A in Borda count requires both $a > b$ and $2b > a$ be true. For example, if $a = 4$ and $b = 3$ then both conditions are true. With these values of a and b B is a Condorcet candidate but A gets $4 \times 2 + 3 \times 3 = 17$ Borda Count points and B gets $4 \times 3 + 3 \times 1 = 15$ Borda Count points.

19. There are many possible answers. Example 4 gives clues. The simplest has only 3 ballots, with the preferences "cycled" (the bottom choice in a column moves to the top of the next column, and everyone else moves down one spot), and the number of votes for each approximately equal, such as the one shown below. Here K beats L 14 to 7, L beats M 15 to 6, and M beats K 13 to 8.

Number of voters:	8	7	6
First	K	L	M
Second	L	M	K
Third	M	K	L

21. If there is a majority candidate that candidate has more than half the first place votes and wins a comparison with any other candidate. So the majority candidate gets the most points possible in the Method of Pairwise Comparisons and wins using the Method of Pairwise Comparisons.

23. If a voting method violates the Majority Fairness Criterion, then there is an election with a majority candidate that is not chosen as the winner by the voting method. Since a majority candidate is always a Condorcet candidate, this is also a violation of the Condorcet Fairness Criterion.

Section 4.3

1. Suppose candidate X wins an election using a voting method. If a second election is done with the only change in the preference schedule being that some voters rank X higher in the second election that the first, then X must win the second election if the same method is used.

2. Plurality, Borda Count, and Pairwise Comparisons.

3. Suppose candidate X wins an election using a voting method. If one of the losing candidates drops out and then the original ballots are used for a second election, X must still win if that same voting method is used.

Section 4.3

4. None.   5. The Method of Pairwise Comparisons.

6. It is not possible to find a voting method that satisfies all four of our fairness criteria.

7. If Houston drops out the following preference schedule results:

Number of Members:	8	6	2	3	3	2
First	T	B	T	B	P	P
Second	B	P	P	P	T	T
Third	P	T	B	T	B	B

The first place votes are: 10 for T, 9 for B, 5 for P. No candidate has a majority, so P is eliminated. The 5 voters in the last two columns to vote for their second choice, T, giving T 15 first place votes to 9 for B. So Tokyo now wins using Plurality with Elimination after Houston drops out. Since Paris won using the original schedule, this is a violation of the Independence of Irrelevant Alternatives Fairness Criterion.

9.   (a) In the original schedule there is no majority candidate, so A is eliminated. This gives:

Number of students:	7	8	10	4	1
First	B	C	D	B	C
Second	C	D	B	D	B
Third	D	B	C	C	D

The first place votes are 11 for B, 9 for C, and 10 for D. There is no majority, so C is eliminated, giving:

Number of students:	7	8	10	4	1
First	B	D	D	B	B
Second	D	B	B	D	D

Now D has 18 first place votes to 12 for B, so D wins using Plurality with Elimination.

(b) With the revised schedule in which the original winner D is moved up in the fourth column, there is no majority candidate so A is still eliminated with the fewest first place votes, yielding this schedule:

Number of students:	7	8	10	4	1
First	B	C	D	D	C
Second	C	D	B	B	B
Third	D	B	C	C	D

Now the first place votes are: 7 for B, 9 for C, and 14 for D. There is no majority, so B is eliminated. Then C has 16 first place votes and wins using Plurality with Elimination.

(c) This is a violation of the Monotonicity Fairness Criterion by the Plurality with Elimination Method.

11.   (a) No majority candidate. With 27 voters 14 first place votes are needed for a majority.

(b) Y is a Condorcet candidate: Y defeats W 15 to 12; Y defeats X 19 to 9; Y defeats Z 15 to 12.

(c) There is no majority candidate, so Y is eliminated with the fewest first place votes, giving:

Number of voters:	10	6	5	4	2
First	W	X	X	Z	Z
Second	Z	Z	Z	X	W
Third	X	W	W	W	X

There is still no majority, so Z is eliminated. The 4 voters in the fourth column now vote for X, giving X 15 first place votes, a majority. So X wins using Plurality with Elimination.

(d) If Z drops out the original schedule becomes:

Number of voters:	10	6	5	4	2
First	W	X	Y	Y	W
Second	Y	Y	X	X	X
Third	X	W	W	W	Y

Now there is still no majority, so X is eliminated with the fewest first place votes. The 6 voters in the second column now vote for Y giving Y 15 votes, a majority. So Y wins after Z drops out.

(e) No violation of Majority Fairness Criterion since there is no majority candidate. Violation of Condorcet Fairness by Plurality With Elimination Method since there is a Condorcet candidate but that candidate was not chosen as the winner by Plurality With Elimination. No violation of Monotonicity was shown in (a) - (d) since there was no revision of the schedule. Violation of the Independence of Irrelevant Alternatives Fairness Criterion by Plurality With Elimination, because when Z dropped out a different winner resulted.

Section 4.3

13. (a) No majority candidate; no candidate has more than half the 21 first place votes.

(b) There is no Condorcet candidate; A beats B 13 to 8, A beats C 11 to 10, A beats D 11 to 10, but E beats A 11 to 10, and D beats E 13 to 8, so every candidate loses at least one pairwise match.

(c) The Borda Counts are: A 66, B 64, C 72, D 65, E 48. C wins if Borda Count is used.

(d) If E drops out the resulting schedule is:

Number of voters:	5	3	5	3	2	3
First	A	A	C	D	D	B
Second	B	D	D	C	C	A
Third	C	B	A	B	B	C
Fourth	D	C	B	A	A	D

Now the Borda Count points are: A 56. B 48, C 54, D 52. So A now wins.

(e) No violation of Majority Criterion since there is no majority candidate. No violation of the Condorcet Criterion by Borda count Method since there is no Condorcet candidate. No violation of Monotonicity was shown in (a) - (d) since there was no revision of the schedule. Violation of the Independence of Irrelevant Alternatives Criterion by Borda Count Method, because when E dropped out a different winner resulted.

15. (a) A has the fewest first place votes and is eliminated, giving

Number of Votes	27	23	22	13	11	4
First:	B	D	C	B	C	B
Second:	C	B	D	C	D	C
Third:	D	C	B	D	B	D

Now D has the fewest first place votes and is eliminated:

Number of Votes	27	23	22	13	11	4
First:	B	B	C	B	C	B
Second:	C	C	B	C	B	C

B wins 67-33

(b) With the change in column 4, C has the fewest first place votes and is eliminated, giving:

Number of Votes	27	23	22	13	11	4
First:	B	D	A	B	D	B
Second:	D	A	D	A	A	A
Third:	A	B	B	D	B	D

Now A has the fewest first place votes and is eliminated, giving:

Number of Votes	27	23	22	13	11	4
First:	B	D	D	B	D	B
Second:	D	B	B	D	B	D

Then D wins 56 - 44.

(c) This shows a violation of the Monotonicity Fairness Criterion. When the original winner, B, was moved up in column 4, the result was then a different winner.

17. We need an example in which a candidate with few first place votes withdraws, causing those who voted for that candidate to then vote for the person who originally lost by Plurality. Here is one:

Number of voters:	8	7	6
First	K	L	M
Second	L	M	L
Third	M	K	K

If M withdraws, the 6 who voted for them first then vote for L, giving L 13 first place votes to 8 for K.

19. Suppose candidate X wins an election using the Borda Count Method. If X is moved up in one or more rankings, X will then have at least as many Borda Count points using the new schedule as it did using the original schedule. Also, no other candidate can have more points with the new schedule than they did with the old schedule since they did not move up in any rankings. So X must still have the most points using the Borda Count Method on the new schedule.

Section 4.3

21. Suppose candidate X is a Condorcet Candidate who does not win by the Plurality method, and that candidate Y wins using Plurality. If the third candidate drops out the election becomes a pairwise match between X and Y. X must win that match, because X is a Condorcet Candidate, so the winner changes from Y to X when the third candidate drops out, a violation of Independence of Irrelevant Alternatives.

Section 4.4

1.

State	Standard Quota	Lower Quota	Extra Seat?
A	3.4	3	
B	2.15	2	
C	5.6	5	+1
D	4.05	4	
E	4.8	4	+1
Total:	20	18	

2.

State	Standard Quota	Lower Quota	Extra Seat?
A	1.335	1	
B	5.415	5	
C	3.5	3	+1
D	4.42	4	+1
E	5.33	5	
Total:	20	18	

3. (a) The standard divisor is $(224 + 346 + 425) / 25 = 995 / 25 = 39.8$ This is the average enrollment per section for the 25 sections. (b) The standard quotas are obtained by dividing the enrollments by 39.8. They are the number of sections each course "deserves".

	Enrollment	Standard Quota
Pre-Algebra	224	$224/39.8 = 5.628...$
Geometry	346	$346/39.8 = 8.693...$
Algebra	425	$425/39.8 = 10.678...$
Total:	995	

4. (a) The standard divisor is $(869 + 1025 + 619 + 187) / 225 = 2700/225 = 12$. This represents the average number of patients per nurse. (b) The standard quotas are obtained by dividing the numbers of patients by 12. These represent the number of nurses each shift "deserves".

Shift	Avg. Number of Patients	Standard Quota
A	869	$869 / 12 = 72.4166....$
B	1025	$1025/12 = 85.4166....$
C	619	$619 / 12 = 51.5833....$
D	187	$187 / 12 = 15.5833....$
Total:	2700	

5. From the standard quotas the Hamilton Method drops the fractional parts, and sums the resulting whole numbers. The states with the largest fractional parts are given 1 extra seat each until the total number of seats reaches the house size.

6. In a legislative apportionment, the standard divisor represents the average number of people per seat, and the standard quotas represent the number of seats each state "deserves".

7. The two apportionments must use the same populations, but different house sizes. Also, there must be a state whose apportionment with the larger house size is smaller than its apportionment with the smaller house size.

8. The two apportionments must have the same house sizes but different state populations. Also, there must be a state whose population decreases from the first to the second apportionment, but whose apportionment increases, and a state whose population increases from the first to the second apportionment but whose apportionment decreases.

9. The Quota Rule says that in an apportionment, each states apportionment should be either its lower quota or 1 more than its lower quota. Hamilton's Method always produces an apportionment that satisfies this because Hamilton's Method starts with all states having their lower quotas, and then given some of the states an additional seat. The latter states end up with 1 more than their lower quota.

10. The sum of the standard quotas always equals the total number of things to be apportioned.

Section 4.4

11. The total population is 30,000. The Standard Divisor is D= 30,000 / 15 = 2,000.

State	Population	Stand. Quota	Lower Quota	Apportionment
Blue	12,600	6.3	6	6
Yellow	6,800	3.4	3	4
Green	10,600	5.3	5	5

Dividing each state population by this 2,000 the Standard Quotas. Dropping the fractional parts of these gives the Lower Quotas. The Lower Quotas total 14, so 1 additional seat is given to Yellow, whose standard quota has the largest fractional part.

13. (a) There are 40,800 eligible voters, so the standard divisor is 40,800 / 50 = 816. It represents the average number of voters for each polling place.

(b) The standard quotas are found by dividing the numbers of eligible voters by 816, and they represent the number of polling places each district is entitled to.

District	Eligible Voters	Stand. Quota	Lower Quota	Apportionment
1	7671	9.40073	9	9
2	9010	11.04167	11	11
3	5497	6.73652	6	7
4	8925	10.9375	10	11
5	3641	4.462	4	5
6	6056	7.42157	7	7

(c) The lower quotas sum to 47, so 3 additional polling places must be awarded. They go to Districts 4, 3, and 5, yielding the Hamilton Apportionment shown above.

15. (a) Standard divisor = 1,003,464 / 50 = 20,069.28. Dividing each state's population by this standard divisor gives the standard quotas shown below (after rounding to nearest hundredth).

County	Population	Stand. Quota	Lower Quota	Hamilton Appor.
Bristol	48,859	2.43	2	2
Kent	161,135	8.03	8	8
Newport	87,194	4.35	4	4
Providence	596,270	29.71	29	30
Washington	110,006	5.48	5	6
Total:	1,003,464	50.00	48	50

The lower quotas sum to 48. Providence and Washington have the largest fractional parts of their standard quotas and so are awarded 1 extra seat each by the Hamilton Method.

(b) If the standard quotas are rounded conventionally, only Providence's rounds up. So the total of the rounded standard quotas is 49. In a valid apportionment the allotments must total the house size 50.

17. (a)

	Enrollment	Standard Quota	Lower Q	Extra?	Hamilton Appor.
Pre-Alg	224	5.628	5		5
Geometry	346	8.693	8	+1	9
Algebra	425	10.678	10	+1	11
Total:	995	Divisor = 39.8	23		25

In June Pre-Algebra gets 5 sections, Geometry 9, and Algebra 11.

(b)

	Enrollment	Standard Quota	Lower Q	Extra?	Hamilton Appor.
Pre-Alg	223	5.413	5	+1	6
Geometry	379	9.199	9		9
Algebra	428	10.388	10		10
Total:	1030	Divisor = 41.2	24		

In August Pre-Algebra gets 6 sections, Geometry gets 9, and Algebra gets 10.

(c) Even though Pre-Algebra's enrollment went down and Algebra's went up, Pre-Algebra gained a section and Algebra lost a section! This is an example of the Population Paradox.

Section 4.4

19. If the legislature is changed so as to have 16 seats, the Standard Divisor is D = 30,000 / 16 = 1875. Dividing each state population by this gives the new standard quotas. Dropping the fractional parts of these gives the new Lower Quotas in shown below.

State	Population	Standard Quota	Lower Quota	Hamilton Apportionment
Blue	12,600	6.72	6	7
Yellow	6,800	3.63	3	3
Green	10,600	5.65	5	6

The Lower Quotas total 14, so 2 additional seats are given to Blue and Green, whose standard quotas have the largest fractional parts. With Problem 11 this is an example of the Alabama Paradox. When the number of seats was raised form 15 to 16, Yellow's apportionment decreased from 4 seats down to 3 seats. That is, raising the House size caused Yellow to lose a seat.

21. (a) There are a total of 7200 fire alarms, so the Standard Divisor is 7200 / 80 = 90, which represent the average number of fire alarms per fireman. The Standard Quotas are shown in the table below; they represent the number of firemen to which each district is entitled.

District	Fire Alarms	Stand. Quota	Lower Quota	Hamilton Apportionment
A	1,843	20.48	20	20
B	2,160	24.00	24	24
C	3,197	35.52	35	36
Totals	7,200	80.00	79	80

(b) The Hamilton Apportionment is shown above.

(c) The adjusted numbers of fire alarms total 7240; the new standard divisor is 7240 / 80 = 90.5. The table below shows the Hamilton Apportionment using the adjusted fire alarm numbers.

District	Fire Alarms	Stand. Quota	Lower Quota	Hamilton Apportionment
A	1,842	20.35	20	21
B	2,200	24.31	24	24
C	3,198	35.34	35	35
Totals	7,240	80.00	79	80

(d) This is the Population Paradox. District A, whose number of fire alarms went down, gained a fireman, while District C, whose number of fire alarms went up, lost a fireman.

23. If there are 51 polling places then the standard divisor is 40,800 / 51 = 800. Dividing the number of eligible voters in the districts by 800 yields the Standard Quotas below.

District	Eligible Voters	Stand. Quota	Lower Quota	Hamilton Apportionment
1	7671	9.58875	9	10
2	9010	11.2625	11	11
3	5497	6.87125	6	7
4	8925	11.15625	11	11
5	3641	4.55125	4	4
6	6056	7.57	7	8

The Lower Quotas sum to 48. To reach a total of 51 Districts 3, 1, and 6, whose standard quotas have the largest fractional parts, get additional seats, as shown above. This is an example of the Alabama Paradox, because when the number of polling places rose from 50 to 51, District 5 lost a polling place (its apportionment went from 5 to 4).

25. (a) The House Size is the sum of the standard quotas, 10.
    (b) Standard divisor = (Total Population) / (house size) = 10,000 / 10 = 1,000.
    (c) State population = (standard divisor)(state standard quota); for C this is 3,660.

Section 4.5

1.

Number	Jefferson Rounded	Webster Rounded
3.499	3	3
5.5	5	6
7.501	7	8
6.99	6	7

2. (a) For Jefferson, The rounded standard quotas sum to 14, too low, so a smaller divisor is needed to produce larger quotients.

   (b) For Webster, The rounded standard quotas sum to 16, the house size, so the standard divisor is a valid divisor.

State	Standard Quota	Webster	Jefferson
A	4.4	4	4
B	3.6	4	3
C	2.4	2	2
D	5.6	6	5
Total		16	14

3. (a) For Jefferson, The rounded standard quotas sum to 15, too low, so a smaller divisor is needed to produce larger quotients.
   (b) For Webster, The rounded standard quotas sum to 17, too large, so a larger divisor is needed to produce smaller quotients.

State	Standard Quota	Webster	Jefferson
A	4.6	5	4
B	3.6	4	3
C	2.7	3	2
D	5.1	5	5
Total		17	14

4. (a) For Jefferson, The rounded standard quotas sum to 15, too low, so a smaller divisor is needed to produce larger quotients.
   (b) For Webster, The rounded standard quotas sum to 15, too low, so a smaller divisor is needed to produce larger quotients.

State	Standard Quota	Webster	Jefferson
A	4.2	4	4
B	3.15	3	3
C	2.35	2	2
D	6.3	6	6
Total		15	15

5. (a) $2{,}500{,}000 / D$ needs to increase from 4.6 to 5 in order to round down to 5, so $2{,}500{,}000 / 5 = 500{,}000$ is the critical divisor.
   (b) $2{,}500{,}000 / D$ needs to decrease from 4.6 to 4.5 in order to round down to 4, so $2{,}500{,}000 / 4.5 = 555{,}556$ is the critical divisor.

6. (a) $1{,}500{,}000 / D$ needs to increase to at least 6 in order to round down to 6, so $1{,}500{,}000 / 6 = 250{,}000$ is the critical divisor.
   (b) $1{,}500{,}000 / D$ needs to increase from 5.45 to more than 5.5 in order to round up to 6, so $1{,}500{,}000 / 5.5 = 272{,}727$ is the critical divisor.

7. With the Hamilton Method the fractional parts of the standard quotas, obtained using the standard divisor, are used to obtain the apportionment. With a divisor method, a divisor is found so that the quotients determined using that divisor, when rounded as specified by the apportionment method, the rounded quotients add up to the house size.

8. The Jefferson Method rounds by dropping the fractional part. The Webster Method rounds by rounding down if the fractional part is ≤ 0.5 and rounds up otherwise.

9. The divisor should be adjusted to be smaller, causing the quotients to be larger.

10. A "valid divisor" is a divisor that produces quotients which, when rounded as prescribed by the apportionment method, sum to the desired house size.

11. (a) In order to round to 11 using Jefferson Method rounding, P/D must be ≥ 11, so $P \geq 11D$ and $P/11 \geq D$. The critical divisor is $D = P/11$.
    (b) In order to round to 11 using Webster Method rounding, P/D must be ≥ 10.5, so $P \geq 10.5D$ and $P/10.5 \geq D$. The critical divisor is $D = P/10.5$.

12. In order to round to 10 using Webster rounding, P/D must be ≤ 10.5, so $P \leq 10.5D$ and $P/10.5 \leq D$. The critical divisor is $D = P/10.5$.

Section 4.5

13. The standard divisor is 10,000 / 50 = 200. The standard quotas are shown below, as well as how they round using both Jefferson and Webster.

State	Population	S. Q.	Jefferson rounded	Webster rounded
Red	2,390	11.95	11	12
White	3,450	17.25	17	17
Blue	2,480	12.40	12	12
Green	1,680	8.40	8	8

(a) The Jefferson Method. The rounded down standard quotas sum to 48, so we must decrease the divisor until two additional seats are obtained. The critical divisors for each state to gain a seat are: Red: 2390 / 12 = 199.17;   White: 3450 / 18 = 191.67   Blue: 2480 / 13 = 190.77   Green: 1680 / 9 = 186.67

Any divisor between the divisors of White and Blue, such as $D = 191$ used in the table below, should produce the Jefferson apportionment in which the rounded quotients sum to 50. Check:

State	Population	Quotients $D = 191$	Jefferson Apportionment	Quotients $D = 198$	Webster Apportionment
Red	2,390	12.513	12	12.07	12
White	3,450	18.063	18	17.42	17
Blue	2,480	12.984	12	12.525	13
Green	1,680	8.796	8	8.485	8

(b) The Webster Method. The rounded standard quotas (in the table above) sum to 49, so we must decrease the divisor until one additional seat is obtained. The critical divisors for the states to gain a seat are: Red: 2390 / 12.5 = 191.2   White: 3450 / 17.5 = 197.14   Blue: 2480 / 12.5 = 198.4   Green: 168 / 8.5 = 197.65

Any divisor between the critical divisors of Blue and Green, such as $D = 198$ used in the table directly above, produces the Webster apportionment; the rounded quotients sum to 50.

15. The table below shows the standard quotas, and how they round.

District	Eligible Voters	Stand. Quota	Jefferson rounded	Webster rounded
1	7671	9.40073	9	9
2	9010	11.04167	11	11
3	5497	6.73652	6	7
4	8925	10.9375	10	11
5	3641	4.462	4	4
6	6056	7.42157	7	7

(a) When the standard quotas are rounded by the Jefferson Method, the sum is 47, so 3 additional polling places must be awarded. The critical divisors for each district to gain a polling place are: District 1: 7671 / 10 = 767.1   District 2: 9010 / 12 = 750.83   District 3: 5497 / 7 = 785.2857   District 4: 8925 / 11 = 811.36   District 5: 3641 / 5 = 728.2   District 6: 6056 / 8 = 757

As D decreases from the standard divisor of 816, it crosses the critical divisors of Districts 4, then 3, then 1. A divisor between the critical divisors of Districts 1 and 6, such as 762, should produce the Jefferson Apportionment. The rounded quotients for $D = 762$ do sum to 50 as shown in the table below

District	Eligible Voters	Quotients $D = 762$	Jefferson Apportionment
1	7671	10.0669	10
2	9010	11.824	11
3	5497	7.2139	7
4	8925	11.71	11
5	3641	4.778	4
6	6056	7.9475	7

Section 4.5

15. (b) When the standard quotas are rounded by the Webster Method, the sum is 49, so 1 additional polling places must be awarded. The critical divisors for each district to gain a polling place are:

District 1: 7671 / 9.5 = 807.47368   District 2: 9010 / 11.5 = 783.478

District 3: 5497 / 7.5 = 732.9   District 4: 8925 / 11.5 = 776.09

District 5: 3641 / 4.5 = 809.1   District 6: 6056 / 7.5 = 807.46667

As D decreases from the standard divisor of 816, it crosses the critical divisor of District 5, then 6. A divisor between these two, such as $D = 808$, the results of which are shown the table below, should produce the Webster Apportionment. The rounded quotients do now sum to 50.

District	Eligible Voters	Quotients $D = 808$	Webster Apportionment
1	7671	9.4938	9
2	9010	11.15	11
3	5497	6.8	7
4	8925	11.046	11
5	3641	4.506	5
6	6056	7.495	7

17. There are a total of 33,348 crimes, so the standard divisor is 33,348 / 42 = 794. The table below shows the standard quotas and how they round using the Jefferson and Webster Methods.

District	Crimes	Stand. Quota	Jefferson rounded	Webster rounded
Inner	7873	9.9156	9	10
North	7124	8.97	8	9
East	5896	7.42	7	7
South	5126	6.46	6	6
West	5005	6.3	6	6
Outer	2324	2.927	2	3
Total:	33,348		38	41

(a) When the standard quotas are rounded by the Jefferson Method, the sum is 38, so 4 additional police cars must be awarded. The divisors for the districts to gain a police car are:

Inner: 7873 / 10 = 787.3   North: 7124 / 9 = 791.555   East: 5896 / 8 = 737

South: 5126 / 7 = 732.3   West: 5005 / 7 = 715   Outer: 2324 / 3 = 774.67

As the divisor decreases from the standard divisor, it crosses the divisors of North, then Inner, then Outer, then East, then South. A divisor between 737 and 732.3, such as $D = 736$, shown in the table below, should give the Jefferson Apportionment. The rounded quotients for $D = 736$ do sum to 42.

District	Crimes	Quotients $D = 736$	Jefferson Apportionment
Inner	7873	10.69	10
North	7124	9.68	9
East	5896	8.008	8
South	5126	6.962	6
West	5005	6.7976	6
Outer	2324	3.156	3

(b) When the standard quotas are rounded by the Webster Method, the sum is 41, so 1 additional police car must be awarded. The critical divisors for each district to gain a police car are: Inner: 7873 / 10.5 = 749.8   North: 7124 / 9.5 = 749.89   East: 5896 / 7.5 = 786.13   South: 5126 / 6.5 = 788.6   West: 5005 / 6.5 = 770   Outer: 2324 / 3.5 = 664

As the divisor decreases from the standard divisor of 794, it crosses the critical divisors of South, then East. A divisor between 788.6 and 786.13, such as $D = 788$, the results of which are shown in the table below, should give the Webster Apportionment. The rounded quotients for $D = 788$ do sum to 42.

District	Crimes	Quotients $D = 788$	Webster Apportionment
Inner	7873	9.9911	10
North	7124	9.0406	9
East	5896	7.4822	7
South	5126	6.505	7
West	5005	6.3515	6
Outer	2324	2.949	3

Section 4.5

19. The total population is 5,000 (thousands), so the standard divisor is 5,000 / 20 = 250. The table below shows the standard quotas for the states and how they round using each method.

State	Population	Standard Quota	Jefferson rounded	Webster rounded
Red	2490	9.96	9	10
White	590	2.36	2	2
Blue	620	2.48	2	2
Green	1300	5.20	5	5

(a) When the standard quotas are rounded by the Jefferson Method, the sum is 18, so 2 additional seats must be awarded. The divisors for the states to gain a seat are:

Red: 2490 / 10 = 249   White: 590 / 3 = 196.67   Blue: 620 / 3 = 206.67   Green: 1300 / 6 = 216.67

As the divisor decreases from the standard divisor of 250, it crosses the critical divisor for Red to gain a seat (249) first, then the critical divisor for Green to gain a seat (216.67). However, the critical divisor for Red to gain a *second* seat (for a total of 11) is 2490 / 11 = 226.36, and the divisor crosses this before it decreases enough for any other state to gain a seat. A divisor between 226.36 and 216.67, like $D =$ 220, the results of which are shown in the table below, produces the Jefferson Apportionment with Red gaining two additional seats. The rounded quotients do sum to 20.

State	Population	Quotients $D = 220$	Jefferson Apportionment
Red	2490	11.318	11
White	590	2.682	2
Blue	620	2.818	2
Green	1300	5.909	5

(b) When the standard quotas are rounded by the Webster Method, the sum is 19, so 1 additional seat must be awarded. The divisors for the states to gain a seat are:

Red: 2490 / 10.5 = 237.14 White: 590 / 2.5 = 236 Blue: 620 / 2.5 = 248 Green: 1300 / 5.5 = 236.36

As the divisor decreases from the standard divisor of 250, it crosses the divisor for Blue to gain a seat (248) first, then the divisor for Red to gain a seat (237.14). A divisor between these, such a $D = 240$, the results of which are shown in the table below, should produce the Webster Apportionment. The rounded quotients for $D = 240$ do sum to 20 as required.

State	Population	Quotients $D = 240$	Webster Apportionment
Red	2490	10.375	10
White	590	2.458	2
Blue	620	2.583	3
Green	1300	5.417	5

(c) The Jefferson Apportionment in (a) violates the Quota Rule. Red has a standard quota of 9.96, and according to the Quota Rule this means Red should be apportioned its standard quota rounded either down or up, that is, either 9 or 10 seats. But the Jefferson Apportionment gave Red 11 seats.

21. The rounded standard quotas, and how they round using the Adams Method, are shown in the table below.

State	Population	Standard Quota	Rounded Up
A	105,200	5.26	6
B	79,800	3.99	4
C	67,200	3.36	4
D	47,800	2.39	3

The sum of the rounded up standard quotas is 17, but the House size is 15 seats, so we need smaller quotients and a larger divisor. For A to get only 5 seats, the divisor would have to be at least 105,200 / 5 = 21,040. For B to get only 3 seats, the divisor would have to be at least 79,800 / 3 = 26,600. For C to get only 3 the divisor would have to be at least 67,200 / 3 = 22,400. For D to get only 2 seats the divisor would have to be at least 47,800 / 2 = 23,900. As the divisor increases from the standard divisor of 20,000, first A loses a seat, then C. A divisor between 22,400 and 23,900, such as 23,000, the results of which are shown in the table below, should produce the Adams Apportionment. Check:

State	Population	Quotient $D = 23,000$	Adams Apportionment
A	105,200	4.574	5
B	79,800	3.469	4
C	67,200	2.92	3
D	47,800	2.078	3

The method seems to favor small states. All the other divisor methods gave D only 2 seats.

Section 4.5

23. In any apportionment problem the sum of the standard quotas equals the "house size" which is the number of things to be apportioned. When we round the standard quotas using the Jefferson Method the result of each rounding is no larger than the standard quota, so the sum of the Jefferson rounded standard quotas is less than or equal to the house size. This means we never have to adjust the divisor up to achieve a smaller sum of the rounded quotients. So any valid divisor for the Jefferson Method must be less than or equal to the standard divisor.

24. (a) Standard divisor = 15,809/180 = 87.8. There are 87.8 students per new computer.

(b) The standard quotas are shown in the table below. Each represents the number of new computers each division is entitled to.

Division	Enrollment	Standard Quota	Lower Quota	Hamilton Apportionment
Arts	3455	39.35	39	**39**
Business	5780	65.83	65	**66**
Humanities	1896	21.59	21	**22**
Science	4678	53.28	53	**53**
Total:	15,809	180	178	180

(c) The Lower Quotas sum to 178. Business and Humanities get the extra seats.

(d) The table below shows the quotients for $D = 86.5$; after rounding using the Jefferson Method these total 180 as desired.

Division	Enrollment	Standard Quota	Quotients $D = 86.5$	Jefferson Apportionment
Arts	3455	39.35	39.94	**39**
Business	5780	65.83	66.82	**66**
Humanities	1896	21.59	21.92	**21**
Science	4678	53.28	54.08	**54**
Total:	15,809	180	178	180

As the divisor decreases from 87.8 it first crosses the divisor for Business to gain a computer, 5780/66 = 87.58, and then crosses the divisor for Science to gain a computer, 4678/54 = 86.62. Any divisor between 86.62 and the divisor for Arts to gain a computer, 3455/40 = 86.375, is a valid divisor.

(e) The Webster Apportionment is the same as the Hamilton Apportionment in this problem, because when the standard quotas are rounded using conventional rounding, their sum is 180 as desired. So the standard divisor is a valid divisor for the Webster Method in this problem.

Section 4.6

1. (a) $3.49 - $2.99 = $0.50, a difference of 50 cents. The price of milk has increased $0.50.

(b) $0.50 / $2.99 = 0.16722... = 16.72%. The price of milk has increased 16.72%.

2. (a) $66,000 - $60,000 = $6,000. His salary increased by $6,000.

(b) $6,000 / $60,000 = 0.1 = 10%. His salary increased 10%.

3. Calculate the states' average constituencies = population / number of seats. The state with the larger average constituency has more people per representative, so its people are more poorly represented, and the apportionment favors the other state.

4. First find the Average Constituency = population / number of seats apportioned for each state. Then the relative unfairness equals the relative difference between these two average constituencies.

5. The relative unfairness of two apportionments equals the relative change from the smaller average constituency to the larger average constituency of the two states.

6. Over the last 100 years the average constituency in the House has risen from about 212,000 to over 710,000. The reason is that the population of the United States has more than tripled in that time, but the size of the House has remained fixed at 435.

7. (a) Average Constituency: Ohio: 11,568,495 /16 = 723,030

Tenn: 6,375,431 / 9 = 708,381 (to the nearest whole number). Ohio is more poorly represented.

(b) Relative unfairness = (723,030 - 708,381) / 708,381 = 7077 / 715,953 = 0.020679...= 2.07%. The average constituency in Ohio is 2.07% larger than the average constituency in Tennessee.

(c) Now the average constituency of Ohio is 11,568,495 /17 = 680,500.

The average constituency of Tennessee is 6,375,431 / 8 = 796,929.

The relative unfairness is now (796,929 - 680,500) / 680,500 = 0.17109.. = 17.11%.

Yes, the relative difference is (much) greater with the switch.

Section 4.6

9. (a) With the 2010 apportionment, the average constituencies are: Indiana: 6,501,582 / 9 = 722,398,   Illinois: 12,864,384 / 18 = 714,688   This is smaller for Illinois, so Illinois is favored.
   (b) The relative unfairness in these is (722,398 – 714,688) / 714,688 = 7710 / 714,688 = 1.08%
   If a seat is switched from Illinois to Indiana, the average constituencies are:
   Indiana: 6,501,582 / 10 = 650,158   Illinois = 12,864,384 / 17 = 756,728
   The relative unfairness in these is (756,728 – 650,158) / 650,158 = 106570 / 650,158 = 16.39%
   So the relative unfairness is much smaller with the actual 2010 apportionment.

11. (a) If the new fireman goes to Crestwood, giving them 14 firemen, the average constituencies are:
   Crestwood: 1750 / 14 = 125, La Grange: 2250 / 15 = 150. (These are runs per fireman.)
   The relative unfairness is (150 – 125) / 125 = 0.2 = 20%.
   (b) If the new fireman is given to La Grange, giving them 16 firemen, the average constituencies are:
   Crestwood: 1750 / 13 = 134.6153846, La Grange: 2250 / 16 = 140.625
   The relative unfairness is (140.625 – 134.6153846) / 134.6153846 = 0.04464 = 4.46%.
   (c) To minimize relative unfairness the new fireman should be given to La Grange.

13. (a) Here are the avg. constituencies. CA: 704,566; FLA. 700,029; NY: 719,298; TX: 701,901;
   New York (with the largest average constituency) is most poorly represented; the apportionment favors Florida (with the smallest average constituency) the most.
   (b) Use the difference between the largest and smallest average constituencies: 719,298 - 700,029 = 19,269 is the largest absolute unfairness; 19,629 / 700,029 = 2.80% is the largest relative unfairness.
   (c) If a seat were transferred from Florida to New York, then Florida would have 26 seats and New York 28. The average constituency of Florida would be 18,900,773 / 26 = 726,953 and the average constituency of New York would be 19,421,055 / 28 = 693,609. The relative unfairness is then (726,953 - 693,609) / 693,609= 0.0481 = 4.81%. Transferring the seat does not make the unfairness between the two states any less.

15. (a) The average constituencies are: A: 9.916,   B: 9.985,   C: 10.042,   D: 10.214   Each average constituency is the average number of patients per nurse on the shift. Shift D is most poorly represented; the apportionment favors shift A which has the smallest number of patients per nurse.
   (b) The largest absolute unfairness is the largest average constituency minus the smallest: 10.214 - 9.916 = 0.298. The largest relative unfairness is the absolute unfairness divided by the smaller average constituency: 0.298 / 9.916 = .0301 = 3.01%.

Section 4.7

1. 5.45 is below its cutoff of $\sqrt{5 \times 6} = \sqrt{30} = 5.477225575...$ and so rounds down to 5.

2. 2.46 is above its cutoff of $\sqrt{2 \times 3} = \sqrt{6} \approx 2.449$ and so it rounds up to 3.

3. 0.23 is above its cutoff of $\sqrt{0 \times 1} = \sqrt{0} = 0$ and so rounds up to 1. (Note: *Any quota in the range from 0 to 1 always rounds to 1 under Huntington-Hill, so each state is guaranteed at least one seat with the Huntington-Hill Method.*)

4. 7.49 is above its cutoff of $\sqrt{7 \times 8} = \sqrt{56} \approx 7.483$ and so it rounds up to 8.

5. To round to 5 the quotient 2500000 / D must be > $\sqrt{4 \times 5} = \sqrt{20} \approx 4.472$. So D must satisfy
   $2500000 / D > \sqrt{20}$ Solving for D gives $D < 2500000 / \sqrt{20} \approx 559017$

6. To round to 3 the quotient 2500000 / D must be < $\sqrt{3 \times 4} = \sqrt{12} \approx 3.464$. So D must satisfy
   $2500000 / D < \sqrt{12}$ Solving for D gives $D > 2500000 / \sqrt{12} \approx 721,688$

7. (a) False   (b) True   (c) True

8. (a) True   (b) False   (c) False

9. Yes; Any divisor method, such as Jefferson, Webster, or Adams.

10. No; This is Theorem 7 (Balinski and Young's Theorem).

11. To round a quotient q, find two consecutive whole numbers n and $n + 1$ so that $n < q < n+1$. The H-H cutoff for rounding q is then $\sqrt{n \times (n+1)}$. If $q < \sqrt{n \times (n+1)}$ round q down to n; if $q > \sqrt{n \times (n+1)}$ round q up to n+1.

12. One reason the Huntington-Hill Method is better is that it minimizes the relative difference among the average constituencies of the various states. One reason the Webster Method is better is that, according to the data of Balinski and Young, it produces apportionments that violate the Quota Rule slightly less often than does the Huntington-Hill Method.

Section 4.7

13. For P/D to round to 11, P/D must be $\geq \sqrt{10 \times 11}$. The critical divisor is $D = \dfrac{P}{\sqrt{10 \times 11}}$.

14. In order for P/D to round to 10, P/D must be $\leq \sqrt{10 \times 11}$. The critical divisor is $D = \dfrac{P}{\sqrt{10 \times 11}}$.

15. (a) The standard divisor is $D = 1500 / 5 = 300$.

College	Enrollment	Standard Quota	H-H Cutoff	H-H rounding
Arts	420	1.4	$\sqrt{1 \times 2} \approx 1.414$	1
Science	375	1.25	$\sqrt{1 \times 2} \approx 1.414$	1
Business	705	2.35	$\sqrt{2 \times 3} \approx 2.449$	2
Totals	1500	5		4

All the standard quotas are below their cutoffs and so round down, giving a sum that is too small. The divisors for each college to get an extra seat are: Arts: 420 / 1.414 = 296.98; Science: 375 / 1.414 = 265.16;   Business: 705 / 2.449 = 287.815. As D decreases from 300, it crosses the divisor of Arts first. Any D between 296.98 and 287.815 should give an additional seat to Arts. The calculations for $D = 290$ are shown in the table below:

College	Enrollment	Quotient $D = 290$	H-H Cutoff	H-H Apportionment
Arts	420	1.448	1.414	2
Science	375	1.29	1.414	1
Business	705	2.413	2.449	2
Totals	1500			5

(b) From the calculations in a) of the standard quotas, we see that they round conventionally to 1, 1, and 2 respectively, giving a sum of 4. The divisors for each college to get an extra seat are: Arts: 420 / 1.5 = 280; Science: 375 / 1.5 = 250; Business: 705 / 2.5 = 282. As the divisor decreases from the standard divisor 300, it first crosses 282 and then crosses 280. A divisor between 280 and 282, such as $D = 281$ should give the extra seat to Business, as shown in the table below.

College	Enrollment	Quotients $D = 281$	Webster Apportionment
Arts	420	1.49466	1
Science	375	1.33	1
Business	705	2.5089	3
Totals:	1500		5

(c) The table below shows the average constituencies for the two schools whose Huntington-Hill and Webster apportionments differ.

College	Enrollment	H-H Apportionment	H-H Avg. Constituency	Webster Apportionment	Webster Avg. Constituency
Arts	420	2	210	1	420
Business	705	2	352.5	3	235

For these two schools, the relative unfairness for H-H is (352.5 - 210) / 210 = 0.6786 = 67.86%, and the relative unfairness for the Webster is (420 - 235) / 235 = 0.7872 = 78.72%. H-H's is smaller.

17. (a) Standard Divisor is 5000/25 = 200. The Standard Quotas, when rounded using H-H, sum to the correct house size and so give the H-H apportionment as shown in the table below.

District	Population	Stand. Quota	H-H Cutoff	H-H Rounded & Apportionment
A	2295	11.475	11.489	11
B	895	4.475	4.472	5
C	1810	9.05	9.487	9

Section 4.7

17. (b) For Webster, $D = 200$ produces rounded quotients with a sum of 24. Clearly A or B will get the additional seat; here are their divisors to do so: A: $2295 / 4.5 = 199.565$, B: $895 / 4.5 = 198.889$. The table below shows the quotients for $D = 199$, when rounded they do sum to 25.

District	Population	Quotients $D = 199$	Webster Rounded & Apportionment
A	2295	11.532	12
B	895	4.497	4
C	1810	9.10	9

(c) The apportionments of Districts A and B differ:

District	Population	H-H Apportionment	H-H Avg. Constituency	Webster Apportionment	Webster Avg. Constituency
A	2295	11	208.6	12	191.25
B	895	5	179	4	223.75

With H-H, the absolute difference in average constituency for A and B is $208.6 - 179 = 29.9$
and the relative difference in average constituency is $29.9 / 179 = 0.16536... = 16.54\%$

With Webster, the absolute difference in average constituency for A and B is $223.75 - 191.25 = 32.5$
and the relative difference in average constituency is $32.5 / 191.25 = 0.16993464 = 16.99\%$.

19. The standard divisor is $1960 / 36 = 54.4444$. The Standard Quotas and their roundings using H-H and Webster are shown in the table below.

Course	Enrollment	Stand Quota	H-H cutoff	H-H Rounded	Webster Rounded
Algebra	286	5.253	$\sqrt{30} = 5.477$	5	5
Trig	133	2.443	$\sqrt{6} = 2.449$	2	2
Precal	678	12.453	$\sqrt{12 \times 13} = 12.490$	12	12
Calc I	568	10.433	$\sqrt{110} = 10.488$	10	10
Calc II	295	5.418	$\sqrt{30} = 5.477$	5	5
Total:	1960			34	34

(a) Using H-H the rounded standard quotas sum to 34, 2 less than 36. Here are the divisors for the courses to gain a section: Algebra: $286 / \sqrt{30} = 52.216$ Trig: $133 / \sqrt{6} = 54.297$
Precal: $678 / \sqrt{12 \times 13} = 54.283$ Calc I: $568 / \sqrt{110} = 54.157$ Calc II: $295 / \sqrt{30} = 53.859$

As D decreases from 54.4444, it first crosses the divisor for Trig, then that of Precal, then Calc. I. A divisor between 54.283 and 54.157, such as 54.2, should produce the Huntington-Hill apportionment, as shown in the table below.

Course	Enrollment	Quotients $D = 54.2$	H-H cutoff	H-H Rounded & Apportionment
Algebra	286	5.276	$\sqrt{30} = 5.477$	5
Trig	133	2.4539	$\sqrt{6} = 2.449$	3
PreCal.	678	12.509	$\sqrt{12 \times 13} = 12.490$	13
Calc I	568	10.4797	$\sqrt{110} = 10.488$	10
Calc II	295	5.4428	$\sqrt{30} = 5.477$	5
Total:	1960			36

(b) Using Webster the rounded standard quotas sum to 34. The divisors for the courses to gain a section using Webster: Algebra: $286 / 5.5 = 52$ Trig: $133 / 2.5 = 53.2$
PreCal.: $678 / 12.5 = 54.24$ Calc I: $568 / 10.5 = 54.095$ Calc II: $295 / 5.5 = 53.636$

As D decreases from 54.4444, it first crosses the divisor of Precal, then of Calc I, then Calc. II. A divisor between 54.095 and 53.636, such as 53.9, should produce the Webster apportionment, as shown in the table below.

Course	Enrollment	Quotients $D = 53.9$	Webster Rounded & Apportionment
Algebra	286	5.306	5
Trig	133	2.4675	2
PreCal.	678	12.5788	13
Calc I	568	10.538	11
Calc II	295	5.473	5
Total:	1960		36

Section 4.7

19 (c) The two apportionments differ in the apportionments of Trig and Calc I. Here are the average
constituencies (actually section sizes in the context of this problem):

H-H: Trig: 133 / 3 = 44.3333   Calc I: 568 / 10 = 56.8

Webster: Trig: 133 / 2 = 66.5   Calc I: 568 / 11 = 51.636

The relative unfairness of these apportionments are:

H-H: (56.8 - 44.3333) / 44.3333 = 0.2812 = 28.12%

Webster: (66.5 - 51.636) / 51.636 = 0.28786 = 28.79% The relative unfairness is slightly
less with the Huntington-Hill apportionment.

21. The total population is 11,000, and the standard divisor is 11,000 / 110 = 100.

(a) Here are the standard quotas and how they round using the Webster Method.

State	Population	Stand. Quota	Webster Rounded
A	10,099	100.99	101
B	430	4.3	4
C	330	3.3	3
D	141	1.41	1

The rounded standard quotas sum to 109, so the divisor must be decreased until another seat is added.
For A to gain a seat the divisor must decrease past 10099 / 101.5 = 99.498; the divisors for the other
states to gain a seat are less than 99. So a divisor of 99 gives another seat to A using the Webster
Method, as shown in the table below. This apportionment violates the Quota Rule because state A got
more than its Standard Quota rounded up.

State	Population	Quotients $D = 99$	Webster Rounded
A	10,099	102.0101	102
B	430	4.34	4
C	330	3.33	3
D	141	1.42	1

Answers to Review Problems for Chapter 4

1. (a) A has the most first place votes and so wins using Plurality. There is no majority candidate.

(b) D has the fewest first place votes with 5, and so is eliminated first. This leaves:

Number of Votes:	5	6	5	3	2	3	2
First	A	B	C	C	C	A	A
Second	B	C	A	B	B	B	C
Third	C	A	B	A	A	C	B

Now A has 10, B has 6, C has 10, so B is eliminated. In A vs C, A gets 10 and C gets 16. C wins.

2. (a) X gets 51 points, Y gets 53 points, Z gets 46 points. So Y wins using Borda Count.

(b) 13 votes are need for a majority, and X has this, so X is a majority candidate.

(c) Yes this illustrates a violation. Borda Count does not pick the majority candidate as the winner.

3. (a) In the pairwise comparisons A beats B and C, and C beats B. So using the Method of Pairwise
Comparisons A wins.

(b) Since A is a Condorcet candidate, but Plurality would pick B (with the most first place votes) as the
winner, this does show a violation of the Condorcet Criterion.

4. (a) P has a majority of first place votes (7 of 13)

(b) Any majority candidate is also a Condorcet candidate.

(c) Using Borda Count: P gets 38 points, C gets 39 points, M gets 27, and S gets 26 points. C wins.

(d) If S drops out the schedule becomes:

Number of voters:	7	4	2
First	P	C	M
Second	C	M	P
Third	M	P	C

Now with Borda Count P gets 29 points, C gets 28 points, and M gets 21 points. P wins.

(e) parts (a) - (c) show a violation of the Majority Fairness Criterion; parts (c) & (d) show a violation of
the Independence of Irrelevant Alternatives Fairness Criterion.

Answers to Review Problems for Chapter 4

5. (a) True. If a candidate has a majority they must win all their pairwise comparisons.

(b) False. Problem 3 above is a counterexample.

(c) True. If candidate X wins using the Plurality Method then X has the most first place votes. If X moves up in some rankings and no one else moves up in the rankings then X must have at least as many first place votes as they did originally, and no other candidate gained any first place votes. So X still has the most first place votes and wins using the Plurality Method.

6. If you are a majority candidate, then only methods that satisfy the Majority Criterion would guarantee that you win. That means any of our methods other than the Borda Count Method.

7. The total population is 5448. (a) With a House size of 24 the standard divisor is 227. The lower quotas sum to 22, so the Hamilton Method awards two additional seats to E and D whose standard quotas have the largest fractional parts. The Hamilton Apportionment with a House size of 24 is shown in the table.

State	Population	Stand. Quota (24 seats)	Lower Quota	Hamilton Apportionment (24 seats)
A	1676	7.38326	7	7
B	1454	6.40529	6	6
C	925	4.07489	4	4
D	778	3.42731	3	4
E	615	2.70925	2	3
Total	5448	24	22	24

(b) With a House size of 25, the standard divisor is 217.92. The lower quotas still sum to 22, but now 3 additional seats must be awarded to reach 25 total. They go to E, A, and B, whose standard quotas have the largest fractional parts. The Hamilton apportionment with a House size of 25 is shown in the table below.

State	Population	Stand. Quota (25 seats)	Lower Quota	Hamilton Apportionment (25 seats)
A	1676	7.69089	7	8
B	1454	6.67217	6	7
C	925	4.24468	4	4
D	778	3.57012	3	3
E	615	2.82214	2	3
Total	5448	25	22	25

This is an example of the Alabama Paradox, because when the House size *increased* from 24 to 25, D's apportionment *decreased* from 4 to 3.

8. A town has four districts A, B, C, and D, and a force of 40 police officers.

District	Population	Standard Quota (D = 111)	Lower Quota	Hamilton Apportionment
A	1,865	16.802	16	17
B	1,269	11.432	11	12
C	712	6.414	6	6
D	594	5.351	5	5
TOTAL	4,440	40.00	38	40

(a) The standard divisor is 4440 / 40 = 111. It represents the average number of people per officer in the town. The standard quotas represent the number of police officers each district is entitled to.

(b) The lower quotas sum to 38, so two more officers are awarded. They go to A and B, since their Standard Quotas have the largest fractional part. The table above shows the result.

(c) Suppose the populations of the districts change as shown below.

District	Population	Standard Quota (D = 112.5)	Lower Quota	Hamilton Apportionment
A	1,924	17.102	17	17
B	1,272	11.307	11	11
C	710	6.311	6	7
D	594	5.280	5	5
TOTAL	4,500	40.000	39	40

The standard divisor is now 4500 / 40 = 112.5, giving the new standard quotas in the table above. The lower quotas sum to 39. The additional officer goes to C.

(d) The results of parts (b) and (c) give an example of the Population Paradox. Even though district B's population increased, it lost an officer, while C gained an officer even though its population decreased.

Answers to Review Problems for Chapter 4

9. A school can offer a total of 20 sections of mathematics in 4 courses according to the table below.

   (a) Jefferson Method

Course	Students	Standard Quota ($D = 150$)	Round Down	Quotients with $D = 135$	Round Down (Jeff. Appor.)
Geometry	980	6.53	6	7.26	7
Algebra	820	5.47	5	6.07	6
Precalculus	670	4.47	4	4.96	4
Calculus	530	3.53	3	3.93	3
Total:	3000	20	18	($\neq 20$)	20

When the standard quotas are rounded down, the sum is 18, too small, so we need a smaller divisor. $D = 135$ (quotients shown above) is a valid divisor, as is $D = 136$.

   (b) Webster Method

Course	Students	Standard Quota ($D = 150$)	Webster Rounded
Geometry	980	6.53	7
Algebra	820	5.47	5
Precalculus	670	4.47	4
Calculus	530	3.53	4
Total:	3000	20	20

When the standard quotas are rounded in the conventional fashion, the sum is 20 as desired, so no further work is required!

   (c) Neither of the above apportionments is a violation of the Quota Rule; each state's apportionment is its standard quota rounded either up or down.

10. Use the Huntington-Hill method to apportion 25 house seats among these three states.

State	Population In thousands	Quotas $D = 200$	H-Hill cutoff	Quotas H-Hill rounded
A	880	4.4	$\sqrt{4 \times 5} = 4.472$	4
B	1,850	9.25	$\sqrt{9 \times 10} = 9.487$	9
C	2,270	11.35	$\sqrt{11 \times 12} = 11.489$	11
Total	5,000			24

The quotas resulting from the standard divisor $D = 200$, when rounded according to the Huntington-Hill rounding rule, sum to 24 as required, so the divisor must be adjusted down to produce larger quotients. The critical divisors for each state to gain a seat are:

A: $880/\sqrt{4 \times 5} = 196.77$;   B: $1850 / \sqrt{9 \times 10} = 195$;   C: $2270 / \sqrt{11 \times 12} = 197.578$

A divisor between the largest two, such as $D = 197$, produces quotients which, when rounded by the H-H rounding rule, sum to 25, as shown below.

State	Population In thousands	Quotas $D = 197$	H-Hill cutoff	H-Hill Apportionment
A	880	4.457	$\sqrt{4 \times 5} = 4.472$	4
B	1,850	9.39	$\sqrt{9 \times 10} = 9.487$	9
C	2,270	11.52	$\sqrt{11 \times 12} = 11.489$	12
Total	5,000			25

Answers to Review Problems for Chapter 4

11. A small country consists of four states A, B, C, and D. The total population of this country is 10,000,000. Given the standard quotas below:

State	A	B	C	D
Standard Quota	0.84	4.14	3.66	1.36

(a) Find the standard divisor for this apportionment problem.
   The *Standard* Quotas always add up to the house size, and here that sum is 10. So the Standard Divisor is 10,000,000 / 10 = 1,000,000.

(b) Find the population of State C
   Since   Standard quota of a state   =   (state population) / (standard divisor),
   (Population of State C) = (its Standard quota) x (standard divisor) = (3.66) x 1,000,000 = 3,660,000.

12. The table below shows the populations and apportionments of Kentucky, Indiana, and Ohio according to the 1990 Census.

State:	Kentucky	Indiana	Ohio
Population	3,698,969	5,564,228	10,877,325
Apportionment	6	10	19
Average Constituency	616,495	556,423	572,491

(a) Find the average constituency of each state.   Divide the state's population by its apportionment.
   The answers in the chart above have been rounded to the nearest whole number.

(b) Which benefits a state, having a large district size or a small district size?   Explain.
   A state wants a small district size, because this means fewer people per representative, or, equivalently, more representatives per person. So the apportionment above favors Indiana.

(c) For these states, what is the largest absolute unfairness between two states?
   The two states with the largest difference are KY and IN: 616,495 - 556,423 = 60,072

(d) For these states, what is the largest relative unfairness between two states?
   KY and IN: 60,072 / 556,423 = .10796 = 10.796%, or about 10.8%

13. (a) State the Quota Rule
   The Quota Rule says that in an apportionment each state should either receive its standard quota rounded either up or its standard quota rounded down.

(b) Which apportionment method(s) we studied always produce(s) apportionments that satisfy the Quota Rule? **Only Hamilton's Method**

14. State Balinski and Young's Theorem. **No apportionment method both satisfies the Quota Rule and always avoids the Population Paradox.**

15. Which apportionment method favors large states the most?   **Jefferson**

16. Which methods we studied are Divisor Methods? **Jefferson, Webster, and   Huntington-Hill.** (All except the Hamilton Method.)
   What are the advantages of a divisor method? **They avoid paradoxes like the**
         Alabama Paradox and the Population Paradox.
   What are the disadvantages of a divisor method? **They may produce apportionments**
         that violate the Quota Rule.

Answers to Review Questions About Apportionment of the U. S. House of Representatives.

Fill in the blanks below using the phrases listed at the bottom to supply some of the highlights of the history of the apportionment methods considered and/or used by the U. S. Congress to apportion the House of Representatives. (Some phrases may need to be used more than once, some not at all; the blank by 1911 requires a number, not a phrase.)

1791 Congress proposes that **the Hamilton Method** be used, but President Washington vetoes this proposal. In its place, **the Jefferson Method** is adopted.

1842 Congress abandons **the Jefferson Method**, primarily because **it violates the Quota Rule**, and adopts **the Webster Method**.

1852 Congress adopts **the Hamilton Method** under a different name.

1880 **The Alabama Paradox** surfaces as a serious flaw in **the Hamilton Method**.

1901 **The Alabama Paradox** resurfaces as the same serious flaw in **the Hamilton Method**, and **the Webster Method** is readopted.

1911 The size of the House of Representative is fixed at its current size of **435**.

1941 The method currently used, **the Huntington-Hill Method**, is adopted. This method has the advantage that **it minimizes the relative unfairness.**

Section 3.3

21. (Continued) The initial simplex matrix is:

x	y	z	$s1$	$s2$	$s3$	P	
2	6	10	1	0	0	0	4800
6	10	8	0	1	0	0	12000
4	8	16	0	0	1	0	12000
-10	-25	-35	0	0	0	1	0

(ii) The software produces this final matrix:

x	y	z	$s1$	$s2$	$s3$	P	
0	1	2.75	0.375	-0.125	0	0	300
1	0	-3.25	-0.625	0.375	0	0	1500
0	0	7	-0.5	-0.5	1	0	3600
0	0	1.25	3.125	0.625	0	1	22,500

(iii) The basic variables are x, y, $s3$ and P. Set $z = 0$, $s1 = 0$, and $s2 = 0$; then $x = 1500$, $y = 300$,
   $s3 = 3600$, and $P = 22{,}500$.

 The meaning of these in the original problem is that the shop should make 1500 arrangements and
300 baskets and no centerpieces, for a profit of \$22,500 for the month. There will be 3600 minutes
(60 hours) of Carol's time left over, but no time of Beth or Joan.

23. The mathematical formulation is:
  Let C = number of cotton-filled jackets to make, W = number of wool-filled jackets to make,
    and D = number of down-filled jackets to make.
  Maximize $P = 24C + 32W + 36D$
  Subject to: $50C + 50W + 50D \le 40000$ minutes of sewing time
         $8C + 9W + 6D \le 4804$ minutes of stuffing time
         $12W \le 3600$ ounces of wool
         $12D \le 2160$ ounces of down.
      $C \ge 0,\ W \ge 0,\ D \ge 0$

(i) Define slack variables: Let s_1 = number of unused minutes of sewing time available,

 s_2 = number of unused minutes of stuffing available, s_3 = number of unused ounces of wool available,

  s_4 = number of unused ounces of down available.

 Using these the constraints become equations:
$$50C + 50W + 50D + s_1 = 40000 \text{ minutes of sewing time}$$
$$8C + 9W + 6D + s_2 = 4804 \text{ minutes of stuffing time}$$
$$12W + s_3 = 3600 \text{ ounces of wool}$$
$$12D + s_4 = 2160 \text{ ounces of down}$$

Rewritten profit equation: $-24C - 32W - 36D + P = 0$
The initial simplex matrix is:

C	W	D	s_1	s_2	s_3	s_4	P	
50	50	50	1	0	0	0	0	40000
8	9	6	0	1	0	0	0	4804
0	12	0	0	0	1	0	0	3600
0	0	12	0	0	0	1	0	2160
-24	-32	-36	0	0	0	0	1	0

Section 3.3

23 (Continued) (ii) The software produces this final matrix:

C	W	D	s_1	s_2	s_3	s_4	P	
0	0	0	1	-6.25	.5285	-1.0416	0	9600
1	0	0	0	0.125	-.09375	-.0626	0	128
0	1	0	0	0	0.0833	0	0	300
0	0	1	0	0	0	.08333	0	180
0	0	0	0	3	.41666	1.4999	1	19152

(iii) The non-basic variables are s_2, s_3, and s_4; these are set equal to 0. The values of the basic variables are: $C = 128, W = 300, D = 180, s_1 = 9600, P = 19{,}152$. Thus the company should make 128 cotton-filled jackets, 300 wool-filled jackets, and 180 down-filled jackets. The profit will be $19,152. There will be 9600 minutes of sewing time left unused by this production policy.

25. Let w = number of barrels of light x = number of barrels of dark
    y = number of barrels of ale z = number of barrels of premium to make.
    The mathematical formulation is: Maximize $P = 6w + 5x + 3y + 7z$
    Subject to: $1w + 1x + \quad + 3z \le$ 50 lbs. malt
        $2w + 1x + 2y + 1z \le$ 150 lbs. hops
        $1w + 1x + 1y + 4z \le$ 80 lbs. yeast.
            $w \ge 0, x \ge 0, y \ge 0, z \ge 0.$
    Define slack variables: Let s_1 = number of unused lbs. malt available,
    s_2 = number of unused lbs. hops available, s_3 = number of unused lbs. yeast available.
    Using these the constraints become equations:

$$1w + 1x + \quad + 3z + s_1 \qquad\qquad = \; 50 \text{ lbs. malt}$$
$$2w + 1x + 2y + 1z \quad + s_2 \qquad = 150 \text{ lbs. hops}$$
$$1w + 1x + 1y + 4z \qquad + s_3 \quad = \; 80 \text{ lbs. yeast}$$

Rewritten profit equation: $-6w - 5x - 3y - 7z \qquad\qquad + P = 0$
The initial simplex matrix is:

w	x	y	z	s_1	s_2	s_3	P	
1	1	0	3	1	0	0	0	50
2	1	2	1	0	1	0	0	150
1	1	1	4	0	0	1	0	80
-6	-5	-3	-7	0	0	0	1	0

The simplex software yields the following final matrix:

w	x	y	z	s_1	s_2	s_3	P	
1	0	0	-4	1	1	-2	0	40
0	0	1	1	-1	0	1	0	30
0	1	0	7	0	-1	2	0	10
0	0	0	7	3	1	1	1	380

The basic variables are w, x, y, and P. The nonbasic variables are z, s_1, s_2, s_3. These are set = 0. The values of the variables in the optimal solution are: $w = 40, x = 10, y = 30, z = 0, \; s_1 = 0, s_2 = 0,$
$s_3 = 0, P = \$380.$

(a)&(b) This means the optimal production policy is to make 40 barrels of light, 10 barrels of dark, 30 barrels of ale, and no barrels of premium. All the resources will be used up, and the profit will be $380.

(c) If we change the available hops to 100 lbs and rerun the software, the final simplex matrix yields this new optimal production policy: Make 50 barrels of dark and 25 barrels of ale, but no light or premium, for a profit of $325.. All the resources are used except 5 lbs of yeast.

(d) By running the software for various profits on the premium, it is found that any profit greater than $14 per barrel for premium will result in a production policy that includes making some premium.

Index

Index

Index